Armoured Fighting Vehicles in Profile
(AFV's of the World Series)
VOLUME 3

British and Commonwealth AFVs 1940-46

Edited by Duncan Crow

Published by
DOUBLEDAY & COMPANY, INC.,
Garden City New York

Uniform with this volume

Armoured Fighting Vehicles of the World Series

Volume 1 AFVs of World War I
Volume 2 British AFVs 1919–1940

Aircraft in Profile Series
(3rd Edition)

Volume 1 (Part numbers 1–24)
Volume 2 (Part numbers 25–48)
Volume 3 (Part numbers 49–72)
Volume 4 (Part numbers 73–96)
Volume 5 (Part numbers 97–120)
Volume 6 (Part numbers 121–144)
Volume 7 (Part numbers 145–168)
Volume 8 (Part numbers 169–192)
Volume 9 (Part numbers 193–210)
Volume 10 (Part numbers 211–222)

Classic Cars in Profile Series
(2nd Edition)

Volume 1 (Part numbers 1–24)
Volume 2 (Part numbers 25–48)
Volume 3 (Part numbers 49–72)
Volume 4 (Part numbers 73–96)

Locomotives in Profile Series

Volume 1 (Part numbers 1–12)

Warships in Profile Series

Volume 1 (Part numbers 1–12)

© *Profile Publications Limited 1971*
Doubleday & Company Inc., edition
1972

First Published in England 1971, by
PROFILE PUBLICATIONS LIMITED
Coburg House, Sheet Street, Windsor, Berkshire, England

Printed in England by
Mears Caldwell Hacker Limited, London, and
Edwin Snell & Sons, Yeovil, Somerset

CONTENTS

Test of Armour	*Duncan Crow*	v
Crusader—Cruiser Mark VI	*Major James Bingham*, R.T.R.	1
Cromwell	*Major James Bingham*, R.T.R.	21
Comet	*Major James Bingham*, R.T.R.	31
Ram and Sexton	*Chris Ellis and Peter Chamberlain*	45
Australian Cruiser Mark 1—Sentinel	*Major James Bingham*, R.T.R.	65
Australian Matildas	*Major James Bingham*, R.T.R.	76
Churchill—British Infantry Tank Mark IV	*B. T. White*	85
Churchill and Sherman Specials	*Peter Chamberlain and Chris Ellis*	105
The 79th Armoured Division	*N.W. Duncan*, C.B., C.B.E., D.S.O.	129
Armoured Recovery Vehicles	*Peter Chamberlain*	177
Wheels, Tracks and Transporters	*N.W. Duncan*, C.B., C.B.E., D.S.O.	182
Armoured Cars		
Guy, Daimler, Humber, A.E.C.	*B. T. White*	197
The South African built Marmon-Herringtons	*B. T. White*	217
Alvis-Straussler	*B. T. White*	228
Light Reconnaissance Cars	*B. T. White*	233
British Armoured Units and Armoured Formations (1940–1946)	*Duncan Crow*	237
Commonwealth Armoured Units and Armoured Formations (to 1946)	*Duncan Crow*	255
Survey of AFVs in British and Commonwealth Service during World War II	*Duncan Crow*	283
Index		309

Coloured illustrations by:

Tom Brittain, Terence Hadler, Martin Lee, James Leech, Michael Trim.

ACKNOWLEDGEMENTS

The Editor, Authors and Publishers wish to acknowledge the help given, especially in the provision of illustrations by Peter Chamberlain; Colonel Peter H. Hordern, D.S.O., O.B.E.; Colonel Robert J. Icks, A.U.S. (Retd.); B. T. White; Australian War Memorial; the Imperial War Museum; the Ministry of Defence Library; the Royal Armoured Corps Tank Museum; the Royal Australian Armoured Corps AFV Museum; the South African National War Museum; and the manufacturers, particularly Alvis Ltd. Examples of almost all the AFVs described in this Volume are on view at the Royal Armoured Corps Tank Museum, Bovington Camp, Dorset, England.

ERRATA

Page 11	Illustration 3: The angle of slope of the turret front in this side-view of Crusader III is incorrectly drawn. The turret front was perpendicular as can be seen in the top picture on page 16 and the bottom picture on page 281. Also the B set aerial in this illustration is incorrectly placed. It should not be at the back of the turret almost in line with the A set aerial, but on the left side about half-way along; for its correct position see top picture on page 16.
Page 17	Right-hand column, lines 38-39: 6th Armoured Division was equipped with Valentines as well as Crusaders.
Page 19	Bottom right caption, line 1: Amend "twin 40 mm." to "twin 20 mm.".
Page 29	Caption, line 1: Amend "tank" to "Tank".
Page 33	Caption, line 2: Amend "Major J. O. Spencer" to "Major J. D. Spencer".
Page 41	Top caption, line 1: Amend "Leading" to "Loading". Centre caption, line 2: Amend "Marshall" to "Marshal".
Page 44	SPECIFICATION, General: After "commander" add "gunner".
Page 96	Delete "*See AFV No. 16" at foot of right-hand column.
Page 97	Footnote at bottom of left-hand column: Amend "See AFV No. 16" to "See pages 105–118, 120–121, and 124–128. Bottom caption: Amend "January" to "April".
Page 100	Left-hand column, line 35: Amend "Le Harve" to "Le Havre". Bottom caption, line 1: Amend "6th Guards Armoured Brigade" to "6th Guards Tank Brigade". Line 8: After "glance" add "similar".
Page 101	SPECIFICATION, Dimensions: Amend "Track centres" to "Track length in ground contact". Track width should be "22 in." not "14 in.".

Leaving the Normandy beaches for the battle inland a 7th Armoured Division Cromwell followed by a Sherman Firefly, another Cromwell, and a string of vehicles, on D + 1 (June 7, 1944). The Firefly was a Sherman re-armed with a 17-pdr. gun to produce the most effective tank in Allied use at this period.
(Imperial War Museum)

Test of Armour

by Duncan Crow

THE events of May and June 1940 proved that French confidence in the Maginot Line was misplaced and that the combination of circumstances was as favourable for a *Blitzkrieg* in France as it had been in Poland the previous September. Those tacticians who maintained that the primary rôle of the tank was to assist the infantry in reaching successive objectives were discountenanced. The tanks of the German panzer divisions operated well in advance of the infantry, motorized or on foot, who followed as quickly as possible to occupy the ground gained. With dive-bomber support and the assistance of the panzer division's own lorried infantry the tanks sliced their way across Belgium and France, frequently disregarding flank protection so long as momentum was maintained, and averaging between 20 and 25 miles a day.

The effect of this success was shattering on its enemies. "After Dunkirk," wrote the historian of the British 11th Armoured Division, "the words 'panzer division' assumed a near-mystical significance. We had to have armoured divisions."

Given that this emphasis was the correct one, the need was indeed urgent. At that time in 1940, apart from the 1st Armoured Division which had been wrecked in France, there were only two British armoured divisions in existence: the 2nd in England and the 7th in Egypt. Both were under strength.

The creation of new armoured divisions was begun. The plan was to increase the total number from three to ten by the end of August 1941. This was achieved.

The 6th, 8th, 9th, 11th, and 10th were formed in that order, and the Guards and 42nd were converted from infantry. But many were armoured divisions in name only; their training was incomplete, their equipment in short supply. Not until July 1942 did the first of these "new" armoured divisions go into action.

The organisation of an armoured division until the spring of 1942 was still based on the "all-armour" concept of the years before the war. Each division had two armoured brigades. By 1942 experience had shown that the "all-armour" idea was dead. The organisation was changed. One armoured brigade was removed and replaced by an infantry brigade; and the division's artillery was increased. "The day of unsupported armour is over," ran the dictum of the RAC Officers' Tactical School at the beginning of 1943. The hindsight of history makes one doubt whether it ever truly existed. Certainly the German armoured commanders, even at the height of their *Blitzkrieg* successes, never under-rated the importance of having all the supporting arms needed to allow the tanks to fight with full effect.

Despite the "near-mystical significance" of the panzer divisions British armoured effort was not devoted exclusively to the formation of more armoured divisions. There was a comparable increase in the number of tank brigades, whose rôle was the close support of infantry. At the maximum, in 1942–43, there was a combined total of 29 armoured brigades and tank brigades in the British Army. In addition, Australia, Canada, India, New Zealand, East Africa

"The best all-round tank this side of the Iron Curtain." A Churchill in the specialised rôle of AVRE (Armoured Vehicle, Royal Engineers) advancing to the attack in France, September 1944. Beside it is another Churchill AVRE with Small Box Girder bridge.
(Imperial War Museum)

and South Africa all had armoured units and armoured formations. At the maximum these totalled over 20 armoured brigades and tank brigades. A short "biography" of each of these armoured formations, British and Commonwealth, appears in this Volume, together with an account of the growth of the armoured forces.

The two tank rôles—close support of infantry by the tank brigades, and independent operations by the armoured divisions— had given rise before the war to two types of tank: "I" tanks for the first rôle, cruiser tanks for the second. This basic philosophy persisted for the greater part of the war, although its influence began to wane from the end of 1942 onwards. It resulted in eight marks of cruiser plus the Comet, and four marks of infantry tank.

Cruisers Marks I (A9), II (A10), III (A13), and IV (A13 Mark II) saw action in France in 1940 and in the Western Desert and Cyrenaica in 1940 and 1941. Cruiser Mark V (A13 Mark III), better known as the Covenanter, was used for training only. Cruiser Mark VI, the Crusader, was produced in greater numbers than any other cruiser tank and became the standard British tank of the armoured brigades in action in North Africa. Cruiser Mark VII, the Cavalier, was not used in action as a gun tank. Cruiser Mark VIII, the Centaur (with Liberty engine) and the Cromwell (with Meteor engine), fought in North-West Europe in 1944-45. The Comet, the last of the cruiser line, also saw action towards the end of that campaign.

The cruiser series was far from being an unqualified success. At the end of his *Profile* of the Comet in this Volume Major Bingham quotes the historian of the 15th/19th Hussars: "The Comet, unlike many previous British Cruiser tanks, was reliable and battleworthy from the first—a statement that bodes well for the

Desert dwelling—a Marmon-Herrington Mark III armoured car beside the Mediterranean at Marsa Lucch, between Tobruk and Bardia. The South African-built Marmon-Herringtons were familiar to all armoured car regiments in the Middle East from the end of 1940 onwards.
(Major K. G. Balfour, M.C.)

future but provides a sorry epitaph on British tank provision before and during the war."

Major Bingham himself, however, in his Crusader *Profile,* which deals with the cruiser tank series Marks I to VI inclusive, is not so critical: "In my own experience with A13s in France and with A10s and A13s in the Western Desert, these cruisers were, in their time and in the balance of gun-power and armour, the equal in quality with their German opponents— PzKpfw III and PzKpfw IV." The Crusader was under-gunned, "a failing shared with most British tanks in the war years," but it was as much superior German tactics, in which anti-tank weapons were skilfully used in close co-operation with tanks, that caused the heavy toll of Crusaders in the Desert. The German tactics were based on the closest possible co-operation between the tanks and the supporting arms and on the assumption that the tank's primary rôle was to kill infantry; the armoured battle was, so far as possible, avoided and on meeting British armour in strength the Germans would fall back to lure the British tanks onto the anti-tank weapons which travelled in a moving box formation and could be quickly organized for all-round defence. The close combination of tanks and artillery was something that the Eighth Army had to learn from German practice.

Nevertheless the Crusader had an unenviable "reputation for unreliability, due largely to the complexity and need for constant maintenance." The Cromwell, on the other hand, though outmatched in firepower was quicker and more reliable than its opponents and responded more rapidly in laying and firing.

The Canadians and Australians also built cruiser tanks. The Canadians designed and built the Ram, which was based on the American M3 Medium chassis; the Australians designed and built the Sentinel, which combined American automotive practice (as demonstrated in the M3 Medium) with British configuration and added some new features of its own. Neither the Ram nor the Sentinel was used in action as a gun tank.

The "I" tank series was, on the whole, more successful than the cruiser tank series. Indeed the Churchill, which was the Infantry Tank Mark IV, earned from Major-General G. L. Verney this accolade in a letter to *The Times:* "I, and others who had the good fortune to fight in Churchill tanks, will always maintain that the Churchill was the best all-round tank this side of the Iron Curtain".

Infantry Tank Mark I, the original Matilda, went out of service after Dunkirk. Infantry Tank Mark II, also called Matilda, was in its day a world-beater; it fought in France in 1940 and in the Desert until July 1942, after which it saw service with the Australians in the Pacific theatre. Infantry Tank Mark III, the Valentine, was produced in greater numbers than any other British tank, many Valentines being built in Canada. Although primarily an "I" tank the Valentine was issued to some armoured divisions as well as to tank brigades because of the shortage of cruiser tanks. It saw action in North Africa from November 1941 until the end of the campaign in 1943, and in other parts of the world, notably in Russia—both the Matilda and the Valentine were sent to Russia in substantial numbers with other British and American

The backbone of German anti-tank defence in the North African fighting was the 88 mm. anti-aircraft gun used in an anti-tank rôle. This 88 was spiked by its crew before being overrun during the Second Battle of Alamein, October-November 1942.

(Major K. G. Balfour, M.C.)

tanks. The Matilda and the Valentine are described in Volume Two, apart from the *Profile* of the Matilda in Australian service which appears in this Volume.

The Churchill first saw action in the Dieppe raid on August 19, 1942, in Canadian hands. Its first sustained test was in the Tunisian campaign, when two tank brigades of Churchills formed part of First Army. These brigades also took part in the Italian campaign, although they were not wholly equipped with Churchills throughout. Churchills also equipped the tank brigades in the North-West Europe campaign.

Apart from their rôle as standard gun tanks Churchills were converted for a number of special rôles, notably as recovery vehicles, AVREs (Armoured Vehicles, Royal Engineers) and Crocodiles (flame-throwing tanks). The Churchill and the American M4 Medium, the Sherman, were the two tanks used for the special purpose equipment developed to enable the invading troops to land successfully in Normandy in June 1944 in the face of strong enemy opposition. This equipment, augmented as the campaign progressed, was operated by 79th Armoured Division. Formed as a normal armoured division with one armoured brigade and one infantry brigade in September 1942, the 79th's rôle was changed in the spring of 1943. It was a unique formation whose organisation and operations are described in this Volume by Major-General Nigel Duncan, commander of its 30th Armoured Brigade.

Despite a total tank production of about 27,000 vehicles during the six years of World War II—a total, incidentally, that was slightly greater than the German—Britain was heavily dependent from 1941 onwards on American tanks.

The first American tank to go into action with a

Sexton self-propelled gun in North-West Europe, October 1944. The Sexton was Canadian designed and manufactured, consisting of a 25-pdr. on a Ram tank chassis. SP artillery was developed from 1941 onwards to provide equipment similar to that which was being used so effectively by the Germans.

(Imperial War Museum)

British crew was the M3 Light, called the Stuart or "Honey" by the British. The date was November, 1941; the place was Sidi Rezegh. The Stuarts were followed into British service by the M3 and M4 Mediums. The M3 Medium was named the Grant or Lee, depending upon which version it was. The M4 Medium was called the Sherman. The Grant was first used in action by the British at Gazala in May 1942, the Sherman at the Second Battle of Alamein in October 1942.

The Sherman became the most important tank in British service. From 1943 until the end of the war in 1945 it was more widely used in the British and Commonwealth armies than any British designed or British produced tank. During those years it was the Sherman which equipped the British, Canadian, Indian, New Zealand, and South African armoured divisions. An account of the American tanks and other American armoured equipment in British and Commonwealth service appears in the Survey of AFVs at the end of this Volume.

The arrival of American Medium tanks in British service was an important contributory factor to the change in British tank policy that was taking place by the end of 1942. It was decided by the Tank Board, a joint War Office-Ministry of Supply organisation which exerted little influence until 1943, that there should be a movement towards some degree of standardisation between the designs for the two classes of tanks, and that what many people considered to be the artificial, and indeed stultifying, distinction between the cruiser and infantry rôles should be abandoned in view of the fact that the Sherman and the Churchill were being successfully used in both. This new policy was strongly supported by General (later Field-Marshal Viscount) Montgomery. It was opposed just as strongly by others, including Lieutenant-General Sir Giffard Martel who, until early in 1943, was Commander of the Royal Armoured Corps. Martel favoured the production of a limited number of really heavy tanks for the assault rôle. But the trend of tank development went against him. What emerged, as the war ended, was the Centurion—the multi-purpose tank that was also capable of conversion to specialised rôles. The Centurion's own test in action began six years later in Korea.

The ubiquitous Universal Carrier in one of its many rôles—as a 3-inch mortar carrier, seen here early in the Italian campaign, 1943.
(Imperial War Museum)

A Crusader II CS with 3 inch Howitzer on the ranges, showing the degree of movement of the independently sprung road wheels which permitted fast and stable cross country mobility. (I.W.M.)

Crusader-Cruiser Mark VI By Major James Bingham

THE aim of Operation "Crusader" in November 1941 was to relieve Tobruk which had been besieged by the German and Italian forces since April, and to drive the enemy out of Tripolitania. The main obstacle in the way of the British forces was Rommel's Afrika Korps, and the immediate object was the destruction of his armour in the major tank battle that was expected. After making a wide sweep through the desert, 7th Armoured Brigade was directed on to the airfield at Sidi Rezegh, 15 miles from the Tobruk defences and, as the Crusaders of 6th Royal Tank Regiment raced up to the surprised airmen, three fighters took off. Nineteen aircraft were captured. The divisional Support Group of infantry and artillery came up next morning to reinforce the position, and the fighting which ensued during the next three days

"was the fiercest yet seen in the desert. Round Sidi Rezegh airfield in particular the action was unbelievably confused, and the rapid changes in the situation, the smoke and the dust, the sudden appearance of tanks first from one direction and then from another, made great demands on the junior leaders."*

No less than three Victoria Crosses were won there in the Support Group.

Combined with a break-out from Tobruk, the Support Group and Crusaders made an attack on the escarpment north of the airfield. As the Crusaders moved down into the valley beyond, they came under fire from very strong enemy gun positions and

suffered heavy losses. The remnants retired to support the infantry and artillery where they were soon engaged in repelling repeated German tank attacks supported by dive bombers. When the Crusaders had been reduced to seven only, they were reinforced by a squadron of the older cruiser tanks and this small force endeavoured, with further losses, to hold the enemy off. Throughout, the legendary Brigadier "Jock" Campbell, commander of the Support Group, was in action with the guns and the tanks, inspiring his dwindling force. On the third day the 22nd Armoured Brigade, now reduced to some 80 Crusaders, came up to find the field artillery concentrated on the edge of the airfield, firing over open sights against a concentrated German/Italian attack by 150 tanks. The Crusaders attacked in line abreast through the guns but, at this stage, all they could do was to prevent the enemy armour routing what remained of the force.

"The Regiments fought magnificently and though greatly outnumbered and out-ranged, fought on and never gave the Germans an opportunity to close with the Support Group or the artillery."**

DEVELOPMENT AND PRODUCTION

The Crusader was the last of the pre-war designs of cruiser tank to see action and it was a development which started in 1936 from a prototype design by the American J. Walter Christie. A War Office party

* *History of the Second World War—The Mediterranean and Middle East.* (H.M.S.O.)

** *Maj. Gen. G. L. Verney. The Desert Rats—History of the 7th Armoured Division.* (Hutchinson.)

An A9 carrying the kit and bedding for a crew of six, in the days when sun helmets were still officially necessary for health in the heat of the desert. (I.W.M.)

The A9 E2, mounting Vickers MGs in two forward sub-turrets. (R.A.C. Tank Museum)

under Major-General Wavell had visited Russia during the summer manoeuvres in 1936, and had seen the *Bystrokhodnii* tanks which were most impressive on account of their speed and mobility, due in great part to the suspension developed from a prototype of the Christie tank. In the following October War Office permission was given to buy the Christie 1932 prototype from America for development of a fast British medium tank, and Lord Nuffield agreed to act as agent in buying the vehicle and patent rights. The tank arrived in November, crated and described as a "tractor" to satisfy suspicious Customs authorities; it was then officially designated A13 E1, and running trials started at once.

But one must go back a little further still in describing the growth of the "cruiser" family of tanks. During the late 1920's and early 1930's, revolutionary concepts of armoured warfare were being evolved in the Tank Brigade in Britain, requiring mobile forces equipped with fast tanks that could strike into the enemy's rear areas; medium tanks—or "cruisers", following the simile of a Fleet action—were to be the main striking force. These concepts, however, received grudging official support when conventional ideas predominated in the General Staff, expecting tanks to be used in slow-moving waves in support of the infantry assault. The conflict of views led to the development of two classes of tank—the slow, heavily armoured "infantry" tank, and the "cruiser" for mobile operations. Even so, money for development of either type was strictly limited, and first priority in tank production was to support peace-keeping operations in "colonial type" wars for which the light tanks were more suitable. It was not until Mussolini's campaign in Abyssinia in 1935 revealed the threat of war against the Axis powers in the Middle East and Europe that the purse strings were loosened. It became imperative to replace the medium tanks of the type that had been in service since 1923. But with no clear General Staff direction upon what was wanted, with a very small design staff and few designs under development, it would take time to achieve production

An A9 of the 1st Royal Tank Regiment in Egypt in 1940, with sand guards over the tracks for desert operations. (I.W.M.)

The A10 prototype modified with dummy Besa MG in front hull mounting. See picture below right for same prototype unmodified
(R.A.C. Tank Museum)

in quantity. Inevitably, production tended to follow the use of known components, without time for major re-design or extensive trials, and at the outbreak of war only 77 of the new cruisers were in service.

A9, CRUISER MARK I

In February 1934 Sir John Carden of Vickers Armstrong was asked to design a reasonably cheap tank to replace some of the mediums, and a pilot model appeared in April 1936 as the A9 E1. It carried only 14 mm. of armour, but it had a speed of 25 m.p.h. and mounted the new 2 pdr. (40 mm.) high velocity gun with a good anti-tank performance. The A9 was not

entirely satisfactory. There were problems with gun fumes, and the suspension gave an uncomfortable and unstable gun platform over rough ground, but in July 1937, after competitive trials against other designs immediately available, the A9 was selected for limited production (125) to meet an urgent but interim need as Cruiser Mark I. First deliveries appeared in January 1939 and the tank saw action in France and the Middle East.

The A9 was a notable advance in one respect in that it was the first to have a powered traverse, the Nash and Thompson hydraulic system which was similar in operation to the Frazer-Nash equipment then being developed for the Vickers Wellington bomber. This

The A10 in desert camouflage. The signalling lamp raised through the roof was similar to one mounted on the Matilda infantry tank. (I.W.M.)

The A10 E1, with dummy guns in the turret and no place for any machine-gun in a hull mounting. (R.A.C. Tank Museum)

3

A13 E2, with a heavier hull than the original Christie 1932 prototype, but running on the same type of track. (R.A.C. Tank Museum)

A13, Mark II, Cruiser Mark IV, the up-armoured version of A13 with spaced armour on the turret. This mark carries the Vickers machine-gun. (I.W.M.)

same system was adapted for all the British cruisers up to Cromwell, and for the Infantry tanks Matilda and Valentine.

A10, CRUISER MARK II

Also in 1936 the pilot A10 appeared from Vickers to a basically similar design but with 30 mm. armour in answer to a demand for a more heavily armoured tank to fight in close support of infantry. With the same engine, and a weight of 14 tons, the A10 had a maximum speed of 16 m.p.h. The added armour protection was provided by attaching extra plates—the first British example of composite armour construction. However, by 1937 it was realised that this armour was insufficient for the role of infantry support, and next year the A10 went into limited production (170) as an interim "heavy" cruiser. First delivery arrived in December 1939, and this basic design was later used by Vickers in development of the Infantry Tank Mark III, Valentine.

A13, CRUISER MARK III AND IV

Neither A9 nor A10 were regarded as fast enough for the cruiser role in the Mobile Division and great hopes were placed upon the development of the Christie tank. The chief merits of this design lay in the suspension, allied to a light but powerful engine which would give a satisfactory power/weight ratio, but the hull of the prototype would have to be enlarged to meet British ideas for the fighting compartment. Two pilots of this project, known as A13, were designed and produced by Nuffield Mechanisations and Aero, Ltd, a newly created armaments firm, and the first was delivered in October 1937, only ten months after the order had been given. These machines were over 2 tons heavier than the original Christie because of the increased armour (14 mm.) and the need to carry a 2 pdr. gun, and these factors, plus inherent defects in the engine and transmission, required extensive re-design and modifications. The initial trials were

A13s, Mk IIA, of the 5th Royal Tank Regiment taking cover beside a hedge in France, 1940. On the side of the turret are the smoke dischargers which projected a 4-inch smoke canister about 150 yards. The furthest tank is a Mk I, without the extra armour on the turret. Mk IIA mounted the Besa machine-gun. (I.W.M.)

An A13, Mk IIA, of the 2nd Royal Tank Regiment in the desert. A later version with an external gun mantlet. (I.W.M.)

country speed of 25 m.p.h. and to weigh about 25 tons; but the projects started under this specification (A14 and A16) proved to have no material advantage over the up-armoured A13.

A13 MARK III, CRUISER MARK V, COVENANTER

A third mark of A13 was then used as the basis for a new "heavy" cruiser project under the Mechanisation Board in conjunction with the L.M.S. Railway (hull), Meadows (engine), and Nuffields (turret); the new tank was to have the same A13 suspension in a lower hull, with a Meadows flat horizontally opposed 12-cylinder engine, and the radiator in the front beside the driver. An important innovation was the Wilson epicyclic steering gears which provided more efficient and flexible steering than the simpler clutch and brake systems used on earlier tanks. The Wilson epicyclic

encouraging but the pilot models suffered many teething troubles. Despite this a production order was given in January 1938, and in December the first deliveries were made of A13 Mark I, as Cruiser Mark III. It was a remarkable achievement in two years from the order for pilot models of a completely new design. To meet the need for 30 mm. armour, a second mark of A13 was then produced as Cruiser Mark IV, but despite the extra weight it could still attain a speed approaching 40 m.p.h. Production of the A13 was also taken up by the L.M.S. Railway, English Electric, and Leylands, and by the time manufacture ceased in 1941 a total of 665 had been made of these two marks.

The A13 was looked upon as a "light" cruiser needing the support of a more powerful "battle" tank, and in April 1937 a specification was drawn up for a "heavy" cruiser as an entirely new medium tank. It was to have a 2 pdr. gun in the main turret plus three machine-guns in sub-turrets, 30 mm. armour, a cross-

A Covenanter I, in which the crew are wearing the protective helmet introduced in the early part of the war but which was seldom, if ever, worn in action. (I.W.M.)

Polish soldiers in Scotland being instructed on the Christie suspension of a Covenanter I. The assembly was mounted on the hull side, protected by the outer skin of armour plate. (I.W.M.)

Covenanter I, followed by Mark II's. The driver's hatch on Crusader was made to open in two halves, so that the forward part could be opened in any position of the turret. (I.W.M.)

Covenanters of 'C' Squadron, 15th/19th The King's Royal Hussars at Ashridge, Herts., July 1941. The nearest is a Mark II. The 15th/19th at this time formed part of 28th Armoured Brigade, 9th Armoured Division. (I.W.M.)

steering units were also fitted in the next mark of cruiser, the Crusader, and later in the Cavalier.

In the haste to produce tanks in quantity, the new design was accepted in April 1939 for production without trials of a pilot model, and a "drawing board order" for production was placed. Deliveries began in the summer of 1940 as Cruiser Mark V, which was later named Covenanter. As trials progressed on the first production models a major weakness was found in the engine cooling system, and tanks were modified in a re-work programme at service workshops and factories. Covenanter Mark II appeared with service modifications to improve the cooling. A third mark then incorporated a new design of air louvres and some internal changes. Finally, Covenanter Mark IV

was produced as a new machine which embodied the improved features of Mark III. Production was given to the L.M.S. Railway, English Electric, and Leylands, who turned out a total of 1,365 Covenanters before manufacture ceased in January 1943.

A15, CRUISER MARK VI, CRUSADER

Meanwhile Nuffields, who had been involved in the development of Covenanter, put forward a proposal in mid-1939 to develop their own version of a "heavy" cruiser from the A13, rather than manufacture Covenanter. This had the advantage of using their own Liberty engine and gearbox, which would minimise

Winston Churchill inspecting the 9th Armoured Division in May 1942, accompanied by Major-General B. G. Horrocks, riding on a Covenanter III of the 4th/7th Royal Dragoon Guards, 27th Armoured Brigade. The Australian Minister for External Affairs, Dr. H. V. Evatt, is on the second tank. The panda's head, formation sign of 9th Armoured, is in the centre of the front plate. The 27th Armoured Brigade was later under command of 79th Armoured Division. (I.W.M.)

Covenanter IV in September 1942, showing air vents in the hull side below the track guard. The air louvres were similar to those on Mark III but the front stowage bins were removed and others mounted on the turret sides. (I.W.M.)

The Covenanter III Bridgelayer could lay, and recover, its Scissors Bridge over a 30 ft. gap for a tracked vehicle load of 30 tons. (I.W.M.)

delays when their production of A13 ceased. As design project A15 it was accepted, and in August 1939, just before the outbreak of war, an initial order was placed without pilot trials. (This designation A15 must not be confused with another and entirely different project for a "heavy" cruiser which was given the same number in 1937. That project did not go beyond design stage.)

The new tank retained the basic engine layout of the A13 Mark II, and mounted an auxiliary machine-gun turret beside the driver, but it incorporated many features of the Covenanter. The hull, however, was lengthened slightly and an extra pair of road wheels was mounted to carry the extra weight and to reduce the ground pressure. In armour protection the new cruiser would have a basic 40 mm. on the front but in mid-1940, even before the first model appeared, demands were made for an increase. This led to the production of Crusader Mark II with 50 mm. armour on the front but identical in other respects.

Initially the armament had included a Besa machine-gun mounted in the front of the driver's hood, but in mid-1940 it was decided to abolish this; a revolver port was fitted in its place. During firing trials at the end of 1940 the auxiliary turret was found to be unsafe because of the very small space and the lack of ventilation, and it was recommended that the auxiliary turret be removed. There was some confusion in the plans for removal, since the tank was well advanced in production, but in practice it was removed from many Crusaders I and II on active service and it disappeared completely from the Crusader III.

The Crusader had been designed to carry the 2 pdr. gun, which was accepted as adequate until experience in France in 1940 emphasized the urgent need for development of the 6 pdr. (57 mm.) as a tank weapon. In fact, the Director of Artillery had anticipated the General Staff in 1938 by initiating the design of a 6 pdr. anti-tank equipment which was accepted in March 1940, generally to replace the 2 pdr. Trials of the gun started in the summer of 1940 but it was not

The Anti-Mine Roller Attachment, mounted here on a Covenanter, consisted of a framework carrying spring-mounted and castoring rollers wide enough to cover the track path of the tank. (I.W.M.)

Crusader prototype which mounted a Besa machine-gun in the front of the driver's hood. This gun was removed and a revolver port fitted in place. (R.A.C. Tank Museum)

Front view of Crusader. (I.W.M.)

until the end of 1941 that first delivery could be made from production for both field and tank mountings. No action was taken initially to mount the 6 pdr. in Crusader because a new cruiser, Cavalier, was to be designed for the purpose, to coincide with delivery of the gun. However, after unforeseen delays with Cavalier, Nuffields were eventually asked in September 1941 to re-design the Crusader turret for 6 pdr. This was quickly done and deliveries of Crusader III were made in May 1942.

The A13 had its mechanical troubles and Crusader inherited many, plus those in new components common to the Covenanter, which were not eradicated until much later when the tank was almost obsolescent. But, a total of 4,350 gun tanks were produced, plus 1,373 in special roles, and Crusader became the standard British tank of the armoured brigades in action until replaced by the American Grants and Shermans.

DESCRIPTION OF CRUSADER

All three marks of Crusader were generally the same, the main differences being in the thickness of armour and the new 6 pdr. turret in Crusader III. The hull was formed by a structure of hardened steel plates to which the homogeneous armour plate was bolted, the whole being braced by three transverse bulkheads and by the cross-tubes through which the suspension axle arm shafts stretched right across the floor. The suspension assemblies were mounted on the hull sides in a space between the inner and outer plates. The bulkheads divided the hull into four compartments, the two at the rear containing the engine and transmission which drove the rear track sprockets. The crew of five were in the two forward compartments.

The driver sat on the right of the front compartment, under a raised hood, separated from the front gunner by a partition with access hole. The gear change lever was between his knees and steering levers on either side were mounted above the compressed air steering control valves. Normal accelerator, brake

and clutch pedals provided driving controls, and a parking ratchet connected to the foot brake held the brakes on for parking. Armoured and prismatic visors were mounted on an outward opening door on the front plate of the driver's hood; the prisms could be quickly changed if damaged but, if necessary, the driver could raise the armoured visor over the aperture to see through narrow slits. A revolver port was fitted to the right of the visor, and on the right side of the hood was a shutter-type look-out. The front gunner was enclosed in the small auxiliary turret mounting a Besa machine-gun which could be traversed through 150° by handwheel. When closed down, the gunner had no vision apart from the telescopic sight. Where this turret was removed, the space below was used for storage of kit and extra ammunition. The unsatisfactory nature of the auxiliary turret led to development of the ball-mounted Besa in the straight front which later appeared in the Cavalier and Cromwell.

The turret was polygonal in shape, formed by welded, hardened steel plates to which the outer armour plate was bolted. The following description of the turret arrangement applies to the Crusader I and II, and material differences in Crusader III will be

Crusader, showing a view of the top deck of the hull with hatches, fuel tank, and auxiliary turret. (R.A.C. Tank Museum)

Test model of Crusader I, which had the A13 type of gun mantlet. The bulbous external mantlet came later, but both types are found on Crusader and Covenanter. Note the hinged aerial base at the rear of the turret, used with the No. 9 set. (R.A.C. Tank Museum)

outlined later. The turntable suspended from the turret carried the crew of three, commander, loader/wireless operator and gunner.

The commander sat in the centre, behind the gun, with a single, standard rotating periscope mounted in the roof for vision. Additionally for the commander there was a look-out with triplex block on each side of the turret. Vision for the gunner was provided by a shutter type look-out in the turret front plate, whilst the loader/operator had a periscope in the turret roof. A single blade vane sight for the commander was fitted on the front edge of the turret roof to help direct the gunner who sat on the left of the co-axially mounted 2 pdr. and Besa guns.

The guns moved freely in elevation under shoulder control and were fired mechanically from trigger grips in the right hand. Traverse was by the left hand,

The Commander-in-Chief Home Forces, General Sir Bernard Paget, following the progress of a major armoured exercise in September 1942 from the turret of a Crusader. (I.W.M.)

either by spade grip on the powered traverse or by handwheel. Under power the turret could be rotated completely in 10 seconds as well as controlled for fine-laying on the target.

Lack of ventilation was a weakness in this turret, even though cooling air for the radiators was partially drawn from the turret when the engine was running; space was made for air to be drawn under the back of the roof door when closed down, but this was not sufficient and an extractor fan was fitted in Crusader III above the guns. Besides attending to both guns and the wireless set, the loader/operator also controlled the 2-inch bomb thrower, which was mounted on the right of the turret front plate but independently of the main gun mounting.

The wireless set was fitted in the bulge at the back of the turret and in earlier models this was the No. 9 set, with a single aerial on a bracket at the back of the turret, providing communication on a single net. However, the majority of Crusaders had the No. 19 set which consisted of two sets ("A" and "B") with two separate aerial bases on the roof.

The Crusader III with 6 pdr. gun carried a turret crew of two, the loader/commander on the right, and the gunner. The roof door was replaced by two doors hinged on the turret sides. Three periscopes were mounted, one for the gunner and two for the loader/commander of which one was in the right hand roof door. The 2-inch bomb thrower was re-mounted to fire through the roof, forward of the loader, whilst the Besa machine-gun was moved across to the left of the main gun.

On both sides of the engine compartment were the fuel tanks, against the hull sides, and between them and the engine were two radiators housed almost vertically. Two chain-driven fans, mounted in the bulkhead at the rear of the engine compartment, drew cooling air through louvres above the radiators and partly from the turret. In addition to the main fuel tanks, an auxiliary fuel tank was fitted at the rear; it

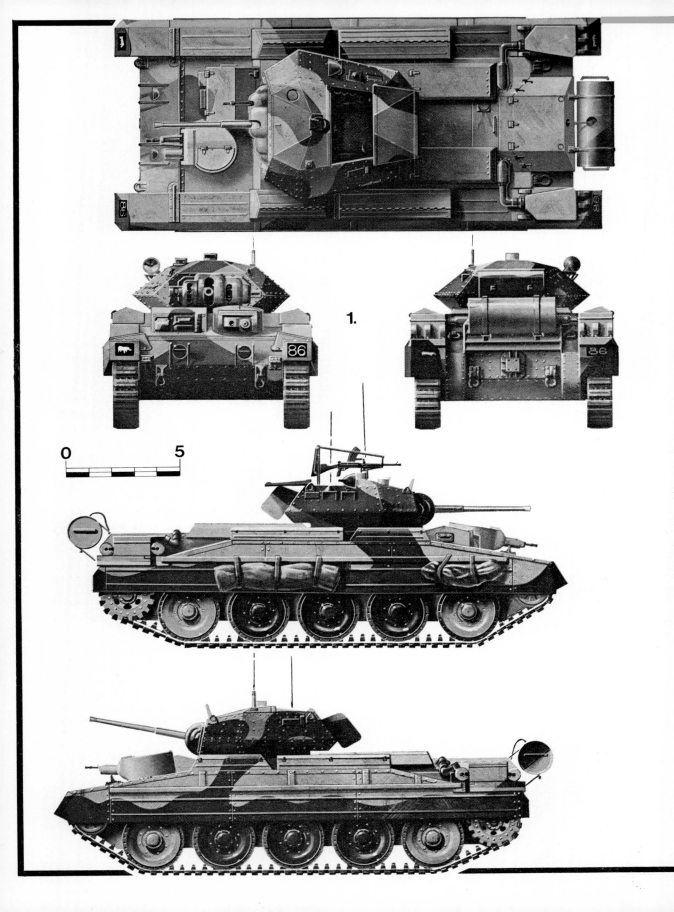

1.

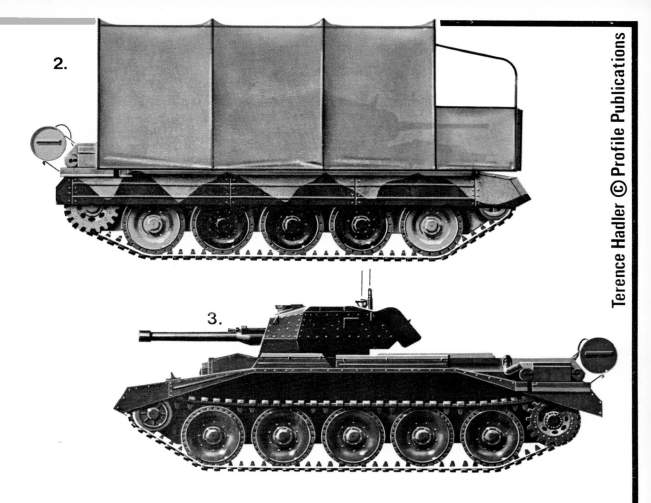

2.

3.

Terence Hadler © Profile Publications

1. Crusader II with auxiliary sub-turret, of the 9th Queen's Lancers, 1st Armoured Division. The 9th Lancers arrived in the Western Desert in December, 1941.

2. Crusader in desert disguise. The ''Sun Shield'' as it was called was a cage of hessian covered tubing intended to make the tank resemble a large lorry at a distance.

3. Crusader III (6 pounder) of 6th Armoured Division in Tunisia where it retained its U.K. camouflage.

4. Formation Signs of Armoured Divisions that fought with Crusaders in North Africa, from left to right:- 1st, 10th, 6th and 7th.

4.

Crusader patrol in the desert. The pennants on the aerials were fixed in different positions each day for identification purposes. (I.W.M.)

could quickly be jettisoned by hand controls from the fighting compartment. Oil bath air cleaners for the carburettors were mounted externally at the rear end of each track guard. To combat fire in the engine and transmission compartments, distributor nozzles were connected to a Pyrene carbon dioxide cylinder in the fighting compartment; the system was released manually.

The Wilson epicyclic steering units were mounted on each end of the gearbox, designed with two brake bands and gear trains to "drive" and "steer". Use of the "steering" gear train, in effect, meant changing gear down for that track and so permitting gradual turns with power to both tracks, but for sharp, skid turns a positive brake was applied to the appropriate track through the main brake drums. Control of the brake bands on steering units and main brake drums was by compressed air which was supplied by a compressor system mounted on the front of the engine.

This system was of vital importance because the tank could neither be moved nor steered if the air supply failed.

Compressed air was stored in a cylinder at the front of the engine compartment and delivered to the control valves operated by the driver's steering levers. The foot brake pedal operated mechanically on both main brake drums simultaneously, but this did not have the power of the pneumatic steering controls.

The suspension was adapted from the original Christie design which provided a fast and stable gun platform. Crusader could not attain the speed of the A13, being nearly 5 tons heavier and powered by the same engine, but the Christie suspension was again to prove itself at speed in the Cromwell.

One external feature was the Lakeman anti-aircraft mounting. It was a simple detachable device mounted on a spigot on the left side of the turret, with springs to balance the weight of the Bren light machine-gun suspended from hooks.

CRUSADERS IN SPECIALIST ROLES

Although Crusader was mechanically unreliable at first, the main faults were overcome in the production of later versions of specialist vehicles for which there was no other chassis available. Some of these saw action in North-West Europe in 1944:

CRUSADER COMMAND TANK

To provide more space for working in command tanks at brigade or divisional headquarters, and for more wireless sets, the turret guns were removed and replaced by a dummy gun to retain the same general appearance. Otherwise these were normal gun tanks.

The tank crews' cooking arrangements were simple but quick to prepare the evening meal before bedding down beside the tank. (I.W.M.)

A heavy lift for a radiator change on a Crusader II from the regimental Light Aid Detachment. (I.W.M.)

CRUSADER III (OP)

These served as observation posts in artillery regiments supporting armoured units equipped with Crusader; the 6 pdr. gun and mounting was removed and replaced by a dummy; the Besa machine-gun was retained for protection. For communication to infantry and armoured units, one No. 18 and two No. 19 sets were carried in the turret with cable reels, extra batteries and auxiliary charging engine in the forward compartment beside the driver. Identification is possible through the extra aerial on the turret and the auxiliary engine silencer on the front hull roof plate.

CRUSADER III ANTI-AIRCRAFT

Three versions were issued, each with three-man crew. Mark I with 40 mm. Bofors was issued to artillery units; this had hydraulic powered traverse driven by a small two-stroke engine in the fighting compartment and controlled by joystick from the gunlayer's seat. The gun could also be controlled by hand in independent traverse and elevation, but the handles were normally removed. Marks II and III were issued to anti-aircraft troops of armoured units and mounted twin Oerlikon (20 mm.) with co-axial gas-operated

A Crusader I towing a captured SP 15 cm. howitzer Lorraine Schlepper (SdKfz 135/1), a German conversion of the French Lorraine tractor. (I.W.M.)

Vickers machine-gun for ground protection; hydraulic powered traverse was adapted from the normal tank arrangement. In Mark III the wireless set was moved from the turret to the left forward compartment where it was operated by the driver, and the turret was extended to give more room for the commander/gunner in the rear of the turret.

The No. 9 set aerial base was made to hinge back so that the aerial and pennants would be less conspicuous in action. The white, red, white stripes on the nose, for recognition, were dropped later. (I.W.M.)

Tank casualties in the desert were heavy, either from enemy action or from breakdowns. Quick recovery for repair during the battle was vital. A Crusader I with No. 9 set. (I.W.M.)

Crusader II moving with Shermans along a well-used track. (I.W.M.)

CRUSADER ARMOURED RECOVERY VEHICLE

The A.R.V. was based on the Crusader hull, fitted with tools and equipment for front line repairs and recovery, and with a jib crane for lifting major assemblies. Twin Bren A.A. machine-guns could be mounted in the space of the fighting compartment. One A.R.V. was normally deployed to each squadron.

CRUSADER GUN TRACTOR

This was designed to tow the 17 pdr. anti-tank gun, with a completely new arrangement of the hull carrying a crew of eight and 40 rounds of 17 pdr. ammunition. The 17 pdr. gave the British forces a weapon which could defeat the Tiger and the Panther, and this gun tractor was reported as mechanically reliable and a success in Normandy in 1944.

CRUSADER BULLDOZER

This had the dozer blade attached by arms to the side of the tank, suspended from a jib and controlled by a

The Atherton Jack fixed to the Crusader turret to lift out the engine. (I.W.M.)

winch in the fighting compartment. The turret was removed.

EMPLOYMENT OF THE EARLY CRUISERS

COVENANTER

The Covenanter was not a success as a fighting vehicle. There was a host of minor defects, particularly affecting the compressed air system which controlled the transmission and steering, and many of the parts needing repair and maintenance were almost inaccessible. The engine cooling system, however, was the main weakness and this restricted the tank's use to temperate areas only until Mark IV was produced. But by then the Crusader was in full production for the battles in the Middle East. Covenanter stayed at home, where it was extensively used as a training vehicle in the re-

In the desert fighting superstructures to disguise cruiser tanks as lorries were widely used, to be discarded in the final stages of the approach march. To complete the illusion the centre roadwheels were blacked out. (I.W.M.)

Crusader II Close Support in a tank column with Shermans moving up at El Alamein. This tank has had extra armour plates bolted on the glacis and nose plates, an unusual addition. (I.W.M.)

equipment and build-up of forces after the losses on the Continent in 1940.

The need for more armoured formations was urgent, whether in preparation for future offensives in Europe or the Middle East, or in defence of Great Britain against the very real threat of invasion. During the next three years the Covenanter was widely deployed in the re-equipment and training of many units converting to the new tactics of armoured warfare, from the 1st Polish Armoured Division in Scotland, to the 9th Armoured Division on the East Coast, to the Guards Armoured Division in the South. Regimental histories write of the value gained from training with the Covenanter and, in overcoming its maintenance problems, of their preparation for more

difficult situations later. Tank crews at the time did not take such a dispassionate view as they struggled to keep their machines fit. But, for all its defects and the mistakes in the hurried production of the tank, Covenanter temporarily filled a vital gap in the build-up and training of new armoured forces.

In the development of mine-clearing devices, the Anti-Mine Roller Attachment was fitted to the Covenanter, as well as to other tanks of that period. It consisted of heavy rollers carried on a frame and positioned so that they covered the track path of the tank, but the device was not an operational success.

The Covenanter Mark IV Bridgelayer, however, was a more promising development, with a Scissors Bridge of the same type as that mounted on the Valentine. It could bridge a gap of 30 ft. and carry a tracked vehicle load of 30 tons. Like the other Covenanters it was used for training and was not called upon for operational use by British forces, but it was used by the Australian Army against the Japanese in 1945. There are at least two recorded instances of the Covenanter Bridgelayer being used in jungle operations on Bougainville Island in support of the Matildas of 2/4 Australian Armoured Regiment.

Not an impressive fighting record for the Covenanter but, at least, it was represented on the battlefield before the end.

A9, A10 AND A13

The other cruiser tanks in production before the war were generally known by their numbers and had no type names. They went into battle in France and the Middle East in 1940 and provided the main striking power of the armoured divisions until replaced by the

The dreaded 88 mm. Flak gun. A First Army Crusader in Tunisia passes one that has been silenced. (I.W.M.)

Crusader. In my own experience with A13s in France and with A10s and A13s in the Western Desert, these cruisers were, in their time and in the balance of gunpower and armour, the equal in quality with their German opponents—Pz Kpfw III and Pz Kpfw IV. The weakness in France lay in numbers, when two armoured brigades of 1st Armoured Division with a total of about 150 hastily issued A9s and A13s landed at Calais and Cherbourg in May in an attempt to check the German *blitzkrieg*. At Calais all were lost but some of the cruisers and light tanks south of the Somme returned to England after a series of long and tiring moves that ended in a grim race for Cherbourg against Rommel's 7th Panzer Division.

In Egypt the 7th Armoured Division was then reinforced to provide each armoured regiment with a balance of cruisers (A9, A10 and A13) and Light Tanks Mark VI. The balance was achieved in different ways and when the 3rd The King's Own Hussars arrived with a full complement of light tanks, one squadron was exchanged for an A10 squadron from the 2nd Royal Tank Regiment which had all cruisers.

In General Wavell's campaign against the Italians in Libya the division struck fast and wide through the desert to hold the ring during December 1940 and January 1941, whilst Matilda tanks with 4th Indian Division broke into the forts at Sidi Barrani and supported the 6th Australian Division in capturing Bardia and Tobruk. Then, striking across 240 miles of desert in Cyrenaica, 7th Armoured Division with only 39 cruisers in action caught the retreating Italians at Beda Fomm and completed the annihilation of the Italian Tenth Army.

Against Rommel's Afrika Korps in 1941 the same cruisers continued the fighting alongside the Matildas in Tobruk, and provided the mobile striking force of 7th Armoured Division in the battles on the Egyptian frontier until replaced by Crusader. The A9 and A10 were the first to go but in General Auchinleck's offensive to relieve Tobruk in November 1941, the A13s still formed half the strength of 7th Armoured Brigade. In the fighting at Sidi Rezegh and in the days that followed, the A13 made a gallant departure from the battlefield.

TACTICAL EMPLOYMENT OF CRUSADER

Crusader first went into action in June 1941 on the western frontier of Egypt, in the abortive operation "Battleaxe" aimed at the relief of Tobruk. The tanks had been shipped in the "Tiger" convoy which had been fought through the Mediterranean in May with urgent reinforcements of tanks, aircraft, and ammunition, and Winston Churchill expected good use to be made of his "Tiger Cubs". In the event there were delays in preparing the tanks for desert operations and in training the crews, and only one regiment of Crusaders was ready in June to fight beside the A9s and A13s in 7th Armoured Brigade. Much was expected of the new cruiser tank, but the attack was shattered against the skilfully deployed and concealed anti-tank guns. It was the first major confrontation between British and German tanks and many were the

The re-designed turret for the 6 pdr. gun in Crusader III provided two sideways opening hatches in the roof. The 2-inch bomb-thrower was positioned to fire through the roof, and an extractor fan was mounted above the guns. (R.A.C. Tank Museum)

Front view of Crusader III. This particular tank is now in the R.A.C. Tank Museum.

complaints afterwards about unreliable tanks which mounted a 2 pdr. gun that could do no damage at the ranges they were themselves receiving punishment from the enemy. The criticisms were not, however, entirely justified in comparison with the German tanks; the Pz Kpfw III with short 50 mm. gun held

Crusader III crossing an anti-tank ditch at Mersa Matruh in the advance after El Alamein, November 1942. (I.W.M.)

A Crusader III of the 6th Armoured Division on the Bou Arada road in Tunisia, wearing the green camouflage of the Anglo-American forces in the fighting during the winter of 1942/43. (I.W.M.)

no advantage in range over the cruisers, and the low velocity 75 mm. gun on the Pz Kpfw IV was not a "tank killer", even though it could shell the British tanks at longer ranges. The main cause of the British tank casualties was the 88 mm. Flak gun, sited and used in the anti-tank role, and the new 50 mm. Pak 38 anti-tank gun.

In the next major action in November 1941, operation "Crusader", the cruiser tank strength was increased by the arrival of three yeomanry regiments in 22nd Armoured Brigade fully equipped with Crusaders. In five weeks of bitter fighting the Afrika Korps was driven from Cyrenaica, but the toll was heavy. Again it was the 88 mm. gun and the 50 mm. Pak 38 in larger numbers which caused the most damage as Rommel skilfully used his anti-tank weapons in close co-operation with his tanks. The most effective British answer to both was the 25 pdr. field gun, but the British formations were neither organized nor trained for such close combination

Crusader II followed by Crusader III advancing in Tunisia with Eighth Army, near the end of the Battle of Mareth, March 19-29, 1943. These are tanks of the 9th Queen's Royal Lancers, 1st Armoured Division. (I.W.M.)

between tanks and artillery. This was improved later but the tank crews wanted a heavier anti-tank gun and their own high explosive weapon.

The armoured brigade in the Middle East in 1941 contained three armoured regiments each totalling 52 cruisers in three squadrons. In each squadron there were four troops each of three tanks, and four tanks at squadron headquarters where two were for close support, armed with a 3-inch Howitzer. The close support tanks were useful in providing protective smoke, but their HE performance was poor both in range and in lethality. Early in the following year the Grant tank began to arrive in the Middle East and was incorporated in the Crusader regiments on the basis of one squadron of Grants to two of Crusaders. With its 75 mm. gun the regiments at last had a weapon with which they could hit back at longer range. At the same time, however, the Afrika Korps began to receive the Pz Kpfw III (J) Special—with long 50 mm. gun—which had the advantage in range over the 2 pdr. Crusader. It was not until the summer of 1942, when the Eighth Army was back on the El Alamein line, that the Crusader III—with 6 pdr.—began to arrive in Egypt.

The 6 pdr. was useless as an HE weapon but it was a most effective anti-tank gun which enabled the Crusader III to compete with the formidable Pz Kpfw IV with the long 75 mm. gun when that too arrived in the desert. The Grant and Crusader III made a strong combination. At the Battle of El Alamein some 300 Crusaders were deployed to all three armoured divisions, and of these about one third were Crusader III. The proportion of 6 pdr. tanks increased steadily as the Eighth Army fought its way westwards to Tunisia, but the Sherman was gradually superseding Crusader.

In the First Army invasion in Algeria and Tunisia, the 6th Armoured Division was equipped with Crusaders until they could be replaced by a special diversion of Shermans in February 1943. At the end of the North African campaign the Crusader went out of service as a combat tank except in the specialist roles.

Crusaders were under-gunned for their time, a failing shared with most British tanks in the war years.

Sir James Grigg, Secretary of State for War, climbing onto a Crusader Command tank of HQ 11th Armoured Division. Extra wireless aerials and a mapboard are mounted on the roof, while a dummy gun is fitted in the mantlet. (I.W.M.)

Repairs to a Crusader III of 6th Armoured Division in Tunisia. Holders for smoke dischargers, known as rear smoke emitters, can be seen on each side. This tank mounts a substantial towing hook. (I.W.M.)

Another common failing was shown in the reputation for unreliability, due largely to the complexity and need for constant maintenance. Tank crews were glad to exchange their Crusaders for Grants and Shermans. But for nearly two years the Crusader was the only modern British cruiser tank fit for operations, and it led, through the Cavalier and Centaur, to the Cromwell which proved in 1944 to be an effective, fast and reliable tank during operations in North-West Europe.

A.F.V. Series Editor : DUNCAN CROW

SPECIFICATION

A15 CRUISER MARK VI—CRUSADER II

General
Crew: Five—commander, gunner, loader/wireless operator, driver front gunner.
Battle weight: 19 tons.
Bridge classification: 19.
Power/weight ratio: 17·9 to 1 b.h.p./ton.
Ground pressure: 14·65 lb./sq. in.

Dimensions
Length overall: 19 ft. 7½ in.
Length including fuel tank: 20 ft. 8½ in.
Height overall: 7 ft. 4 in.
Width over track guards: 8 ft. 8 in.
Width over sand shields: 9 ft. 1 in.
Width over tracks: 8 ft. 5½ in.
Track centres: 7 ft. 6¾ in.
Track width: 10·7 in.
Length of track on ground: 11 ft. 4 in.

Armament
Main—QF 2 pdr. Mark IX or X.
Auxiliary—Two 7·92 mm. Besa machine-guns one co-axially mounted and one in auxiliary turret (which was often removed). Bomb thrower 2-in. mounted in turret front plate. ·303 Bren light machine-gun.

Crusader fitted for wading trials. (I.W.M.)

The Crusader Armoured Recovery Vehicle showing the method of staying the jib crane by brackets fixed to the tracks. Twin Bren light machine-guns could be mounted in the cockpit. (I.W.M.)

Crusader III AA Mark I with 3-man crew, mounting the 40 mm. Bofors gun, used by light anti-aircraft artillery units. Normally operated by hydraulic power in traverse and elevation by joystick from the gunlayer's seat. (I.W.M.)

Standing-by to protect a column of tanks moving forward in Normandy, a Crusader III AA Mark III of the East Riding Yeomanry of 27th Armoured Brigade. (I.W.M.)

Fire Control

Turret: Shoulder controlled in free elevation ($+20°$ to $-15°$). Traverse by hydraulic power from variable flow pump driven by main engine, with auxiliary hand traverse. Mechanically operated firing gear from pistol grips.

Auxiliary turret: Mechanical firing gear, free elevation. Traverse 150° by handwheel.

Ammunition

2 pdr.: 110.
Besa: 4,500 (20 boxes)—with auxiliary turret.
Bren: 600.
Bomb thrower: 26.

Crusader III AA Mark III, of the 4th/7th Royal Dragoon Guards, loading on to a tail flat. The co-axial Vickers MG is clearly visible. (I.W.M.)

Sighting and Vision

Commander: Periscope centrally in roof. Look-out with visor and Triplex block on both sides of turret.
Loader: Periscope in roof.
Turret gunner: Telescopic Sight No. 30 Mark I and IA, or No. 33. Shutter type look-out in turret front plate.
Front gunner: Telescope.
Driver: Armoured visor in front plate of hood and shutter type look-out on right side.

Communications

Wireless Set No. 19. Two sets "A" (squadron/regimental net) and "B" (troop net). Intercommunications between all crew.

Armour

Hull: Riveted skin of hardened steel, outer armour bolted. Detachable armour plate over suspension assemblies mounted on hull sides of hardened steel plate.
Thicknesses are aggregate of steel skin and armour plate.
Front: 30 mm./30°.
Driver's hood front: 40 mm. (cast visor and pistol port nominal 50 mm.).
Glacis: 20 mm./60°.
Nose: 33 mm./29°.
Side inner: 14 mm.
    outer: 14 mm.
Rear: 28 mm./11°.
Top: 7 mm.
Floor: 10 mm.
Turret: Welded skin, outer armour bolted.
Front: 49 mm./7°.
Sides: 24 mm./45°.
Rear: 30 mm./32°.
Top: 12 mm.

Engine

Nuffield Liberty Mark III, petrol, 45° V-12 cylinder, water cooled, 27 litres. 340 b.h.p. at 1,500 r.p.m. Fuel—110 gallons in main tanks, 30 gallons in auxiliary tank.

A Crusader Dozer which was specially protected and fitted with a crane and grab for removing unexploded ammunition after fires at the Royal Ordnance Factory, Kirkby. Salvage work extended over three months without a single casualty. (I.W.M.)

Crusader III AA Mark II, with twin 40 mm. Oerlikon. The sign on the turret is that of a trials establishment. (R.A.C. Tank Museum)

The Crusader III Gun Tractor for the 17 pdr. gun, with a re-designed hull to carry a crew of eight. It was a reliable and successful vehicle in the 1944 campaign in North-West Europe. (I.W.M)

Transmission

Clutch: Multi-plate, dry.
Gearbox: Mechanisations and Aero Ltd., constant mesh second, third and fourth gears. Four forward speeds and reverse.

Steering: Dual two-speed Wilson epicyclic steering units, or skid steering. Both pneumatic operation.
Brakes: External contracting.
Final Drive Reduction: 4·08 to 1.

Suspension

Christie Type, five road wheels each side on pivoting axle arms supported in cross tubes fixed to bottom plate of hull. Hydraulic shock absorbers fitted to all except centre assembly. Track rests on centre road wheels returning round idler (tensioner) at front.
Track: 118 links each side with centre lug, manganese steel.
Pitch: 4·035 in.

Electrical System

12 volt system, with two 6 volt batteries mounted in fighting compartment.

Performance

Maximum speed: 27·5 m.p.h. (governed engine).
Vertical obstacle: 2 ft. 6 in.
Trench: 7 ft. 6 in.
Wading depth: 3 ft. 3 in.
Road range: 200 miles.
Cross country range: 146 miles.

CRUISER TANK SERIES

Name	Weight Tons	Armament	Armour	Engine	Remarks
A9 Cruiser Mark I	12·5	1 2 pdr. 3 Vickers ·303 MG	14 mm.	AEC Petrol 150 b.h.p.	Close support version mounted 3·7-in. Mortar
A10 Cruiser Mark II	13·75	1 2 pdr. 1 Vickers ·303 MG	30 mm.	AEC Petrol 150 b.h.p.	Close support version mounted 3·7-in. Mortar. Mark IIA mounted 2 Besa (one in hull)
A13 Mark I Cruiser Mark III	14·2	1 2 pdr. 1 Vickers ·303 MG	14 mm.	Nuffield Liberty I 340 b.h.p.	
A13 Mark II Cruiser Mark IV	14·75	1 2 pdr. 1 Vickers ·303 MG	30 mm.	Nuffield Liberty I 340 b.h.p.	Spaced armour on turret Mark IVA mounted Besa instead of Vickers MG
A13 Mark III Cruiser Mark V Covenanter	18	1 2 pdr. 1 Besa	40 mm.	Meadows D.A.V. 280 b.h.p.	Four marks of Covenanter. Close support version mounted 3-in. Howitzer
A15 Cruiser Mark VI Crusader I	18·8	1 2 pdr. 2 Besa	40 mm.	Nuffield Liberty II 340 b.h.p.	Auxiliary turret with Besa MG sometimes removed. Close support version mounted 3-in. Howitzer
Crusader II	19	1 2 pdr. 2 Besa	49 mm.	Nuffield Liberty III 340 b.h.p.	
Crusader III	19·75	1 6 pdr. 1 Besa	51 mm.	Nuffield Liberty III or IV 340 b.h.p.	Three-man crew
Crusader III (OP)	19·5	1 Besa	51 mm.	Nuffield Liberty III or IV 340 b.h.p.	Artillery observation post tank. Extra wireless sets, dummy 6 pdr. gun
Crusader III AA Mark I	19	1 40 mm. Bofors		Nuffield Liberty III or IV 340 b.h.p.	
Crusader III AA Mark II and III	19	2 20 mm. Oerlikon 1 Vickers, gas operated ·303 MG		Nuffield Liberty III or IV 340 b.h.p.	Mark III with extended turret at rear and wireless aerial on front hull compartment
Crusader Gun Tractor	23			Nuffield Liberty III or IV 340 b.h.p.	Redesigned hull to carry crew and ammunition for 17 pdr. gun

Cromwell's war of movement begins: August 15, 1944 and a Cromwell IV finds the turn of speed for which it was designed, racing eastward towards Falaise at the spearhead of the pincer movement which trapped the remnants of 15 German divisions.

(Photo: Imperial War Museum)

Cromwell

by Major James Bingham, Royal Tank Regiment

THE Cromwell tank first went into action in June 1944 in Normandy with the 7th Armoured Division, known from its famous insignia as the "Desert Rats". The Division had fought in all the campaigns in the Western Desert of Egypt since June 1940, from Alamein to the capture of Tunis, and then in Italy up to the River Volturno when it was withdrawn to England. Re-equipped with the new British Cromwell, faster and more powerful than its predecessors in the family line of cruisers, the Division landed in Normandy on D+1. The country through which they had to fight during the next two months, the *bocage*, is not attractive for tank action, being heavily wooded, with many small fields, farms, high-banked hedgerows and narrow roads. It hampered the light, nimble cruisers and favoured the defensive use of the more heavily armoured and powerfully gunned German Tigers and Panthers. It was only after the breakout from the bridgehead, which the German armour had tried desperately to prevent, that the Cromwell came into its own, in the rôle for which it had been designed.

The History of the Royal Tank Regiment illustrates the rôle of the Cromwell in these operations:

"It was on September 2, when the other armoured divisions made only a limited advance, that the 7th Armoured Division made its deepest thrust—with 1st R.T.R. led by Pat Hobart as its spearhead. Starting at dawn 60 miles behind the line already reached by the 11th and Guards Armoured Divisions, at midnight that spearhead was further north than either of them had gone by that time. It had advanced over 70 miles, despite more resistance and threat of interference than they had met—as it was travelling closer to the back of the German Fifteenth Army in the Pas de Calais sector. The 'Desert Rats', now free from the cramping conditions of Normandy, were recovering the form that had made them famous." (Captain B. H. Liddell-Hart, Vol. II, *The Tanks*, Cassell, 1959, pp. 404-5).

DEVELOPMENT HISTORY

The Cromwell belonged to the family of cruiser tanks which had been developed from the General Staff policy of the 1930's that stated a need for two quite different types of tank. One was the "infantry" tank, slow and heavily armoured, designed to support infantry against strongly held positions. The other was the "cruiser", lightly armoured and mobile, which was seen in the traditional cavalry rôle of exploiting a breakthrough. This basic philosophy persisted in Britain for most of the war and, even though the so-called infantry tank had sometimes to be used in the rôle considered appropriate to the cruiser, it governed the development of separate types until a reliable general purpose tank, the Centurion (the A.41), could be produced with adequate gun and armour. Experience against the Germans in 1940 produced demands for a tank gun bigger than the 2-pdr. (40 mm.) then in use but policy on the cruiser still stressed the importance of speed over armour and armament until November 1940 when the War Office stated their need for more heavily armed tanks. In January 1941 designs were sought for a cruiser with front armour 75/65 mm., weight 24 tons, mounting a 6-pdr. (57 mm.) gun on a 60-inch turret ring. This was a significant advance upon the cruisers of pre-war design then in production, the Cruiser Mk. V Covenanter (A.13 Mk. III) and Cruiser Mk. VI Crusader (A.15), but a full year was to pass before prototypes of the new design were to appear. In that period of 1940–41, quantity in production was all important.

Three designs emerged from the 1941 specification for a heavier cruiser and were to go into service:

A.24 Cruiser Mk. VII Cavalier. Nuffield Mechanization and Aero were initially approached by the Ministry of Supply and a design was produced incorporating the Liberty engine and other components of the Crusader. Six pilot models were ordered and the first appeared in January 1942 although a production order for 500 had already been placed in June 1941. This was one of the last "off-the-drawing-board" orders to be placed as a short cut to production before thorough testing of pilots.

A.27 Cruiser Mk. VIII. Leyland Motors were later asked to accept parentage of a design similar to the A.24 Cavalier after they had themselves, in collaboration with Rolls-Royce, put forward a suggestion early in 1941 for the Rolls-Royce Merlin aircraft engine to be adapted as a tank engine. This engine, to be called the Meteor, was to be used with the Merritt-Brown gearbox with controlled differential steering which had already been installed in the Churchill (Infantry Tank Mk. IV). However, the Meteor engine could not be made available in sufficient numbers at first and Leyland were asked to develop an alternative design with the Liberty engine, which was the only developed engine of sufficient power available in adequate numbers. These two designs were allotted numbers and

D+1—A Centaur IV 95-mm. howitzer assault tank of "H" Troop, 2nd Battery, 1 Royal Marine Armoured Support Regiment moves inland from the Normandy beaches.
(Photo: Imperial War Museum)

A troop of Cromwell IVs poised on July 18, 1944 for the opening of General Montgomery's offensive east of the River Orne, Normandy.
(Photo: Imperial War Museum)

The ancestry of the A.27 Centaur and Cromwell cruisers is clearly seen in this A.15 Crusader III 6-pdr. gun tank, N. Africa 1943.
(Photo: Imperial War Museum)

names: A.27 (L) Centaur—Liberty engine; A.27 (M) Cromwell—Meteor engine.

Leyland Motors accepted parentage of the Centaur and in 1942 turned their factory over completely to tank production. Design work on Centaur started in November 1941 in conjunction with Morris Engines (engine) and David Brown (transmission). The first pilot model appeared in June 1942 and early production tanks were delivered by the end of the year.

The Centaur was designed to accept the Meteor and when this engine was fitted to a number of these tanks in 1943 they were renamed Cromwell X. Meanwhile, the Birmingham Railway Carriage and Wagon Company had temporarily accepted parentage of the Cromwell in September 1941 and working in conjunction with Rolls-Royce (engine), David Brown (transmission) and Leyland Motors (tracks and sprockets), produced the first pilot model in January 1942 at about the same time as the Cavalier emerged from Nuffield Mechanization.

Cavalier's performance was no better than the pre-war Crusader, using the same unreliable engine, and there was clearly no reserve of power available to enable further progress with the project. Production vehicles were initially used only for training purposes until 1943 when half of them were converted to armoured OPs for artillery regiments. In this guise some were used in North-West Europe in 1944-45 by the artillery regiments of armoured divisions. Some other Cavaliers were converted to armoured recovery vehicles.

The Meteor, however, with 600 b.h.p. offered scope for use in heavier tanks while still retaining a satisfactory power/weight ratio. In fact, the Meteor with the Merritt-Brown gearbox together provided the answers to many problems in the power plant and transmissions of fast or heavier tanks, and the Cromwell became the basic tank upon which to build specialist vehicles and variations in armament or armour. Production of Cromwell started in January 1943.

Up to this point the Cromwell had been designed to mount the 6-pdr. gun. Official policy in 1941–42 required a tank gun which was primarily a good anti-tank weapon and, within its class, the 6-pdr. answered this need. During this period the 6-pdr. tank was the principal demand from production. But experience in the open warfare in North Africa had shown that tanks infrequently fought tanks when effecting a breakthrough; the main targets were anti-tank guns, infantry and other soft targets. This called for a weapon with a better high explosive (HE) shell. The American 75-mm. gun used in the Sherman was a good dual-purpose gun and strong demands were made for a similar weapon in British tanks. This led to a reversal of the General Staff policy with a statement on January 3, 1943 which required the greater proportion of tanks of the medium class to mount a weapon which was effective both with HE and also against enemy armour of the type so far encountered. It was agreed that tanks so armed would be supported by others either mounting high-powered armour piercing (AP) or close support weapons. Work was started at once to develop a 75-mm. gun which used American ammunition and many parts of which were interchangeable with the 6-pdr. It was mounted in Cromwell IV and later marks and also fitted retrospectively into modified 6-pdr. mountings. Tanks with the new 75-mm. gun were issued to troops in October 1943.

DESCRIPTION

The visible and external differences between the various marks of Centaur and Cromwell were few, apart from the changes in armament and the additional armour plate welded to front plates on Mks. VII and VIII. The layout conformed to standard British design with rear engine and transmission driving rear track sprockets. The crew of five were in three forward compartments. The driver and hull gunner sat in front, separated by a plate with an access hole. The commander, gunner and loader/radio operator sat in the central fighting compartment. The hull was of single skin armour plate on front, rear and top, either rivetted or welded. Welded hulls appeared on variations of Mks. V and

Cromwell VI 95-mm. howitzer close support tank. Cromwell VIII was similar but with additional armour on hull front and wider tracks.

One of six pilot models of A.24 Cruiser Mk. VII Cavalier produced in January 1942.   (Photo: R.A.C. Tank Museum)

Cromwell IV F—identifiable by 75-mm. gun, driver's side opening hatch and lack of armour thickening on hull front.
(Photo: Imperial War Museum)

Cromwell III D—sub-mark indicated by hull gunner's side opening hatch. This vehicle was fitted with track sand shields for Middle East trials.   (Photo: Imperial War Museum)

VII. Detachable armour plate on the sides provided protection for the suspension assemblies which were mounted on a second inner plate of hardened steel. It was a simple and rigid hull design with two transverse bulkheads mounted in front of and behind the fighting compartment.

The driver sat on the right, with the gear change lever between his knees and steering levers on either side. The clutch, steering brakes and main brakes were all hydraulically operated, the systems being fed by a common oil reservoir in this compartment. A parking ratchet was fitted to the main brake pedal but, to avoid straining the hydraulic system, this method could only be used temporarily. The tank had to be put in gear for permanent parking. For vision, apart from two periscopes, the driver had an armoured visor which could be fully opened or, when closed for better protection, he could open a small wicket door in the visor. Access to the driver's compartment was through doors above his seat or through the bulkhead from the turret. In the earlier marks the pair of doors in the roof could only be opened when the turret was in certain positions. This was a serious design fault, making this forward compartment virtually a man-trap if the tank was disabled in action. To remedy this, three further types of door were later fitted to give greater freedom of movement, one providing a loose flap in place of a door, one being similar to the hull gunner's door, where a hinged section of the roof and hull side plates swung horizontally sideways, and ultimately a single upward opening door which incorporated one of the periscopes. An extractor ventilation fan was mounted in the roof

between the driver and hull gunner, and a similar fan was mounted in the turret above the guns. The 7·92-mm. Besa machine-gun in the hull gunner's compartment was in a ball mounting, controlled and fired manually. A telescopic sight gave direct view through the mounting. One of the few identifying features in the hull of earlier marks before Cromwell IV was a rounded hood over a periscope sight in the roof above the hull gunner. When this was fitted the gunner had no alternative viewing periscope (but Cavalier had both).

The turret crew were carried in the turntable basket which was suspended from and rotated with the turret. The commander sat on the left behind the gunner. There were two types of cupola, both rotated by hand and fitting almost flush with the roof. The early model mounted two episcopes. The later all-round vision cupola, which was introduced with the Mk. VII and later installed in all service vehicles, mounted eight episcopes, one of which could be extended and tilted to give a better view of the ground closer to the tank. The commander had no direct control over the sighting of the guns but a three-pronged sighting vane mounted externally on the forward edge of the turret roof helped him to direct the gunner. The gunner, in his turn, normally used a telescopic sight but, for targets beyond the range of the telescope or which he could not see, he used the AFV sighting gear with range drum and clinometer. The gun elevation was controlled by a handwheel on the gunner's right. Turret traverse was operated by the gunner's left hand, either through a spade grip on the hydraulic powered traverse system or manually by a handwheel which was marked with a line indicator for semi-indirect shoots. The powered traverse gave complete rotation of the turret in 14 to 15 seconds at top speed, and yet its accuracy was such that it could also be used for fine laying in direct fire. The 75-mm. gun and a co-axially mounted Besa machine-gun were fired mechanically from a pedal on the floor, although later modifications introduced an electrical firing gear operated through a switch on the elevating hand-wheel with a foot pedal mechanism as an auxiliary. The 75-mm. used many parts in the breech mechanism which were identical with the 6-pdr. gun. The barrel was similar, the main external difference being the addition of a muzzle brake. Ammunition stowage for 23 rounds of 75-mm. was provided in the turret for "ready rounds" while the balance of up to 41 rounds was stowed in various positions around the walls of the fighting compartment. The loader/wireless operator was responsible for a two-inch bomb-thrower mounted in the turret roof. This weapon was used for firing protective smoke over variable ranges up to 150 yards (later bombs increased the range to 450 yards). But this crewman's main duties were the operation of the No. 19 Wireless Set in the rear of the turret and listening in to one of the two nets covered.

In the engine compartment, the fuel tanks and two oil bath air cleaners were mounted on either side of the engine. Twin fans and radiators were mounted vertically behind the engine with cooling air being drawn mainly through air louvres in the top and sides, and exhausted to the rear. A Merritt-Brown gearbox, originally used in the Churchill "I" tanks in 1941, was mounted here for the first time in a cruiser tank. From this time forward through to the latest marks of Centurions, this excellent system has been preferred to all other British systems. It was certainly superior to and simpler than the Merritt-Maybach system adapted

both by Germany and the U.S.A. The gearbox incorporated steering controls at each end which, through differential and epicyclic gears, controlled the transmission of power from the engine to either or both tracks. Pulling on one steering lever had the effect of selecting a differential steering gear and slowing the track on the same side while simultaneously speeding up the other, with the radius of turn being dependent upon the gear selected—the lower the gear the tighter the turn. Track brakes were mounted separately for normal braking, both being operated simultaneously from the main brake pedal. The final drive assembly on each side incorporated fixed reduction gears in transmitting power to the track drive sprockets. The high speed (38 m.p.h.) of the earlier marks was too much even for their remarkable Christie-type independent suspension and later models had the reduction ratio in the final drive further reduced to limit the speed. The suspension was adapted from the original Christie design used on the earlier cruisers (A.13 onwards) with stronger components to take the extra weight. The original 14-inch track was also later replaced by a 15·5-inch track to achieve a better weight distribution or ground pressure ratio in modifications to all marks in service.

Externally on the hull, stowage bins for tools, rations, and bedding were fitted on both track guards, one on the left and two on the right, plus a small bin sometimes fitted on the back of the turret. When the driver's compartment was fitted with a side opening door—like the hull gunner's—there was only one bin on the right track guard and extra bins would be fitted to the turret sides.

Other external features on the hull were an exhaust flame deflector cowl—known as the Normandy cowl—fitted over the exhaust pipes at the rear of all Cromwells on operations in Europe to conceal exhaust

A.30 Challenger Tank Destroyer mounted the 17-pdr. (76·2-mm.) gun on a lengthened Cromwell chassis.
(Photo: Imperial War Museum)

Snow camouflage—used for the first time by British armour—assists identification of additional armour plates welded on nose and hull front which characterize this Mk. VII photographed near Sittard, Holland, January 16, 1945.
(Photo: Imperial War Museum)

flames at night. It was easily detachable and could be added to all marks in service.

CROMWELL VARIANTS

The few early Centaur chassis completed as tanks were used primarily as training vehicles. The principal combat version was a batch of 80 Centaur IVs armed with 95-mm. howitzers to operate in the support rôle and issued to the Royal Marine Armoured Support Group for the Normandy Invasion. They were shackled to landing craft and primarily intended to support the beach assault while firing afloat and standing off-shore. However, the Marine tank crews swiftly followed ashore and landed their tanks to support the infantry inland. Centaur chassis were also employed in special rôles:

Cromwell AOP. The simplest conversion was for use as an Artillery Observation Post. This involved internal modifications and additional wireless sets which left the tank with the same gun and appearance as that of the armoured units it was supporting.

Centaur AA Tank. For use in an anti-aircraft rôle the Centaur AA tank was produced with a twin 20-mm. Polsten turret mounting adapted from the Crusader AA tank. These tanks were on the establishments of armoured units and were landed in Normandy. They were discarded when the threat of enemy air attack diminished.

Centaur Bulldozer was based on the Centaur III with turret removed but retaining the hull gunner's position. The dozer blade was attached by arms to the sides of the tank and suspended from a winch. It was used on the basis of one per squadron and it remained

Cromwell ARV. Hatches over centre compartment conceal twin Bren AA machine-guns on a raisable mounting.

in service in the Regular Army for many years after the war.

Cromwell ARV. This armoured recovery vehicle was a conversion of the basic Cromwell (R-R. Meteor) chassis which dispensed with the turret but retained the forward hull Besa machine-gun. The vehicle was equipped with a two-ton jib crane, hand-operated winch, drawbars, detachable track grousers and sundry recovery equipment. Twin Bren AA machine-guns were mounted in the converted fighting compartment.

Above left and right: *A.30 Challenger Tank Destroyer mounted the 17-pdr. (76·2-mm.) gun on a lengthened Cromwell chassis. Note six road wheels and characteristic high turret.*
(Photos: Imperial War Museum)

A.30 Avenger—SP AT 17-pdr. gun on modified Challenger chassis with open-topped turret.
(Photo: Imperial War Museum)

Charioteer was the ultimate development of the cruiser tanks designed in 1950 to mount the Centurion's 20-pdr. gun.
(Photo: Imperial War Museum)

A.33(1) Assault Tank—this version used the U.S. T.1 track.
(Photo: Imperial War Museum)

A.30 CHALLENGER AND AVENGER

The 17-pdr. (76·2-mm.) gun had been developed from 1941 both as a tank and anti-tank gun and it proved later to be a weapon in the same class as the famous German 8·8-cm. The Birmingham Railway Carriage and Wagon Company was asked early in 1942 to develop the A.30 mounting the 17-pdr. The first pilot model appeared in August 1942, based on a lengthened Cromwell with an extra suspension unit—i.e. six road wheels on each side. The performance of this vehicle was disappointing because the gun was really too big for any of the 6-pdr. tanks, but the design was approved in February 1943 and a limited production order for 200 was completed the following year. The vehicle was named Challenger. The high performance of the 17-pdr. had been a potent factor in the continuing controversy over a dual-purpose gun and Challenger was given the specific rôle of a "tank killer" in support of the other cruisers.

An alternative version of A.30 was also developed in 1943–44 as a self-propelled anti-tank gun and called the Avenger. This was also based on the lengthened Cromwell with a modified suspension incorporating three top rollers above the six road wheels on each side. The gun was mounted in a fully rotating turret with an open top covered by a mild steel plate supported above the armoured sides.

A.33 ASSAULT TANK

The main components of the Cromwell were used as the basis for design of a new heavy assault tank which was being sought in 1942–43. This was to weigh about 40 tons, mount a 75-mm. gun and have six inches of armour on the front. The English Electric Company undertook this in 1942 and three pilot models were built by May 1944. A.33(1) used the U.S. T.1 track and A.33(2) had a British suspension. With an uprated Meteor engine of 620 b.h.p. it had a speed of 24 m.p.h. and was fast enough in its rôle, but there was no tactical use for a 40-ton tank which only mounted a 75-mm. medium velocity gun. In fact, policy was already changing towards the need for an all-purpose tank and A.33 was overtaken by the Comet, developed by Leyland Motors from the Cromwell.

CHARIOTEER

Yet another late derivative appeared on the scene when in 1950 work started on the design of the Charioteer, intended for service with the Territorial Army as a self-propelled anti-tank gun. This mounted the Centurion's 20-pdr. gun in a rotating two-man turret carried on the normal Cromwell hull. It was in service in 1954 and models also went abroad to Austria and Jordan.

TACTICAL EMPLOYMENT

The Cavalier, Centaur and early Cromwells played a most important part in the training of crews and units in the United Kingdom, and this secondary rôle continued when the American Shermans became available in considerable numbers in 1942–43 and inevitably were adopted as the standard medium tanks for British armoured formations in North Africa and Italy. For the planned invasion in North-West Europe, the ubiquitous hosts of Shermans continued to provide the backbone of medium tank strength of British armoured units. But Cromwell was now available with a comparable performance in firepower and mobility, and it was planned to equip a proportion of regiments with the new tank. The change was not universally welcome at first because the British cruiser tanks used in the early part of the war had not established a high reputation.

At that time the British armoured division had one armoured brigade (three armoured regiments and a motorised infantry battalion), one lorried infantry brigade and supporting arms and services. Amongst

Cromwell IV dug in, hull down and replenishing with ammunition. The photograph was taken in January 1945 probably during 7th Armoured Division's advance between the Rivers Meuse and Roer.

divisional troops there was an armoured reconnaissance regiment intended to carry out close tactical reconnaissance on the divisional front. The rôle of the division had changed little since the beginning of the war and an instruction upon its employment, issued shortly before the invasion, described its main purpose as exploitation. This was the rôle for which Cromwell had been designed, but which it was not able to fulfil until after the break-out from Normandy. The Cromwell went to Europe in the hands of 7th Armoured Division and in the armoured reconnaissance regiments of both the Guards and 11th Armoured Divisions. Later it was issued to the 6th Airborne Reconnaissance Regiment in place of the 'Tetrarch (Light Tank Mk. VII). The 1st Polish Armoured Division, formed in the United Kingdom in 1942, was also among the units trained on Crusader and Centaur. Their armoured brigade converted to the Sherman in 1943 but the armoured reconnaissance regiment was equipped with Cromwells when they landed in Normandy in August 1944 to fight in 21st Army Group.

In 7th Armoured Division on the Continent of Europe the armoured regiments were organised on the basis of three squadrons of four troops, each of three

Cromwell IV adapted as Brigade HQ tank. The vehicle carries additional aerials, collapsible hood and brackets for mounting map boards.

Cromwell 75-mm. and one Sherman Firefly. At Squadron HQ there was a Cromwell 75-mm. for command and two Cromwell 95-mm. assault tanks to give close support with a heavier HE weapon and smoke. The armoured reconnaissance regiments of all British divisions were initially organised on similar lines but with a larger light reconnaissance troop and with three squadrons of five troops, each of three Cromwell 75-mm. In the event they became, in effect, a fourth armoured regiment of the division. Soon their squadrons were re-organised with four troops like the armoured regiments and Challengers were issued on the basis of one per troop to support the Cromwells.

When Cromwell went into action it was already out-matched in firepower by its German opponents but it was superior to them in speed, reliability and, notably, in quick response in laying and firing—qualities which were rewarding when freed from the restrictions of close country when it could out-manoeuvre the heavy tanks and seek out their weak spots. It thus made an effective contribution to decisive actions by the armoured divisions in North-West Europe and, as a proved and efficient weapon, led directly to the design of its successor, the Comet with its hard-hitting 17-pdr. gun.

SPECIFICATION:
A.27(M) CRUISER MK. VIII CROMWELL IV
General
Crew: 5, Commander, gunner, loader/wireless operator, driver, hull gunner.
Battle weight: 27·5 tons.
Bridge classification: 28.
Power/weight ratio: 21·8 to 1 b.h.p./ton.
Ground pressure: 14·7 lb. per sq. in.

Dimensions
Length overall, gun to front: 21 ft. ¾ in.
Height overall: 8 ft. 3 in.
Width overall: 10 ft.
Width over tracks: 9 ft. 3¾ in.
Track centres: 8 ft. 1¾ in.
Track width: 14 in.
Length of track on ground: 12 ft. 3 in.

Armament
Main: QF 75 mm. gun Mk. V and VA.
Auxiliary: Two 7·92 mm. Besa machine-guns, one co-axially mounted with main armament and one in front of hull.
Bomb thrower 2 in. mounted in turret roof, right side.
·303 in. twin Vickers K Type machine-gun with AA mountings or ·303 Bren light machine-gun. Twin machine-gun and AA mounting later discarded.
Rear smoke generators: two pairs mounted at rear of hull, fired electrically from driver's compartment.

Fire Control
Turret: Manual control of elevation by hand wheel. Traverse by hydraulic power from variable flow pump driven by main engine, with auxiliary hand traverse. Mechanically operated firing gear from pedal on turret floor. (Electrically operated firing gear from switch on hand-wheel introduced in Cromwell VII and VIII, with auxiliary mechanical gear).
Hull: Ball mounting with limited movement 12° to right and 20° to left, in elevation and depression. Hand control.

Ammunition

75 mm. { HE M48 / APC M61 / AP M72 / Smoke WP M64 / Smoke Emission } 64 rounds, proportions varied by types.

N.B.: All types except Smoke Emission were American.
Besa machine-guns: 4,950 ((22 boxes).
Vickers machine-guns: 2,000, or Bren light machine-gun: 600.
Bomb thrower: 30.

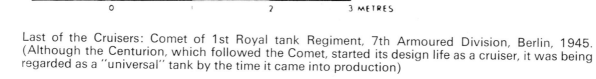

Last of the Cruisers: Comet of 1st Royal tank Regiment, 7th Armoured Division, Berlin, 1945. (Although the Centurion, which followed the Comet, started its design life as a cruiser, it was being regarded as a "universal" tank by the time it came into production)

Martin Lee © Profile Publications Ltd

Cromwell IV F OP tanks of 3rd Royal Horse Artillery, 7th Armoured Division in Berlin Victory Parade.

Sighting and Vision

Commander: Standard cupola mounted 2 episcopes. Later all-round vision cupola mounted 8 episcopes giving 360° vision. Both types rotated by hand. Sighting vane mounted externally on turret roof.

Turret gunner: Telescopic sight No. 50 × 3L Mk. I or 2. AFV Sight Gear 75 mm.

Hull gunner: Telescopic sight No. 50 × 1·9 Mk. 1.

Five periscopes (rotating and tilting) mounted in turret and hull roofs for loader, each gunner and driver (2).

Communications

Wireless Set No. 19. Two sets. "A" (squadron/regimental net) and "B" (troop net). Intercomm. between all crew. Infantry telephone on rear of hull.

Armour

Hull: Rivetted or welded. Detachable armour plate over suspension assemblies mounted on hardened steel plate.

Turret: Rolled or cast. Side armour bolted to welded inner structure.

Hull: Front 63 mm. vertical; Glacis 30 mm./70°; Nose 57 mm./20°; Side 32 mm.; Lower side 25 mm. outer; 14 mm. inner; Rear 32 mm.; Top 20 mm.; Floor 8 mm.; Turret Front 76 mm.; Sides 63 mm.; Rear 57 mm.; and Top 20 mm.

Engine

Rolls Royce Meteor, Petrol. 60° V-12. 12-cyl., Water-cooled. 1,649 cu. in. (27 litres). 570–600 b.h.p. at 2,550 r.p.m. Fuel: 116 gallons.

Transmission

Clutch: Dry, twin plate, hydraulically operated.

Gearbox: Merritt Brown, type Z.5. Five forward speeds and reverse.

Final Drive: Reduction 4·5 to 1 or 3·71 to 1, according to type.

Suspension

Christie type, five road wheels each side independently sprung, on pivotting axle arms supported in cross tubes fixed to bottom plate of hull. Hydraulic shock absorbers fitted to front, second, fourth and rear suspension units. Track rests on top of centre road wheels returning round idler (tensioner) at front.

Track: Manganese steel, 125 links each side with centre lugs.

Pitch: 3·93 in.

Electrical System

12 volt system, with two 6 volt 150AH batteries mounted in fighting compartment. Auxiliary charging set (single cyl. 4 stroke, air-cooled) mounted behind driver.

Performance

Maximum speed: 3·71:1 final drive ratio—38 m.p.h.
4·5:1 final drive ratio—32 m.p.h.

Maximum gradient: 24°.

Vertical obstacle: 3 ft.   Trench: 7 ft. 6 in.

Wading depth: 3 ft., of 4 ft. with fording flap closed.

Road range: 173 miles.   Cross country range: 81 miles.

ARMOURED UNITS EQUIPPED WITH CROMWELL FOR OPERATIONS IN N.W. EUROPE

Guards Armoured Division	2nd Batt. Welsh Guards.
7th Armoured Division	8th King's Royal Irish Hussars.
22nd Armoured Brigade	1st Royal Tank Regiment.
	5th Royal Tank Regiment.
	4th County of London Yeomanry (Sharpshooters), (until July 1944).
	5th Royal Inniskilling Dragoon Guards (from July 1944).
11th Armoured Division	2nd Northamptonshire Yeomanry (until August 1944).
	15th/19th The King's Royal Hussars (from August 1944).
6th Airborne Division	6th Airborne Reconnaissance Regiment, R.A.C.
1st Polish Armoured Division	10th Mounted Rifle Regiment.
Royal Marine Armoured Assault Group (with Centaur IV)	

A.27 CRUISER MK. VIII SERIES

	Weight Tons	Armament	Engine		Remarks
A24 CRUISER MK. VII					
Cavalier	27	1-6 pdr. 2 Besa	Nuffield Liberty 395 b.h.p.		Fitted to carry auxiliary fuel tank at rear
A27 (L) CRUISER MK. VIII					
Centaur I, II	27·5	1-6 pdr. 2 Besa	Nuffield Liberty 395 b.h.p.		Fitted to carry auxiliary fuel tank at rear
Centaur III	—	1-75 mm. 2 Besa	Nuffield Liberty 395 b.h.p.		Limited number with 75 mm.
Centaur IV	—	1-95 mm. 2 Besa	—		Support tank: 80 issued to Royal Marine Armoured Support Group
A27 (M) CRUISER MK. VIII					
Cromwell I	27·5	1-6 pdr. 2 Besa	Rolls Royce Meteor 570-600 b.h.p.		
Cromwell II	—	1-6 pdr. 1 Besa	—		Wider track, 15·5 in.
Cromwell III (Formerly Cromwell X)	—	1-6 pdr.	—		Centaur with Meteor Fitted to carry auxiliary fuel tank at rear
Cromwell IV	—	1-75 mm. 2 Besa	—		New 75 mm. gun
Cromwell V	—	1-75 mm. 2 Besa	—		Mk. Vw with welded hull Few produced
Cromwell VI	—	1-95 mm. 2 Besa	—		See also Mk. VIII. 95 mm. howitzer for close support
Cromwell VII	28	1-75 mm. 2 Besa	—		Mk. VIIw with welded hull. Both Marks, armour increased mainly on front to 101 mm. Wider tracks, 15·5 in.
Cromwell VIII	—	1-95 mm. 2 Besa	—		

There is little external difference in hull and turret of Centaur III, IV and Cromwell IV-VI. Type differences occurred in each of these Marks:

D—With hull gunner's side opening door.
E—4·5 to 1 final drive reduction ratio replaced 3·71 to 1.
F—With driver's side opening door.

Cromwell VII, VIII are mainly distinguished by extra armour plate fixed to hull and turret fronts, nose and rear.

Multi-barrel smoke dischargers were fitted after the War, as on other armoured vehicles, arranged in three pairs on each side of the turret. This Comet tank has been renumbered in the new system. (Photo: R.A.C. Tank Museum)

Comet

by Major James Bingham

THE demand for a tank with the performance of the Comet can be said to have started in September 1941, although it was not until 18 months later that detailed work began on the A34 project that produced the Comet. But it was in late 1941, after the reverses suffered against German armour in the Middle East, that the General Staff told the Tank Board of their need for both a cruiser and an infantry tank which mounted a high velocity anti-tank gun capable of defeating any enemy armoured fighting vehicle. The infantry tank project to meet this demand got as far as mounting the 3-in. 20-cwt. anti-aircraft gun in a few Churchill hulls, but these were never used for the purpose intended. The cruiser development was more productive and, known as the A30, led to the production of the Challenger which eventually went into service in 1944.

The Challenger, however, was not a great success. The Birmingham Railway Carriage and Wagon Company, the design parents of the A27 (Cromwell) at the time, started development early in 1942 and the first prototype appeared in August, mounting the new 17-pdr. high velocity anti-tank gun on a modified Cromwell hull. Results were disappointing. Specifications demanded a turret crew of four (two loaders), and trials revealed weaknesses which were attributable mainly to the size, weight and stresses of a big gun mounted on a comparatively small hull. Despite the

weaknesses, however, a limited production order was made for the Challenger in February 1943, to be pursued as a matter of high priority, as it was the only vehicle under development which could compete with the German tanks coming into action armed with the long 75-mm. and the 88-mm. guns (Pz Kpfw IV and Tiger).

It was in this same period, in January 1943, that official policy on tank armament changed, whereby the majority of medium tanks were to be armed with a dual-purpose, medium velocity 75-mm. instead of the 6-pdr. anti-tank gun. The Tank Board recognized the short-comings of the Challenger against the corresponding demand for a fast, high-powered anti-tank weapon to support the Cromwells armed with the 75-mm., and, at a lower priority than production of the Challenger, turned to the development of another tank, mounting the 17-pdr. or an equivalent type, on the Cromwell chassis—to be known as the A34.

The choice of gun for the new tank was crucial, and the designers were allowed the relative freedom of developing the most effective high velocity gun which could be mounted in the Cromwell, a line of development which was confirmed at War Cabinet level in April. The 17-pdr. was considered but, in effect, the choice remained between a new British gun, known as the High Velocity (HV) 75-mm., and the American 76-mm. which was already in production to arm their

© JAMES LEECH

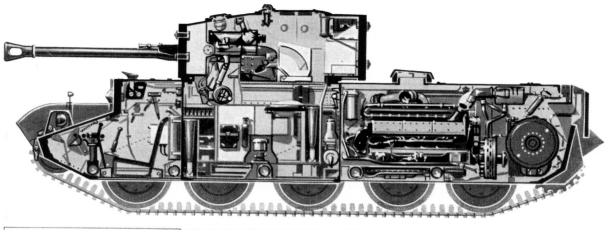

The tank shown here was inspected by Mr. Winston Churchill on a tour of British units "somewhere in England" shortly before D-Day, June 1944. It was commanded by Major J. O. Spencer, Commanding 2 Squadron, 2nd Battalion, Welsh Guards, and driven by Sergeant T. W. Dredge. The Battalion was the Armoured Reconnaissance Regiment of the Guards Armoured Division. It fought throughout the campaign in N.W. Europe to the end of the war. For the Prime Minister's visit the tank carried the Squadron colour—the red dragon pennant—on the "A" Set (right hand) aerial. The signs on the nose plate are (left to right): Unit number 45 on blue and green indicating the armoured reconnaissance regiment of the Division; 26 indicating the bridge classification (later increased to 28); the white square indicating 2 Squadron and the A showing it is the Commander's tank; the shield is the insignia of the Guards Armoured Division. The yellow square on the glacis plate is gas-sensitive paint. The five-pointed Normandy stars were added shortly before D-Day for identification from the air. In these paintings the Commander's hatch in the right and rear elevations and the driver's visor in the front elevation are shown open.

The first prototype of the A34, ready for firing tests in March 1944. The Cromwell suspension had been strengthened; and the return rollers and a wider track were fitted later.
(Photo: R.A.C. Tank Museum)

Tank Destroyers. Selection of the 76-mm. would have involved material alterations to the gun to match British practice in crew positions and turret layout, and the length of the rounds would have restricted handling and loading within the space available. On balance, the only advantages of the 76-mm. lay in interchangeability of ammunition and some relief on British production, and the British gun was eventually chosen. The HV 75-mm. was, in fact, a modified and somewhat less powerful version of the 17-pdr. (76·2-mm.), designed by Vickers-Armstrong to match the tank on which it was to be used. It fired the same shells as the 17-pdr., but had a shorter barrel, reduced muzzle velocity, and a re-designed chamber to accept shorter and wider cases that permitted

easier ammunition handling. To avoid confusion with other British and American guns in service, the new gun was re-named the 77-mm.

Leyland Motors had turned over their factory completely to tank production in 1942 and work started on the new A34 project when the firm was confirmed in February 1943 as design parents for further development of the Centaur/Cromwell series. Taking advantage of the lessons already learned on the Challenger, and also on the three experimental projects A31, A32 and A33 to produce a heavy assault tank based on the Cromwell, design proposals for the new tank were laid before the General Staff in July 1943. By the end of September the mock-up was ready for inspection. The design was based on the

An early model of Comet, before fitting the 17-pdr. tow bar, and lacking the tank telephone box on the rear armoured plate.
(Photo: R.A.C. Tank Museum)

standard Cromwell hull, with additional armour protection and an estimated 3½ tons extra weight. The larger gun naturally required a larger turret but the increased turret ring diameter (57 in. to 64 in.) was achieved without adding a wider centre section to the hull, as had been necessary on the Challenger.

The General Staff confirmed in October their requirement for the A34, mounting the 77-mm., but it was already being regarded as a stop-gap pending the long-term development of a larger cruiser tank carrying heavy armament (the A41 which was to become the Centurion). In the meantime, however, the Challenger had encountered serious production delays and the A34 was the only other tank which met the cruiser requirement; production of the A34 was to proceed with all speed, to get as many as possible in service for the planned operations in Europe in 1944. Orders were placed for three prototypes, plus a hull to be fired at in trials, and it was expected that 20 pre-production models would be ready in June 1944.

Above: *The first A34 Prototype, in mild steel. Side-opening roof doors for both driver and front gunner were fitted on all Comets, as on the later types of Cromwell. This meant that both could get out, whatever the position of the turret.*
(Photo: R.A.C. Tank Museum)

Top left: *An early model of the Comet. Later production models had a bracket welded on to the centre of the nose plate to hold up the tow rope when stowed on the glacis plate.*
(Photo: R.A.C. Tank Museum)

Below: *Rear of the Comet Type A, which retained the Cromwell exhaust system. A cowl was normally fitted over the back end for concealment and protection against exhaust flames projected upwards. Note the addition of the 17-pdr. tow bar, which has caused the two smoke dischargers to be moved up on to the rear armoured plate.*
(Photo: R.A.C. Tank Museum)

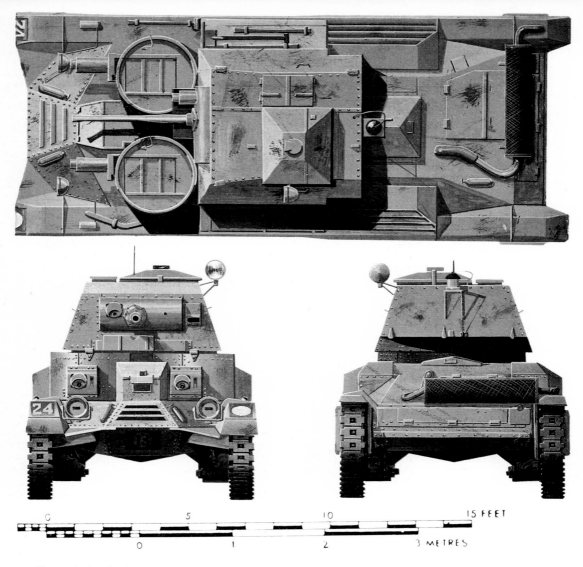

First of the Cruisers: A9 of 1st Royal Tank Regiment, 7th Armoured Division, Egypt, 1940.

Martin Lee © *Profile Publications Ltd*

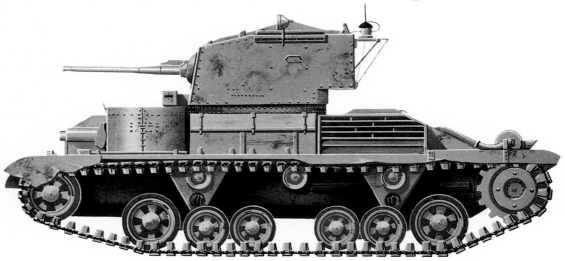

The Comet Type B, in which the exhaust pipes have been led to twin armoured fishtails mounted on the rear armoured plate. Note that the top of the armoured plate has been raised to the level of the engine deck.   (Photo: R.A.C. Tank Museum)

The first mild steel prototype was delivered in February and firing trials started the following month. Results this time were encouraging. The performance of the 77-mm. as an anti-tank gun was only slightly inferior to that of the 17-pdr., but the gun made up for this, at least in part, by its impressive accuracy and by the demonstration of its power with high explosive. Thoughts on further development of the A34 to mount the 95-mm. close support weapon were quickly dismissed, since the next stage in major development was to be the A41, and further design work on the A34, now named Comet, was confined to modifications and minor improvements.

There were criticisms from those with battle experience, particularly on the retention of the hull gunner and on the protection afforded by the belly armour against mines, but, even though these were set aside in order to avoid re-design, the optimistic early forecasts of production were not achieved. Modifications and changes of equipment caused delays and it was not until September 1944 that the first production models were delivered. Operational tanks were ready in November and were sent to Belgium to start the training and conversion of armoured regiments which would be re-equipped with the Comet.

Overhead view of the Comet, showing the basic similarity to the Cromwell hull fittings and layout, and emphasizing the overhang of the large turret bin.   (Photo: R.A.C. Tank Museum)

Soon after the start of operations with Comets, tanks of the 3rd Royal Tank Regiment move through a devastated German town, March 1945.
(Photo: Imperial War Museum)

A Comet of the 2nd Fife and Forfar Yeomanry, named Saint Andrew, *moves up at Petershagen to the Weser bridgehead, April 1945.*
(Photo: Imperial War Museum)

Replenishing ammunition for a Comet of the 2nd Fife and Forfar Yeomanry in position overlooking the River Elbe, with infantry of the 1st Bn. Herefordshire Regiment, April 1945.
(Photo: Imperial War Museum)

DESCRIPTION

The Comet was essentially an up-gunned, up-armoured Cromwell, retaining the same lay-out, the same armament except for the main gun, and using many of the same components, but for all practical purposes it was a new tank. It was never extended to more than one Mark, and there was only one Type variation, introduced in post-war tanks, in which the visible change was the addition of fish tail exhaust pipes on the rear armoured plate.

The hull was of all-welded construction, and incorporated the side-opening door for both driver and hull gunner which had been features of some later Type variations of the Cromwell. The turret, also, was all-welded, with the sides and rear consisting of three bent armour plates, and cast armour at the front. Additional thickness of armour plate was incorporated in construction and this, with the larger turret and weapon system, put the weight of the tank up to nearly 33 tons, almost 5 tons heavier than the latest

Soldiers of the 1st Bn. Herefordshire Regiment being carried forward on Comets of the 3rd Royal Tank Regiment. The nearest tank has the Cromwell exhaust cowl, with no space in the centre for the gun when in the travelling position in the gun crutch.
(Photo: Imperial War Museum)

39

Field Marshal Montgomery taking the salute as Comets of the 1st Royal Tank Regiment drive past in Berlin, September 1945. The tanks carry the sign of 7th Armoured Division, as well as the 22 Armoured Brigade sign above the unit number.

(Photo: Imperial War Museum)

up-armoured Cromwell. The Meteor engine had the power to absorb this weight penalty and, with strengthened suspension units, a wider track and return rollers, the tank retained the performance of a fast cruiser tank with good cross-country ability.

Fire control arrangements in the turret were essentially similar to those in the Cromwell VII and VIII, with improved sighting gear, but, instead of the hydraulic power traverse system which had been used on all cruisers since the A9, the Comet mounted an electrical power traverse adapted from that successfully used on the Churchill. The electrical system was powered by a generator driven by the main engine. A welcome improvement in ammunition stowage provided armoured bins that reduced the risk of fire caused by flying splinters and molten metal if the tank hull were penetrated, while additional space for stowage was provided in racks beneath the turntable floor. The increasing emphasis on good communications between tanks and infantry, demanded in 1944, is shown by the addition of the No. 38 Set (Infantry) mounted alongside the No. 19 Set at the rear of the turret, thus allowing the tank commander to talk on three separate frequencies, on the squadron/regimental net, to tanks in his own troop and to the infantry with whom he was working.

With only two stowage bins on the track guards, one each side, extra space was provided in the large, external turret bin at the rear for the larger and heavier items of equipment. This, with spare track plates slung near the back, served a dual purpose as counter-weight in balancing the turret.

On the original, Type A, Comet two exhaust flame deflector cowls were normally fitted, with a space between for the gun when traversed to the rear and clamped in the travelling crutch. These cowls, similar to the single unit originally fitted on the Cromwell for operations in Normandy to conceal exhaust flames at night, became important also as a protection for the infantry who might be carried into battle on the engine deck. On the Type B Comet, with fish tail exhaust pipes, the cowls were not necessary.

COMET IN SERVICE

The armoured units of 11th Armoured Division were selected to be the first for re-equipment with the Comet, and early in December 1944 29th Armoured Brigade was withdrawn from the fighting in southern Holland to hand in their Shermans near Brussels. This had hardly been completed when the Germans opened their surprise offensive through the Ardennes in December, and the brigade hastily drew up their Shermans again to take part in the fighting to hold and drive back the German threat. Three weeks later, in mid-January, 29th Armoured Brigade was back in North-West Belgium to resume its training and conversion programme.

The armoured brigade units converting were the 23rd Hussars, the 3rd Royal Tank Regiment and the 2nd Fife and Forfar Yeomanry, and the change was generally "viewed with enthusiasm, for though (the) Shermans had given excellent service mechanically— many had survived a far greater mileage than anybody had anticipated—a new toy is always good for morale and this toy looked attractive enough."*

Taurus Pursuant—A History of 11th Armoured Division.

40

Above: *Leading on to a transporter, a Comet Type B clearly shows the fittings on the engine deck and the turret top, including the armoured deflector shield in front of the commander's cupola.* (Photo: R.A.C. Tank Museum)

Right: *The Commanding Officer of the 1st Royal Tank Regiment, in his tank* Iron Duke IV, *passing Field Marshall Sir Bernard Montgomery during an inspection in Berlin, September 20, 1945. The C.O. was Lt.-Col. P. R. C. Hobart. In the foreground of the picture is Maj.-Gen. Sir Percy Hobart, who commanded 79th Armoured Division. At that time Field Marshal Montgomery was a Colonel Commandant of the R.T.R.* (Photo: R.A.C. Tank Museum)

Below: *A post-war Comet Type A—with exhaust cowl—showing clearly the blade vane sight on the turret roof for the commander. Also shown is the protection piece welded on to the glacis plate to protect the join with the vertical front plate.* (Photo: R.A.C. Tank Museum)

Changing the 77-mm. gun barrel in workshops.

(Photo: R.A.C. Tank Museum)

"At first, crews were inclined to compare them unfavourably with the Shermans. Everyone, however was unanimous that the new gun was a miracle of accuracy. There was some disappointment, though, about its penetrative powers. When it was tried against a German Panther it did not have the expected effect against the front plate. For two months the thorough training in the new tank and increasing familiarity with it bred an increasing respect for this speedy and ·splendid fighting weapon."**

The 15th/19th The King's Royal Hussars, the divisional armoured reconnaissance regiment which had been equipped with Cromwells, was also converted to Comets, and at the end of March 11th Armoured Division moved forward to concentrate in the Wesel bridgehead across the Rhine. From then until the end of the fighting five weeks later, when the division reached the Baltic coast at Lubeck, the Comets proved themselves to be effective, fast and thoroughly reliable. There was no occasion then for the Comets to be tested in a major tank *versus* tank battle, although they frequently came up against stubborn resistance by tanks in one's and twos supported by guns and infantry armed with "bazookas", and in these circumstances the comparative weakness of the 77-mm. as an anti-tank weapon was not so vital. Its superior performance with HE, as compared with the 75-mm., was a particular advantage. As the advance progressed against centres of fierce oppo-

** *The Fife and Forfar Yeomanry 1919-1956* by R. J. B. Sellar. William Blackwood & Sons Ltd.

sition, it became normal for infantry to be carried with the leading tanks in closely knit groups.

When the fighting in Europe was over, the re-equipment programme continued and by the end of the summer 22nd Armoured Brigade, in 7th Armoured Division, which had fought throughout the campaign with Cromwells, had converted to Comets, retaining their Cromwell 95-mm. at squadron headquarters as close support tanks. In August the 1st Royal Tank Regiment entered Berlin with their Comets and took part there in the Allied Victory Parade.

Successively, armoured units deployed amongst the Occupation Forces were re-equipped with Comets (and Cromwells for their squadron headquarters and reconnaissance troops), and were then deployed to the Canal Zone in Egypt and amongst those who were keeping the peace in Palestine. It is said that one commanding officer was offered £250,000 for every Comet he was prepared to "lose", payable in any currency! The Comet was an effective deterrent where a show of force was required, but it was still a stop-gap pending the introduction of Centurion, and in early 1949 re-equipment with Centurion reached the Middle East after the programme was virtually completed in Europe. Nevertheless, Comets remained in service with the Regular Army for many more years, in Berlin until 1957 and in the armoured regiment in Hong Kong until late 1959. Some of the Centurions that went to Hong Kong were already veterans of battles in Korea and of trouble spots in the Middle East.

The Comet's greatest contribution to training in the United Kingdom was in the Territorial Army which was re-constituted in 1947, and for the next decade Comets and Cromwells together met the extensive demands for tanks in the training of armoured regiments in the Territorial Army. Even in 1969 the Comet and Cromwell, albeit non-runners, were represented in service with the Territorial and Army Volunteer Reserve.

COMMENTARY

The Comet was the last developed British tank to be used in battle during World War II, and the last in the line of cruiser tanks, if one discounts the Centurion to which it contributed in development but which, by the time it came into production, was being regarded as the "universal" tank.

As mentioned earlier, there was strong criticism of the Comet from users, over the retention of the hull gunner's position behind the vertical front plate, and over the weakness of belly armour as a protection against mines, which became an ever increasing threat in the later stages of the European campaigns. These criticisms might have been met without incurring undue delay in production had they been foreseen during the early stages of design but, as it was, the Comet was ready only just in time to take part in the fighting. In fact, it was the finest tank for its rôle that the British tank crews had had, and the

A Comet and Cromwell still in service in 1969, but no longer as runners, being used for training in loading tank transporters of the Territorial and Army Volunteer Reserve.
(Photo: *The Waggoner*)

Taking a jump at a demonstration. The Christie suspension allowed a fast and stable platform for the gun, but it was not a strong enough system for the heavier Centurion tank that was to follow the Comet in British service.
(Photo: R.A.C. Tank Museum)

Comet went a long way towards catching up with its nearest German equivalent, the Panther. This one would have expected in the last few months of the war after years of experience, but let the historian of the 15th/19th Hussars have the last word.

"The Comet, unlike many previous British Cruiser tanks, was reliable and battleworthy from the first —a statement that bodes well for the future but provides a sorry epitaph on British tank provision before and during the war."*

*History of 15/19 The King's Royal Hussars 1939-1945 by Major G. Courage. Gale and Polden.

AFV Series Editor: DUNCAN CROW

SPECIFICATION—A34, CRUISER TANK, COMET
General
Crew: 5—commander, loader/operator, driver, hull gunner.
Weight, laden: 32·7 tons.
Bridge classification: 32.
Power/weight ratio: 18 to 1 b.h.p./ton.
Ground pressure: 13·85 lbs/sq. in..

Dimensions
Length overall, gun front: 25 ft. 1½ in.
              gun rear: 21 ft. 6 ins.
Height overall: 8 ft. 9¼ ins.
Width overall: 10 ft. 1 in.
Width over tracks: 9 ft. 10¼ ins.
Track centres: 8 ft. 4¼ ins.
Track width: 18 ins.
Length of track on ground: 12 ft. 11 ins.

Armament
Main: QF 77-mm.
Auxiliary: Two 7·92-mm. Besa machine-guns, one co-axially mounted with the main armament and one in the hull front.
Bomb thrower 2-in. mounted in turret roof.
Bren ·303 light machine-gun stowed in rear turret locker.
Rear smoke dischargers, two pairs mounted at rear of hull.

Fire control
Turret: Handwheel control of elevation (+20° to −12°).
Power traverse by Lucas electric motor (max. 15°/sec.), with auxiliary hand traverse. Electrically operated firing gear with auxiliary mechanical gear.
Hull: Ball mounting, hand control.

Ammunition
77-mm.: 61 rounds (APCBC and HE).
Besa machine-guns: 5,175 (23 boxes).
Bren light machine-gun: 600.
Bomb thrower: 20.

Sighting and Vision
Commander: All-round vision cupola, rotating 360°, mounting 8 episcopes, Sighting vane mounted externally on turret roof.
Turret gunner: Telescopic sight No. 57 × 3 ML Mk. 1, AFV Sight Gear 77-mm. Comet No. 1, Mk. 1.
Hull gunner: Telescopic sight No. 57 × 1·9 Mk. 1.
Five periscopes (rotating and tilting) for each gunner, loader and driver (2).

Communications
Wireless sets No. 19 and No. 38 B. Intercomm. between all crew. Infantry telephone on rear of hull (in box incorporating First Aid kit).

Armour
Hull: Welded. Detachable armour plate over suspension assemblies.
Turret: Welded, cast front.
Hull: Front 76 mm. vertical.
       Glacis 32 mm./70°.
       Nose 63 mm./20°.
       Side 32 mm.
       Lower side 29 mm. outer; 14 mm. inner.
       Rear 32 mm.
       Top 25 mm.
       Floor 14 mm.
Turret: Gun mantlet and Front 101 mm.
       Sides 63 mm.
       Rear 57 mm.
       Top 25 mm.

Engine
Rolls Royce Meteor Mk. 3, Petrol. 60° V-12, water-cooled, 600 b.h.p. at 2,550 r.p.m. Fuel 116 gallons.

Transmission
Clutch: Borg and Beck, dry, twin-plate, hydraulically operated.
Gearbox: Merritt-Brown, type Z.5.
Final Drive: Reduction 4·5 to 1.

Suspension
Christie type, five pairs of road wheels each side—similar to that on Cromwell but strengthened. Return rollers mounted above road wheels.
Track: Web-spudded.
Pitch: 4·39 in.
Links: 114.

Electrical System
12 volt system. Tiny Tim auxiliary charging set.

Performance
Maximum speed: 32 m.p.h.
Maximum gradient: 35°.
Vertical obstacle: 3 ft.
Trench: 8 ft.

The 3rd/4th County of London Yeomanry (Sharpshooters) training with a Comet and a Cromwell 95-mm.
(Photo: 3rd/4th County of London Yeomanry (Sharpshooters)

"Mount" — crews of 2nd Canadian Armoured Brigade mount their Ram tanks.

Ram and Sexton

by Chris Ellis and Peter Chamberlain

THOUGH a small Canadian Tank Corps had been formed in 1918, few Canadian officers had experience of tanks by the time of the Armistice. The most significant armour development in 1918 was the establishment of machine-gun companies using armoured lorries as carriers, a very early application of the idea of armoured infantry. The unit involved was a Canadian machine-gun battalion, one of whose officers was a young subaltern named F. F. Worthington. This same officer was destined some 20 years later to become the driving force behind the establishment of the Canadian armoured forces which served with such distinction during World War II.

After the Armistice of November 1918, the huge Canadian Army contracted rapidly to its tiny peacetime strength of a few thousand men, and Worthington resumed his career as an infantry officer with Princess Patricia's Canadian Light Infantry, though he maintained an interest in mechanical transport. In 1930 a dozen Carden-Loyd machine-gun carriers were purchased from Britain to equip the machine-gun platoons of the few Canadian regular infantry battalions, these being the first tracked AFVs to go into military service in Canada since 1918. The Canadian Tank Corps itself—which had had a handful of British Mark V and French Renault FT tanks—was disbanded after 1918. However, by 1936 the international situation was worsening rapidly and the Canadian Defence Department decided to resurrect an armoured element, initially in cadre strength, to train men in tank warfare in the event of war.

Selected to command the newly formed cadre was F. F. Worthington, now a Captain (Brevet Major) and one of the few serving officers in Canada with any experience at all of armoured warfare. A Canadian Tank School was set up at London, Ontario, commanded by Worthington who had five officers and 18 other ranks forming the entire personnel of the unit. At this time six cavalry militia regiments were re-organized as tank units on paper, which meant that they carried out training in tank handling and tank warfare even though they were not allocated any tanks. The dozen Carden-Loyd carriers were taken to London to provide training vehicles and these were supplemented by two Vickers light tanks purchased from Britain. The tiny defence budget of the period did not allow the purchase of spares, however, and prodigies of improvisation were needed to keep the vehicles running. Facilities at London were minimal so Worthington arranged for trainees to go to the nearby R.C.A.F. airfield at Trenton, Ontario, to learn about the mechanical aspects of tanks—using aero engines as a basis.

Meanwhile Worthington was sent on an intensive ten month course at the Royal Tank Corps depot, Bovington, England, to bring his knowledge of the subject up-to-date, and one of his first acts on returning to Canada was to arrange for the Tank School to be moved to Camp Borden where there were ample facilities for cross-country training as at Bovington. The fall manoeuvres of 1938 saw the first official use of tanks on exercises when all 12 carriers and the two light tanks formed one squadron, while a horsed dragoon squadron was used to represent the "enemy" tanks. In the summer of 1939, 14 Light Tanks Mk VI were ordered from Britain and arrived in Canada just before the outbreak of war. No attempt had previously been made to acquire tanks in quantity for Canada, partly on the grounds of expense, but mainly because it was considered that any tank requirements would be met by Britain in the event of a Canadian Expeditionary Force being sent once more to Europe. Production of tanks in Canada was thought to be out of the question because government arsenals were far too small to build them.

When war was declared, all remaining cavalry militia units were re-designated as tank units, and Worthington's small—but now expanding—staff were fully engaged in an increased training programme despite the pitiful shortage of vehicles. At this time a Royal Tank Corps officer, Colonel E. J. Carter, who had been spending his retirement leave in Canada at the outbreak of war, was invited by the Defence Department to report on future tank training needs and organization. Predictably, Carter severely criticized the inadequate training facilities then available. Partly as a result of this and partly as a result of the almost complete inactivity on the Western Front in the early months of the war, influential members of the Defence Department were able to get the Tank School closed down in December 1939 on the grounds that it was not worth maintaining and that there appeared to be little requirement for Canadian tank forces in any case. Worthington and his staff had their task changed to training infantry in the operation and use of the Bren Gun Carrier.

Events in 1940, needless to say, brought a rapid change in the fortunes of Worthington and the Canadian tank forces. The German invasion of France and Flanders in May 1940 found Britain embarrassingly short of tanks, and likely to remain so until new production facilities reached full output. Even before the disaster of Dunkirk it was realized that additional production facilities would be needed outside Britain with the Americas as the obvious choice. One result of this was the eventual despatch of a British Tank Mission to Washington in June 1940 with the initial idea (soon changed) of getting British tank designs built by United States firms. Similarly, in May 1940, the newly-formed Ministry of Supply made contact with the Canadian Pacific Railway Co. and asked if they could undertake production of the latest British tank, the Infantry Tank Mk. III, Valentine, to meet British requirements. Initially Canadian automobile firms had been considered for the task, but these were all already committed to military truck and Universal Carrier production, and Canadian Pacific happened to be the one large firm with spare productive capacity at its workshops in Angus.

THE CANADIAN VALENTINE

The formal contract for Valentine production was signed with Canadian Pacific in June 1940 and called for 300 complete vehicles, less engines, guns, and minor ancillary parts which would be fitted after the tanks arrived in Britain. The drawings would be supplied by Vickers, the builders in England. As it happened there was some delay with these; the

To provide vehicles for training when the Canadian Armoured Corps was almost completely without tanks in 1940, these old M1917 6-tonners were purchased at scrap value from the U.S.A.; here a consignment arrives at Camp Borden in August 1940.
(Canadian Official)

Valentine had been ordered "off the drawing board" the previous July and the first production model, ready in May 1940, was also the pilot model with detail drawings being made almost literally as the vehicle was built.

With the fall of France at the end of June, the original arrangements were further changed, Britain now stood threatened with imminent invasion and the

Colonel F. F. Worthington, Commandant of the Canadian Armoured Corps, takes a look at the engine of one of his newly acquired M1917 ex-U.S. Army tanks on its arrival at Camp Borden, summer 1940.
(Canadian Official)

Valentine Mk. IV tanks lined up outside the Canadian Pacific Works at Angus, Montreal, awaiting installation of their 2-pdr. guns, early in 1942. (Canadian Official)

The pilot model of the Ram makes a ceremonial "roll-out" from Montreal Locomotive Works on June 30, 1941, watched by workers. On the stand on the left are the Hon. J. L. Ralston, Minister of National Defence, and the Hon. D. C. Howe, Minister of Munitions and Supply, who accepted the vehicle on behalf of the Defence Department. Censor has painted out interior of vehicle visible through open sponson door. Note absence of dustguards on this and early production Rams. (Canadian Official)

virtual certainty of disruptive bombing of industrial areas. The majority of the British tanks had been lost in France and only a motley assortment of vehicles was immediately available for home defence. Canadian Pacific were now asked to build and deliver the complete Valentine tank, using Canadian-built 2-pdr. guns (which were made by Dominion Engineering Ltd.), and finding a suitable power plant in lieu of the AEC gasoline engine used in the British-built Valentines.

Meanwhile the Canadian Defence Department had not been inactive. The need for tanks had been amply demonstrated by the turn of events in Europe and on August 18, 1940, the Canadian Armoured Corps was formally embodied with Worthington—now a Colonel and soon to be a Brigadier—as commandant. Camp Borden was to be headquarters and training centre, and all the regular cavalry regiments were to become

tank battalions forthwith. The only flaw in these arrangements was the almost complete lack of tanks— just the few existing light tanks, now almost worn out, and absolutely no prospect of any further deliveries from hard-pressed Britain.

With characteristic initiative, Worthington met the challenge by visiting the United States and purchasing all the 1919 vintage tanks he could lay his hands on. These vehicles, mainly M1917 light tanks (known as "Six Tonners", the U.S.-built version of the Renault FT), with a smaller number of Mk. VIIIs, had been withdrawn from U.S. Army service in the early 'thirties but had been laid up rather vaguely against further contingency needs. Already completely obsolete by 1930, in 1940 they were literally museum pieces but in Worthington's view they were better than nothing—at least for training. He bought the lot, 219

The first 30 Canadian-built Valentines were kept in Canada for training where three of them are seen here at Camp Borden. These very early vehicles had fabricated noses of riveted construction, though most Canadian Valentines had the cast nose. (Canadian Official)

WRC-2666

in all, with spare engines and spare parts at scrap value. This was, in fact, necessary to conform with American neutrality laws, and to maintain the fiction they were formally consigned to "Mr. Worthington, Camp Borden Iron Foundry".

The veteran American tanks saw hard service in the next year or so: 40 were allocated to each of the new armoured battalions. Though of negligible fighting value they did at least give crews an idea of tactics and maintenance problems, providing valuable experience all round.

The initial stage in the expansion of the Canadian Armoured Corps called for the establishment of the 1st Canadian Army Tank Brigade with a further expansion, announced in August 1940, involving the formation of two complete armoured divisions.

To equip the tank brigade, the Department of National Defence placed an immediate order with Canadian Pacific for 488 Valentines in addition to those which the British had ordered. Building the complete Valentine in Canada now meant a certain amount of re-design and, indeed, original design work. When drawings were eventually received in Canada numerous changes were needed to suit the vehicle for home production. Detail measurements were altered to match Canadian engineering standards, a completely new electrical system was designed and new electrical traverse gear was evolved using Canadian components. Major changes involved the engine and armament. The original British Valentine had an AEC gasoline engine, but for the Canadian version a GMC 6-cylinder two-stroke commercial diesel engine (made by General Motors of Canada) was adopted. This was later tested by the British, proved slightly superior to the AEC installation, and was subsequently used in some British-built Valentines. The Besa machine-gun used in the British Valentine was in short supply, so for Canadian vehicles after No. 16 the machine-gun mounts were adapted to take the American Browning ·30 cal. machine-gun. The final, and most distinctive change on the Canadian Valentine was the replacement of the fabricated hull nose by a cast one-piece nose which was intended to simplify production. Later, in 1942, when British designers were up-gunning the Valentine from a 2-pdr. to 6-pdr. gun, the Canadian Army Engineering Design Branch (responsible for tank design from December 1941) drew up plans for a home-produced cast turret with 6-pdr. gun for the Valentine. The idea was shelved, however, for by then Valentine contracts were being run down and the development work involved could not be justified.

Altogether Canadian Pacific built 1,420 Valentines —for orders were subsequently increased—the first being delivered in June 1941 and the last in May 1943, by which time the design was well and truly obsolete. The Valentines built in Canada ran to three marks, designated Mks. VI, VII, and VIIA, all with detail changes. By the time the first Valentines were produced, however, the 1st Canadian Army Tank Brigade had gone to Britain (in February 1941) where it was equipped with Matildas and, later, Churchills. Valentines never did see much service with the Canadian Army. The first 30 were kept for training at Camp Borden and the other 1,390 were shipped to Russia under Lend-Lease arrangements. Some, at least, of these were used in combat and the Russian

Views of an early production Ram I, actually the pilot model, show the main characteristics of the design. Note the cast turret front, later replaced by a bolted front, the sponson side doors, the protectoscopes, and absence of dustguards.
(Imperial War Museum)

Government paid rare and uncharacteristic tribute to their quality stating: "After proof in battle we consider the Canadian-built Valentine Tank the best tank which we have received from any of our allies and we propose to ask . . . for more." Rarely during the war, or after, did the Russians make any other mention or acknowledgement of the many types of weapon supplied to them under Lend-Lease.

THE CRUISER TANK

For the two new armoured divisions it was estimated that there was an immediate requirement for about 1,200 cruiser tanks. In August 1940 the Defence Department had set up an Inter-departmental Tank Committee to co-ordinate tank requirements and procurement for the future. At this time the chances of ever receiving tanks from Britain were remote; similarly, purchasing opportunities in America were severely limited because tank production was only just expanding and Britain had placed prior orders which absorbed all spare capacity. The only alternative, therefore, was to build tanks in Canada. It was decided to set up a Tank Arsenal to be run by the Montreal Locomotive Works, a subsidiary of American Locomotive Co., which was already involved in tank production in the United States.

In the late summer of 1940, the U.S. Ordnance Department commenced work on the M3 medium tank design, the British Tank Mission having knowledge of progress since they proposed to order this vehicle for British use. First inclination on the part of

A view which contrasts the two types of American rubber shoe tracks used on most Rams. (Canadian Official)

the Inter-departmental Tank Committee was to commend production of the M3 at the Canadian Tank Arsenal in the interests of standardization. By late autumn of 1940, however, the M3 design was sufficiently far advanced for the British Tank Mission in Washington to report on the features which were unsatisfactory by British (and thus Canadian) standards. The major objection was the excessive height and the sponson-mounted main armament which imposed tactical limitations. Further, the armour protection was considered inadequate and the radio was carried in the hull instead of in the turret as was British practice. One result of the British Tank Mission's objections was a specially designed low turret (with radio in the rear bulge) to further meet British requirements, and this version of the M3 became the Grant.

In January 1941, the Inter-departmental Tank Committee decided on a compromise. Worthington and other senior officers were convinced that Canada could design and build a cruiser (or medium) tank superior to the M3 design. The committee therefore decided to utilize the very satisfactory chassis and mechanical components of the M3, but to design a new superstructure and adopt a layout and armament which was in line with British requirements and standards. What was needed was a main armament of a 2-pdr. (subsequently amended to 6-pdr.) in a fully traversing turret, with a standard British No. 19 wireless set in the turret bustle, and a low overall height. Other contemporary British features then thought desirable were an auxiliary hull machine-gun turret and right-hand drive.

Montreal Locomotive Works were given responsibility for detail design under the direction of the Department of Munitions and Supply via the Inter-departmental Tank Committee. Features retained from the M3—apart from the chassis—were the sponson side doors and the 60-in. diameter turret ring. The British Tank Mission and the Defence Department were involved in the design and planning of the new vehicle in a consultative capacity.

Colonel Worthington contributed enthusiastic advice, his main contention being that the new vehicle should have a larger turret ring and mount the 75-mm. gun in the turret, so overcoming the main objection to the M3. Unfortunately his advanced view was not heeded and the Inter-departmental Tank Committee kept rigidly to the conventional British "rule" of the period that cruiser tanks should have 2-pdr. guns. The need for a tank with a 75-mm. gun had been appreciated in the U.S. Army from as early as May 1940 when the Germans first invaded France, and this had been the very reason for the design of the

Production Ram Is on first delivery to Canadian troops at Camp Borden in 1942. Note that they lack guns, and the turrets are trained from the camera to conceal this fact in this "official" photo which was among the first released of the new vehicle. (Canadian Official)

In July 1941 the pilot model Ram was sent to Aberdeen Proving Ground where the U.S. Ordance Department ran comparative trials with the M3 medium tank. Col. R. J. Icks was in charge of the tests. This is one of the official pictures taken of the vehicle at the time. Note that it lacks the commander's periscope. Later the U.S. Ordnance Department gave this vehicle the "paper designation" M4A5 in the M4 tank series.
(U.S. Official)

M3; it was not until nearly a year later, in the spring of 1941, that the British fully appreciated the urgent need for a heavier gun than the 2-pdr. and ordered the 6-pdr. (57 mm.) into production for use in tanks.

Thus the opportunity was missed of having an Anglo-Canadian tank with turret-mounted 75-mm. gun in production and in service by 1942, a crucial error of judgement in the otherwise creditable history of the Ram, though it was not, of course, realized to be an error at the time. In fact the Ram had a very advanced design feature by British standards of the period in that the turret incorporated a completely separate bolted front plate which made provision for up-gunning when the 6-pdr.—then (February 1941) going into production—was available. Up-gunning the

Many production Ram I tanks were sent to equip Canadian divisions in Britain. Here one is seen in January 1942. Note the added mudguards. This vehicle also has mud chutes between the bogies, features added to most Canadian M3 Lee tanks but rarely seen on the Ram.
(Canadian Official)

design would merely involve replacing the front plate and 2-pdr. mount with a new front plate incorporating the 6-pdr; there would be no need to re-design the complete turret as was the case in some of the British tanks which were retrospectively fitted with 6-pdrs.

It should be remembered that at the time Worthington was mooting the 75-mm. gun turret idea, the U.S. Ordnance Department had not even started work on the design of the M3's successor, the M4 (Sherman), which was to be built from the start round a turret-mounted 75-mm. gun. Ironically, the British did not begin to consider the 75-mm. gun *officially* until the M3 and M4 medium tanks had given proof of their effectiveness in British hands during the latter part of 1942 and it was late in 1943 before the first British tanks appeared with a 75-mm. gun. By 1944 when British tanks so armed were available in quantity, the German tanks had guns which were superior still.

Worthington went to Britain in February 1941 to organize the reception, training and equipment of the 1st Canadian Army Tank Brigade which actually arrived and took over its Matildas and Churchills in June. Though he had been severed from direct contact with development of the new tank, Worthington's interest in the design and the important part he played in establishing the Canadian Armoured Corps was recognized in the name bestowed on the vehicle—Ram. This was taken from the central feature of the Worthington family crest which incorporated such a beast with suitably pugnacious horns.

The prototype vehicle was completed by Montreal Locomotive Works in June 1941, a considerable feat considering that detailed design had started only six months previously. Of course, work was somewhat

A fine line-up of Ram IIs from one of the Canadian armoured regiments in Britain in April 1944. The nearest three vehicles have the Mk. III 6-pdr. gun and the next two have the longer Mk. V 6-pdr. gun but with the usual muzzle counterweights removed. Note that the nearest vehicle is a late production Mk. II with the sponson doors eliminated but retaining the ventilator and the auxiliary machine-gun turret. (Canadian Official)

simplified by the use of the M3 medium tank chassis, Wright R-975 radial engine, transmission, and vertical volute suspension all virtually unchanged. A major alteration which presented problems was the re-siting of the driving position on the right to conform with the practice in British cruiser tanks. The driving seat which was high (and to the left) in the M3, was placed on the floor and all the controls were re-designed, shortened, and placed on the right. The floor position also allowed the overall height of the hull to be reduced. In July 1941 the prototype Ram was sent to Aberdeen Proving Ground for comparative

trials with the M3 medium. Colonel R. J. Icks was the testing officer, with a British/Canadian crew. While legend has it that the Ram influenced the Sherman design as a result, this is not strictly true for the T6 (Sherman prototype) was already designed by this time and any features derived from the Ram would have affected details only.

THE RAM DESCRIBED

The entire hull top and turret was cast, a considerable design feat for the period. At the time the pilot model was built such extensive armour plate casting was

The Ram Mk. II had a 6-pdr. gun which necessitated a new turret front, clearly shown in this view. Another production change visible here is the replacement of the protectoscope in the side door by a ventilator. (Canadian Official)

Another late production Ram II in Britain, November 1943, this time lacking the ventilator and side doors. (Imperial War Museum)

beyond the capabilities of any Canadian engineering plant and General Steel Castings in U.S.A. undertook this work, later assisting in establishing casting facilities at Montreal Locomotive Works' Tank Arsenal for production vehicles. The turret ring was identical to that used on the M3 medium tank and the turret was offset slightly to the right. The chassis structure was of riveted rolled plate, and layout followed that of the M3 in that the Wright R-975 9-cylinder radial air-cooled engine was mounted in the rear of the hull. The drive shaft led forward above the hull floor to the transmission which was of the controlled differential type with five forward speeds and reverse as in the M3. Final drives and differentials were at the extreme front of the vehicle driving the front sprockets. A three-piece bolted nose casting protected the transmission and final drive.

The driver sat to the right of the transmission housing with his steering levers, clutch and accelerator pedals immediately ahead of him. Forward vision was via an opening port which incorporated a protecto-scope offering a limited view ahead when closed down. In these conditions the main vision device was a periscope in the hull roof just behind the vision port. The instrument panel was mounted in front of the driver but to his left, immediately over the transmission casing. To the left of the transmission was the hull gunner's position. In the early Rams he had a free-turning auxiliary turret which was, in fact, identical to the turret cupola of the M3 medium tank. This featured a hatch in the top and a Browning ·30 cal. machine-gun pivoted for elevation only. The machine-gun traversed the turret. The hull gunner had a circular seat on a rotating pintle attached to the hull floor. In later Rams the auxiliary turret was dispensed with, the hull shape was modified to match the driver's side, and a ·30 cal. machine-gun in a ball mount was provided in the hull front as on the Sherman tank. The other major feature of the cast hull was the sponson

door in each side. Each door incorporated a pistol port but it was mainly intended as an escape hatch. Though a convenient feature for the crew and useful for re-ammunitioning, the sponson door was soon eliminated from production vehicles. Not only did the openings weaken the hull, they also complicated manufacture. As a substitute a belly escape hatch was provided when the side doors were discontinued. The hull rear had bolted cover plates giving engine access, and fuel filler caps. In the hull backplate were engine servicing doors and muffled exhaust pipes.

The cast turret had a bolted front plate holding the gun and mantlet and a small bolted backplate which could be removed for servicing the gun or radio equipment, etc. Each side of the turret was a pistol port incorporating a protectoscope. These protecto-

Ram IIs of a Canadian armoured division training in Britain are subjected to a mock air attack by U.S.A.A.F. Mustangs, December 1942. (Imperial War Museum)

A late production Ram II in 1944 exhibiting all the final modifications. The auxiliary machine-gun turret is eliminated as are the side doors and the pistol ports in the turret. It has U.S. type steel tracks and bogies with trailing return rollers as fitted to the Sherman tank. Note the long Mk. V 6-pdr. gun with muzzle counterweight. Vehicle at rear is the earlier production type with pistol ports, auxiliary turret and Mk. III 6-pdr. gun.

(Imperial War Museum)

scopes were later eliminated, and in later vehicles still the pistol ports themselves were dispensed with. From the early production Ram II the protectoscopes were also removed from the hull side doors and replaced by ventilators.

Vision devices in the turret consisted of a periscope for the commander in one flap of his rotating hatch with another periscope for the gunner in the turret roof. In the Ram II the gunner's periscope was replaced by a mushroom ventilator.

As originally envisaged the Ram was to have the 2-pdr. gun, but while still being designed at Montreal Locomotive Works the decision was taken that all future British tanks should have the 6-pdr. gun, and provision was made for future installation as previously recounted. The story of the 6-pdr. gun was one of bureaucratic muddle and monumental indecision

which delayed its appearance in British tanks. Suffice it to say that no clear go-ahead for production was given until spring 1941 when Rommel's early successes in the Western Desert fighting finally showed up the inadequacy of the British 2-pdr. It was clear that no 6-pdr. guns would be available by the time Ram production was scheduled to start in November 1941. So as an expedient it was planned to fit 2-pdrs. in the first 50 vehicles. The gun and mount was the same as used in the Valentine and was simply adapted to a suitable front plate. This version of the Ram was subsequently designated Mk. I.

In the planning stages for the Ram the British had undertaken to supply 6-pdr. drawings and information for the tank mountings. However, possibly due to the confusion surrounding the 6-pdr. programme, nothing arrived. Fortunately the Canadian Department of Munitions and Supply had acted on its own initiative in October 1940 and asked Dominion Engineering Ltd to go ahead with a Canadian version of the 6-pdr., with production to start at the end of 1941. A suitable tank mount and elevation gear was designed by the Montreal Locomotive Works, so Rams with 6-pdr. guns were in production early in 1942 at the same time as the 6-pdr. was being fitted to British tanks. With the 6-pdr. the vehicle was designated the Ram Mk. II and all subsequent production vehicles after the first 50 were of this type. The turret traverse mechanism (hand and hydraulic) in the Ram was copied from the M3 medium and the same gyro-stabilizer (which worked in elevation only) was installed. In terms of fire-control the Ram was thus superior to British tanks with 6-pdr. guns. In both the Ram I and II there was a co-axial ·30 cal. machine-gun in the mantlet and a ·30 cal. weapon could be pintle-mounted on the turret for AA defence, though this was very rarely fitted.

PRODUCTION CHANGES

The Ram was designed with the benefit of very little 'user' experience, other than that which came second-hand from Britain *via* the British Tank Mission. Thus it became subject to numerous detail modifications during its production life once units in the field had a chance to report back. It says much for the soundness

Another view of a very late production Ram Mk. II, this time fitted with C.D.P. steel tracks. Note the Mk. V 6-pdr. gun and the absence of the auxiliary turret. Date: May 1944.

(Canadian Official)

25 pdr. S.P. Tracked, Sexton of 147 Field Regt., (Essex Yeomanry), 8th Armoured Brigade, October, 1944.

Variation of 8th Armoured Brigade formation sign as carried on this particular vehicle.

Ram Mk II of 'C' Squadron. Lord Strathcona's Horse, 5th Canadian Armoured Division, April, 1943.

Lee /Brittain /Hadler © Profile Publications

Late production Ram IIs displaying the absence of side openings in hull and turrets. These are on exercises in England in December 1943.
(Imperial War Museum)

of the design, however, that there were no fundamental changes necessary. Like the Sherman—which it pre-dated in design by a few months—the Ram proved relatively viceless, being mechanically reliable and easy to maintain. The detail changes are best given in summary form:

Vehicle	WD Numbers (range)	Features
Ram I	CT-39781—CT-39830 (50)	2-pdr. gun, no gyro-stabilizer, auxiliary machine-gun turret, side doors.
Ram II	CT-39831—CT-40937 (1107) CT-159402—CT-160193 (792)	6-pdr. gun with gyro-stabilizer; splash beading added round turret.

Ram II Modifications	From vehicle
Side doors removed from hull	CT-40131
Pistol ports added in hull in place of side doors	CT-40131
Pistol ports eliminated	CT-40546
Access plate in turret rear eliminated and belly escape hatch provided	CT-159502
Auxiliary machine-gun turret removed from hull	CT-159502

Ram II Modifications	From vehicle
Improved 6-pdr. gun mantlet	CT-159599
Improved R-975-CI engine, new silencers, improved air cleaners, improved clutch, and transmission oil cooler	Late production
Improved volute suspension brackets with trailing return rollers and heavier springs. C.D.P. tracks.	Very late production

This view of a production Ram I with the Fort Garry Horse shows very clearly the origin of the 2-pdr. mantlet which was taken straight from the Valentine tank. (Chamberlain Collection)

The Fort Garry Horse were one of the first units to receive Ram Is in Britain, in April 1942. Here they are pictured on the first exercise, the vehicles still painted with shipping instructions.
(Canadian Official)

Farewell to the Rams . . . . one of the new Shermans arrives to replace the Rams of a Canadian armoured regiment in April 1944 during the invasion preparations. (Imperial War Museum)

Early Ram IIs had the OQF 6-pdr. Mk. III gun and later vehicles had the longer OQF 6-pdr. Mk. V which was distinguished by its muzzle counterweight. The engine changes listed above were to allow for the use of a lower octane fuel. One feature unique to the Ram and its derivatives was Canadian Dry Pin track, designed in Canada as a substitute for the American type track, rubber bushed, used on the Sherman. This was both heavy and expensive and C.D.P. track proved very successful. American tracks were used on the early Rams, however.

RAM IN SERVICE

First Ram Is were completed at Montreal Locomotive Works in November 1941 and the change-over to the Ram II came in January 1942. By the time the Ram started to appear the Canadian Armoured Corps had started to expand at a rapid rate. By late 1942 the

The first Canadian regiments with Rams frequently had M3 Lees or Grants (as here) to make up the numbers. This picture was taken on an exercise in England in December 1942. (Canadian Official)

4th and 5th Armoured Divisions had been formed, the 4th by converting an infantry division with Worthington appointed its G.O.C. In mid-1942 these two divisions were shipped to Britain, equipped with a mixture of Rams and M3 Lees.

The majority of the Rams built, including the Mk. Is, came to Britain in this way, equipping the Canadian armoured divisions, but none were to see service in their primary fighting rôle. By the time of the invasion of Europe in June 1944, tanks with 75-mm. guns were to equip the British/Canadian armoured divisions and the Canadian tank battalions had their Rams replaced by Shermans in the months preceding D-Day. In early 1943, in fact, consideration had been given once more to mounting a 75-mm. gun in the Ram in place of the 6-pdr. One vehicle had a 75-mm. gun installed and firing trials were said to be successful. However, no decision was made to produce Rams with 75-mm. guns. No precise reasons have been traced for this, but undoubtedly the main reason was that the turret was too small to hold the 75-mm. gun in comfort. It was a tight fit even with the 6-pdr. and to be wholly satisfactory it would have been necessary to use a larger turret ring and a redesigned turret. The vast amount of work this would have involved could not be justified in late 1943 by which time Ram production had ended and sufficient M4 series vehicles were being turned out in America to suit all Allied medium tank requirements for the year ahead.

A decision to terminate production of the Ram was taken as early as August 1942, when production of the M4 medium tank was in hand on a grand scale in the United States. In the interests of standardization it was planned that the M4A1 would also be produced in Canada at the Montreal Locomotive Works after completion of the Ram contract. In fact, another year was to go by before the last Ram was built in July 1943. The delay was mainly due to the difficulty of introducing the new plant and components needed to build M4A1s in Canada without interrupting production at the Montreal works for too long a period. Also there was an increased demand for M4 series vehicles in the winter of 1942-43 which diverted attention from setting up new production lines when it was simpler for existing facilities to increase their output.

RAM VARIANTS

Ram OP

It was in the last six months or so of Ram production that the first of several variants appeared. This was the Ram OP, which was designed to act as a command and observation vehicle for SP artillery, specifically to complement the Sexton SP 25-pdr. which was then just going into production at the Montreal Locomotive Works. As described later, the Sexton shared a common chassis with the Ram and it was logical to utilize the Ram as an OP vehicle. The last 84 Rams built were completed as OP vehicles and the conversion entailed removal of the 6-pdr. gun and its replacement by a dummy barrel. The interior was completely re-arranged with elimination of the turret

A Ram II used for infantry training in 1943 with its 6-pdr. gun removed.　　　　　　　　(Canadian Official)

Above and below. The Ram converted experimentally as a SP AA mount for the 3·7-in gun. This project was abandoned at an early stage, 1943.
(Canadian Official)

basket and the siting of an observation position (with stereoscopic telescope) in the turret front. Vision slots were cut in the front plate. The hydraulic traverse gear was removed and the turret was limited in hand traverse to 45° each side. The commander's hatch was calibrated and marked so that the hatch periscope could be used as a direction finder and sight. Two No. 19 and one No. 58 wireless sets were carried, and field telephone cable reels were mounted behind the turret.

The detail design for this conversion was carried out by the Canadian Army Engineering Design Branch to meet Royal Artillery requirements. Subsequently a number of standard Ram II tanks were converted as OP vehicles to the same standards and these Ram OPs were widely used by the field regiments equipped with Sextons in the N.W. Europe campaign.

Kangaroo

The other important rôle for which the Ram is best remembered is the Kangaroo troop carrier. This was a significant development as far as the British Army was concerned for it demonstrated, in 1944, the value of the tracked armoured troop carrier for the infantry battalions of armoured brigades; this type of vehicle, latterly in a specially developed form, has been used by the British ever since. Appropriately enough, the Kangaroo as developed in 1944 was a Canadian idea, though at first it did not involve the Ram at all. Lieut.-General Guy Simonds, the young 41-year-old commander of 2nd Canadian Corps, first thought of carrying up troops in tracked armoured vehicles during "Operation Totalise", the offensive against Falaise in early August 1944. Here infantry had to be transported over the big expanse of open ground in the Orne valley to support a tank attack and occupy villages beyond the German defence lines. While a limited number of half-tracks was available, this was nothing like sufficient, for it was necessary to carry up six infantry battalions for this major assault. However, at that time the Priest had just been replaced in British and Canadian SP field regiments by the Sexton, and Simonds arranged for R.E.M.E. workshops to remove the 105-mm. howitzers from as many displaced Priests as were available. Known popularly as "Unfrocked Priests", and later as Priest Kangaroos, these vehicles had the gun embrasure plated in and carried 12 infantrymen. Though the overall operation was not entirely successful, the idea of using the makeshift armoured personnel carriers proved highly satisfactory. Strictly speaking, the Kangaroo idea at this time was simply a revival of what had been done in the first world war, and what the Germans had been doing in the second; but immediately prior to 1944 the British had not used APCs save for a limited number of half-tracks in armoured divisions.

The Kangaroo idea was later taken up by 79th Armoured Division which was responsible for 21 Army

Ram OP tank of a Sexton-equipped SP field regiment passing through a village street in Holland in January 1945.

(Imperial War Museum)

Group's specialized fighting vehicles. By September 1944 the Canadians had formed a special Kangaroo unit, 1st Canadian Armoured Carrier Regiment, this time using converted Ram tanks of which plenty were available. The turret was removed and the No. 19 wireless set was moved into the left sponson. Rungs and footsteps were welded to the hull sides to provide a means of getting aboard, and bench seats were fitted in the turret space to hold eight to eleven infantrymen. Crew of the vehicle was two, driver and commander/wireless operator. The Ram Kangaroos were used by the Canadians in the taking of Boulogne

and were so successful that it was decided to equip a British regiment for the specialized APC rôle. One armoured brigade workshop converted 120 Ram tanks for British use as Kangaroos within a month, and the 49th RTR was redesignated as 49th APC Regt. to operate them. From the end of 1944 until the cessation of hostilities in Europe the two APC regiments operated under 79th Armoured Division control and gave valuable service, despite the limited numbers available and the improvised nature of the adaptation a major failing of which was the lack of an armoured top. In Italy, meanwhile, 8th Army took

Below and top facing page: Two views of the Ram ARV Mk. I shows the simple nature of this conversion. (Imperial War Museum)

up the Kangaroo idea using Priests once more, plus some "war weary" Shermans which were converted in similar style to the Rams. Ram Kangaroos remained in British Army service for some years in small numbers post-war until specialized APCs like the Saracen became available. Rams were also used as tractors for 17-pdr. anti-tank guns and as ammunition carriers for Sexton-equipped SP field gun regiments; in this latter form they were known as Wallabies. The Canadians also fitted some Ram Kangaroos with Wasp II flame-throwing equipment, the flame projector replacing the hull machine-gun. These vehicles were called Badgers and post-war some Canadian Shermans were similarly altered. Badgers were first in service in February 1945 and were used to great effect by the Lake Superior Regt. (4th Canadian Armoured Brigade) during "Operation Veritable". They were also used by 5th Canadian Armoured Brigade in Holland in March 1945, but in this case standard Rams were used, retaining their turrets, perhaps the

nearest the Ram came to action in its original tank configuration.

Ram ARV

Other special-purpose variants of the Ram were produced in smaller numbers. The Ram ARV Mk. I was a recovery vehicle which featured tool boxes on its rear hull decking and a winch fitted to the hull front. This was a towing vehicle only and the few vehicles so altered were mostly Ram Mk. Is. The Ram ARV Mk. II was a more sophisticated conversion, produced in Canada to the same design as the British Sherman ARV Mk. II. This vehicle had all the same fittings as all British "Mk. II" standard ARVs of the time, including dummy fixed turret and dummy gun, rear jib, earth spade at rear, and electric winch (with 25-ton pull) installed in the former turret space. The Ram ARV II was more widely used than the ARV I but no precise figure for the number of vehicles so converted appears to have been recorded.

Experimentals

Minor versions of the Ram included a few test vehicles or prototypes. After Dieppe, when a special engineer assault tank was proposed, the Ram was considered as a possibility for the rôle. Two test vehicles were converted for trials in 1943, but in the event the Churchill proved a more suitable vehicle for what was later known as the AVRE. One project tried in Canada in 1942-43 was a SP AA version of the Ram which featured a cut down hull and a 3-in. gun, later replaced by a 3·7-in. weapon, in place of the turret. In its final form, a shield was incorporated for the gun, but the project was abandoned, possibly because it was unstable. The strangest rôle of all for the Ram, however, was as a searchlight carrier for the C.D.L. functions, some of which were also used to illuminate forward airstrips. The outfit simply consisted of a complete 40-in. searchlight mounting carried in a Ram Kangaroo. So far as is known, only very few vehicles were so fitted in the winter of 1944-45.

Picture shows Ram Kangaroo, a troop carrier made by removal of the turret from the standard Ram tank, in Holland in October 1944.
(Imperial War Museum)

THE SEXTON

Destined to become much better known and more widely used than the Ram was the Sexton, more formally designated "25-pdr. SP, Tracked". The design owed much to that of the Priest or M7 105-mm. Howitzer Motor Carriage which had been developed for the U.S. Army. Priests had been ordered early in 1942 and were delivered to the 8th Army in time for the Battle of Alamein where they were an immediate success. The British General Staff had put out a requirement for a similar vehicle which mounted the British 25-pdr. howitzer instead of the American 105-mm. howitzer. This led to a prototype being built in July 1942, the T51, by the U.S. Ordnance Department. It was virtually a M7 with a 25-pdr. howitzer replacing the 105-mm. weapon. However, U.S. resources could not be devoted to producing this vehicle specially for British service. Hence the Canadian Army Engineering Design Branch were asked *via* the Canadian Defence Department to utilize a Ram chassis to mount the 25-pdr., incorporate British features, and produce a vehicle embodying the general layout of the M7.

Superstructure of the new SP 25-pdr. was very similar to that of the M7 but the driving position was, of course, on the right as in the Ram. Considerable problems were experienced in mounting the 25-pdr., though all were very successfully overcome. A new saddle and pintle was needed for the cradle, and new traverse gear was necessary to speed up traverse and make it easier. Traversing shields were fitted each side of the gun aperture, features not found in the M7 Priest. In order to give 40° elevation it was necessary to limit the normal recoil throw of the 25-pdr. from 36 to 20 inches. Finally the weapon had to be re-balanced to compensate for the absence of the trail and carriage used on the normal 25-pdr.

The pilot model of the new vehicle, now called the Sexton, was shipped to Britain for trials at the beginning of 1943. Approved subject to minor changes, the Sexton entered production at Montreal Locomotive works early in 1943 and 424 had been completed by the end of the same year. When production ceased at the end of 1945, 2,150 had been built. Since Ram tanks were in production in the Montreal works, the howitzer assemblies and other parts were made at Sorel and assembled into the vehicle at

The Badger was a Kangaroo with Wasp flame-throwing equipment replacing the hull machine-gun. This picture shows the same conversion on a Canadian Sherman just post-war with the flame projector arrowed. (Canadian Official)

Montreal. The Sexton long outlived the Ram in production and numerous detail modifications were made as time went by to bring the Sexton chassis up to later standards similar to those of the M4. For instance, early Sextons had three-piece bolted nose assemblies and the original type of bogie bracket. From 1944 these fittings were changed respectively to cast one-piece noses and the M4 type bogies with trailing return rollers. Later additions included provision of a tow-hook for an ammunition trailer, mounting of an auxiliary generator, and provision of pintles for AA machine-guns.

Sextons went into wide service with the British and Canadian divisions in 21 Army Group in June 1944 just after the Normandy landings. They replaced Priests under an agreement with the U.S. Army so that all stocks of 105-mm. ammunition—then in big demand—could be made over to U.S. divisions at Normandy. The displaced Priests were converted to Kangaroos, as previously described. In British service the Sexton remained in use for many years post-war and did not finally disappear until the late '50s.

Early production Sexton with riveted chassis and early type bogies. Note the very crude weld seams on the essentially simple superstructure. (Imperial War Museum)

The Grizzly was simply the Canadian-built version of the M4A1 Sherman with only minor detail changes. (Canadian Official)

Late production Sexton with later Sherman type bogies and cast one-piece nose. C.D.P. tracks are fitted.

(Imperial War Museum)

Though a very large vehicle for such a relatively small weapon, the Sexton, like the Priest, was a very successful and much-liked vehicle with all the inherent virtues of its M3/M4 pedigree. One variant produced based on the Sexton was the Sexton GPO (gun position officer) which was simply a Sexton with the gun removed and fitted out to carry map tables, extra radio and telephones, and Tannoy equipment for the battery control rôle.

THE GRIZZLY

Closely related to the production of the Ram and the Sexton was the Grizzly. It has already been related how Ram production was to be phased out in favour of the M4A1 which was to take over the Ram assembly lines at Montreal Locomotive Works. This changeover took place in the summer of 1943, Ram production ceasing in July and M4A1 production starting in September. The Canadian-built version of this vehicle was called Grizzly and it was identical in all respects to the M4A1 except for the installation of the British 2-in. Smoke Mortar in the turret roof,

The Skink AA tank with its four Polsten 20-mm cannon was based on the Grizzly with re-arranged interior layout and new Canadian-designed turret. (Canadian Official)

and the British No. 19 radio set in the turret. The Wright Continental engine and many other components were similar to those being used already in the Ram, and there was little technical difficulty in effecting the change of production. It is interesting to note that the installation of the 2-in. Smoke Mortar was a feature subsequently adopted for U.S.-built M4 series vehicles. However, Grizzly production was short-lived and terminated in December 1943. By this time it had become apparent that American plants could produce sufficient M4 series tanks to meet all Allied medium tank needs for 1944 and that Grizzly production was an unnecessary duplication of resources. Montreal Locomotive Works was thus left to build only the Sexton and this type was, in the event, built in larger numbers than any other Canadian AFVs except carriers.

THE SKINK

Final Canadian design of the war was the Skink AA tank, an ingenious adaptation of the Grizzly, which was not ultimately required. The Skink originated in 1943 when there was a need for anti-aircraft tanks for the planned invasion of Europe. Several types were designed in Britain as adaptations of existing tanks and the Canadian Department of Defence were asked to produce a similar type. The Waterloo Manufacturing Co. undertook development using the Grizzly as a basis. The Grizzly hull was used with revised interior layout which included armoured racks to hold the magazines for the automatic 20-mm. guns which were to be fitted. At first Hispano guns were specified, later changed to Polstens. A new cast turret was designed to hold the quad gun mount, and this itself presented problems since the shape was difficult to cast and precision was necessary to achieve perfect balance for high speed traverse. A new electro-hydraulic traverse and elevation system was designed, operated by handlebar joystick from the aimer's position in the turret. A much modified auxiliary generator was necessary to provide higher power for the fast traverse system.

The guns could be fired singly, in pairs, or all together. The aimer/gunner was provided with a reflector sight which fitted in the turret roof. This necessitated exposing his head through the turret roof, but for ground fire—a secondary rôle—tracer ammunition was used and the guns were aimed by direct sights from within the turret.

The pilot model of the Skink was completed early in 1944 and production plans were made. Aside from complete Skinks, it was proposed to make conversion kits consisting of the turret and internal equipment so that existing Grizzlies and Shermans could be altered to Skink configuration. However, immediately after the invasion of Europe in June 1944 it became apparent that the expected aerial threat from the Luftwaffe against field forces was negligible. Existing AA tank troops were disbanded and the orders for the Skink were cancelled after only three vehicles and eight conversion sets had been completed. One of the Skinks was brought to England for War Office trials but no further work was done on the project and this promising design ended Canada's energetic and inventive contribution to Allied AFV development in World War II.

THE ROYAL CANADIAN ARMOURED CORPS

By 1945 the Canadian Armoured Corps had grown mightily; Worthington's 24 men of 1936 had become 20,000 by 1945, five times the strength of the entire Canadian Army of pre-war days. Canadian tank men had fought with distinction in Italy and North-West Europe, and a Canadian tank regiment spearheaded the gallant but abortive Dieppe raid in 1942 when much was learned to influence the use of tanks in the Normandy landings. Worthington's lusty infant had indeed grown fast and learnt much inside nine years. Worthington was probably the proudest "father" of all in August 1945 when the Canadian Armoured Corps, which was virtually his creation, was awarded the title "Royal" by King George VI in recognition of its outstanding wartime record.

A.F.V. Series Editor: DUNCAN CROW

SPECIFICATION:

RAM CRUISER TANK/25 pdr. SP TRACKED, SEXTON

	Ram II	Sexton
General		
Crew:	5	6
	(Driver, co-driver, gunner, loader, commander)	(Driver, co-driver, commander, gunners (3))
Combat weight:	65,000 lbs.	57,000 lbs.
Power/weight ratio:	12·3 h.p./ton	14 h.p./ton
Ground pressure:	13·1 lbs./sq. in.	11·5 lbs./sq. in.
Bridge class:	30	30
Dimensions		
Length overall:	19 ft.	20 ft. 1 in.
Height overall:	8 ft. 9 in.	8 ft.
Width overall:	9 ft. 10 in.* 9 ft. 6 in.†	8 ft. 11 in.
Track centres:	83 in.	
Track width:	16½ in. (U.S. T54E1 or T49)	15½ in. (CDP tracks)
Ground contract:	147 in.	147 in.
Armament		
Main:	OQF 6 pdr. Mk. III, IV	OQF 25 pdr. 'C' Mk. II or III
Secondary:	3 × ·30 cal. MG 2 in. Bomb Thrower	2 × Bren ·303 cal. LMG
Fire control:	Gyro-stabilizer in elevation. Direct sight telescope	Direct sight telescope and sight dial for indirect fire
Ammunition		
Main:	92 rds.	112 rds.
Secondary:	880 rds., 24 bombs	1,500 rds.
Sights/vision devices		
	Protectoscopes and periscopes	Protectoscope for driver
Communications	No. 19 set	No. 19 set Loudspeaker (Tannoy)

	Ram II	Sexton
Armour	Cast armour steel Chassis: Armour plate, riveted and/or welded	
Hull		
Front:	1¾ in.	¾ in.
Nose:	1½ in.	1½ in.
Sides:	1½ in. to 2½ in.	⅜ in.
Belly:	1 in.	½ in.
Rear:	1½ in.	1¼ in.
Top:	1½ in. to 3 in.	1¼ in.
Turret		
Front:	3½ in.	
Sides:	2½ in.	Not applicable
Rear:	1½ in.	Front shields: ½ in.
Roof:	1½ in.	
Engine	Wright Continental R-975/CI or R-975/EC2‡ Gasoline/petrol, 9 cylinders radial, air-cooled 400 b.h.p. at 2,400 r.p.m.	
Transmission	Borg-Warner or Lipe clutch, controlled differential gearbox	
Suspension	Vertical volute spring bogies	
Performance		
Maximum speed:	25 m.p.h.	25 m.p.h.
Vertical obstacle:	2 ft.	2 ft.
Trench crossing:	7 ft. 5 in.	8 ft. 3 in.
Wading depth:	3 ft. 4 in.	3 ft. 10 in.
Road radius:	144 miles	180 miles
Fuel capacity:	150 gals. (Imp.)	146 gals. (Imp.)
Special features/remarks	Ram I as for Ram II but with OQF 2-pdr. Mk. IX or X gun. Wt.: 64,000 lbs. OP version had dummy gun and carried second No. 19 wireless set, plus portable No. 54 set.	Could be fitted with canvas tilt over fighting compartment. G.P.O. version lacked gun and carried extra Tannoy and telephone cable reels.

*Vehicles with side doors
†Vehicles without side doors but with vents
‡R-975/C4 in later Sextons

Prototype of AC1. Note the steel track and trailing return rollers on top of suspension units. (Photo: R.A.C. Tank Museum)

Australian Cruiser Mark 1—Sentinel

by Major James Bingham, Royal Tank Regiment

SOON after the outbreak of the Second World War in 1939 it was foreseen in Australia that most of her military equipment would have to be made at home, rather than continuing to rely upon British sources, and steps were taken to build light armoured vehicles from British designs.* The urgency of this programme was suddenly increased when the Allied forces collapsed against the German blitzkrieg in France in May 1940, and when the products of British factories were fully committed to building up their own forces against the threat of invasion. In this situation, and with the intention of equipping the Australian forces in the Middle East, the Department of Defence recommended in June that an attempt be made to manufacture cruiser tanks in Australia. With the approval of the War Cabinet, the project began, although hedged with doubts in some quarters.

The task of designing and producing a tank was a technically ambitious programme, since Australia had a comparatively limited engineering industry and had not even manufactured a motor car. Indeed, apart from some opposition within Australia, there was a disbelief abroad that their industry was capable of producing tanks. Nevertheless, the Army and Department of Munitions accepted the challenge with enthusiasm and soon established a close liaison between their two sections which were responsible, respectively, for design and production.

One of the first steps in gathering information and

*See Volume Two, page 120.

resources for the project was to send an Ordnance Production engineer, Mr. A. Chamberlain, to the United States to study tank production there. Also, a request was made to Britain for the help of an expert in tank design, and Colonel W. D. Watson arrived in December 1940 to join the Army Design Directorate.

DEVELOPMENT AND PRODUCTION

In November 1940 the General Staff issued the specification of the tank required—one weighing between 16 and 20 tons, mounting a 2-pdr. gun with one or two machine-guns, a speed of 30 m.p.h. and an armour basis of 50 mm. It was, of course, desirable that the tank should conform to standard designs used in Britain or the United States, but, within the specification, the design had to take account of what components were already being or could be made in Australia, or which could be imported. Experience in France in 1940 had shown that there was no proven British tank in service which was a suitable model for an Australian tank. Nor was there a battle-tried American tank, but the medium tank M3 was selected as the one offering best scope in meeting the General Staff requirement.

Colonel Watson, on his way to Australia, visited the United States where, in company with Mr. Chamberlain, he studied the M3. He was impressed by the automotive features of this tank and when he got down to the basic design of the new Australian tank he aimed to retain many of the components of the M3. The design which eventually emerged, as the Australian Cruiser Tank Mark 1 (AC 1), was a

The Sentinel in camouflage paint, mounting a bin on the back of the turret and a jettison tank. (Photo: R.A.A.C. A.F.V. Museum)

blend of American automotive practice with British ideas on armour with a low silhouette.

There were, however, considerable difficulties ahead for manufacture within the capacity of Australian industry and there was little tangible progress in the early part of 1941. Early designs showed the hull as being formed by a combination of cast and rolled armour plates, but firms which could produce heavy rolled plates were already fully committed. After considering plans for the hull to be made up in cast sections, proposals were made for the hull to be cast as one solid unit—a method never attempted anywhere before in so large a tank. Despite criticisms from experts, experiments started in mid-1941 to perfect the method of casting and to find a formula for suitable armour using alloys indigenous to the country.

The type of power unit required had been under investigation since July 1940 and it was expected that this would have to be imported. Despite the heavy commitments on American industry, there had been hopes of obtaining the Guiberson diesel; later, however, when the armour thickness was increased to 65 mm. and the design weight went up to 25 tons, Cadillac motor car engines were chosen to form a single power unit made up with three engines. This revolutionary arrangement provoked keen controversy, even from the parent firm of General Motors in America, but by April 1941 tentative agreement had been reached.

The design of the Medium M3 gearbox and final drive, which was to be incorporated in the AC 1, presented a more intractable problem as the machine tools needed to cut the intricate gears in these units

The suspension unit adapted for the Sentinel. Note the escape hatch in the hull side of AC1; this hatch was moved in AC3 to a position behind the driver's head.

(Photo: R.A.A.C. A.F.V. Museum)

Two 25-pdr. guns mounted on an AC1 test vehicle. When fired simultaneously, the twin 25-pdrs. gave a recoil approximately 20% greater than that of the high-velocity 17-pdr.

(Photo: R.A.C. Tank Museum)

The 17-pdr. and turret mounted on an AC1 test vehicle.

(Photo: R.A.C. Tank Museum)

did not exist in Australia; nor was there any prospect of obtaining the tools from Britain or America for at least a year.

In this situation of apparent impasse, Mr. Chamberlain returned from the U.S.A. in May 1941 with proposals for a second Mark of tank, to be known as the AC 2, which would be lighter and simpler, and would use imported power and transmission units produced commercially for heavy trucks in the U.S.A., thereby eliminating the delays inherent in setting up Australian production. In June the Army reluctantly accepted the AC 2 project on the understanding that delivery would start at the end of the year. But the feasibility of the project depended on the weight being kept down to 16-18 tons, within the capacity of the transmission units. Nothing had been settled.

There was continued divergence of opinion, and in July the Government set up a new Directorate of Armoured Fighting Vehicles Production that would take over within one agency the problems of design and production, within the Ministry of Munitions. Mr. A. R. Code, who was an automotive engineer with considerable experience in the industry, became the Director, and he was joined by Colonel Watson for the design work. A re-examination was made of the position on tank production and the AC 2 project was found to be less practical than at first believed. The design weight had emerged at about 22 tons, which could not be reduced without sacrificing armour; and the forecast dates for delivery of the imported components, upon which all depended, seemed to be ever receding while the danger of Japanese intervention in the Pacific was becoming more threatening. In

September, 1941 the Minister for the Army issued instructions that work on the AC 2 should stop, and that the AC 1 be taken in hand as first priority.

In the meantime, design work on the AC 1 had progressed. Drawings had been made of a modified M3 gearbox and final drive which eliminated the syncro-mesh gears and other manufacturing complexities, and it was found possible to make the units

A troop of Sentinels deployed for training.

(Photo: R.A.C. Tank Museum)

The AC1 mounting 2-pdr. gun, with water-cooled Vickers machine-guns in co-axial and front hull mountings.
(Photo: R.A.C. Tank Museum)

The AC3 mounting 25-pdr. and co-axial Vickers machine-gun. Note the difference from the AC1 in the new, sharply sloping hull front and the changed aspect of the hull top.

(Photo: R.A.A.C. A.F.V. Museum)

completely in Australia. Also, in October the casting of the first hull as a single unit was successfully completed. The major obstacles were now overcome for production of the tank entirely in Australia, except for the Cadillac engines and a few small items, and planning went rapidly ahead on a firm overall design. In January, 1942 the first of three AC 1 pilot models was completed, and the first production model was delivered in August—only eleven months after a firm order had been given to go ahead, and 22 months since the idea had taken shape as a General Staff specification.

Despite the comparative speed with which the AC 1 had been produced, experience abroad had shown the need for major improvements and it was decided to

Rear view of AC3. The power unit cover plate on AC1 was similar, giving access to engines, radiators and fuel tanks through hatches.
(Photo: R.A.A.C. A.F.V. Museum)

limit production of AC 1 to 66. Weaknesses included the quick wearing out of the bogie wheel tyres, a weak turret drive gear when the tank was on a slope, and an unsatisfactory engine cooling system, but the main shortcoming was the poor firepower provided by the 2-pdr. gun. Allowance had been made in the design for the 6-pdr. gun to be mounted when available, but, with the urgent demand for anti-tank guns in the Middle East in 1942, none was allotted for the AC 1 project. In order to give the tank a heavier "punch", a pilot model AC 1 was taken for testing with the Australian produced 25-pdr. gun. On 29 June, 1942 the tank was successfully test-fired at Williamstown, Victoria, and work started on the prototype of what was to be called the AC 3, mounting the 25-pdr. gun and incorporating other improvements. A fully equipped model was tested at Wakefield, South Australia, in February, 1943, and it was decided in April to mount the 25-pdr. on a production basis in the AC 3 when the order for the AC 1 was completed.

The next stage in development was to mount the high-velocity 17-pdr. gun, also being manufactured in Australia, in a fourth and heavier Mark known as AC 4. This did not go beyond the stage of design and testing of new components but it was sufficiently far advanced for the Army to state in March, 1943 a requirement for some 700 AC 3 and AC 4, including a second version of the AC 4 mounting the 25-pdr.

The production programme so far had centred upon

The AC3. The co-axial Vickers machine-gun was retained within an armoured shield beside the 25-pdr.
(Photo: R.A.A.C. A.F.V. Museum)

New South Wales where the Government Railways acted as the major co-ordinating contractors and operated a specially built assembly plant at Chullora which had been completed in July, 1942. Plans were in hand to double the production programme by the end of 1943, by opening additional foundries and another assembly plant in Victoria, but these were not taken into use for the purpose.

Driving shafts from each of the three engines in AC1 led forward to the transfer box beneath the turret turntable.
(Photo: R.A.A.C. A.F.V. Museum)

The Perrier-Cadillac 41-75 arrangement of three engines mounted radially on a steel frame around a common crankcase—AC3 and AC4.
(Photo: R.A.A.C. A.F.V. Museum)

American observers were impressed by the AC 3, and General MacArthur commented favourably upon the Australian tank production programme, but Lease-Lend authorities in the U.S.A. could not encourage this diversion of labour and materials. They held that more in the war effort could be achieved in Australia with work on maintaining the American

The triangular case on which the three Cadillac engines were mounted radially to form the Perrier-Cadillac power unit for the AC3 and AC4. (Photo: R.A.A.C. A.F.V. Museum)

tanks which had already arrived in 1942 to equip the Australian forces; also, that the factories should build more railway engines and wagons to sustain the increasing use of the railway system for war work. By 1943 the threat of Japanese invasion on the mainland of Australia had passed and, with General Grant and Matilda tanks being made available from the Middle East also, there was no longer the same need for a home-produced tank. In July the Government ordered production of the Australian Cruiser tank to cease. At that time the initial order for the AC 1 was on the point of completion, and pilot models of AC 3 were being assembled. Those which had been produced were taken into use for training, under the name of Sentinel.

DESCRIPTION OF THE SENTINEL

There were four main castings of armour plate which made up the tank—the main body, to which was bolted the nose section, the power unit cover plate, and the turret.

In the front compartment, on the right side, was the driver, who was separated from the hull gunner's position by the gearbox and the ball-mounted, water-cooled Vickers ·303 machine-gun. In the middle compartment was the turret, supported on the main body and carrying the turntable which held a crew of three

The fans and radiators were mounted at the front of the Perrier-Cadillac power unit. (Photo: R.A.A.C. A.F.V. Museum)

The front compartment and driver's controls in the partially completed hull of an AC3. (Photo: R.A.A.C. A.F.V. Museum)

—commander, loader/wireless operator and gunner. The commander sat on the left, behind the gunner, and he had a flat, revolving cupola which held two periscopes. The loader/operator on the right attended to both guns and to the wireless set in the bulge at the rear of the turret.

The power unit cover plate completely covered the rear compartment, containing the power unit which consisted of three Cadillac 75 engines, fuel tanks, radiators and fan assembly mounted on a subframe. The three engines were arranged in "clover leaf pattern" with two engines side-by-side and one centrally behind, each transmitting power to the transfer box mounted transversely across the floor of the main body, beneath the turret. The combined power of the three engines was transmitted by a single shaft from the transfer box forwards to the main clutch and gearbox. Drive to the sprockets passed through the front axle assembly and the final drive housed in the nose casting; the brakes were operated by the steering levers and were integral with the differential.

The electrical system was complex. A 6-volt system operated the lights, ignition and starter motors, for which the normal engine generators charged three separate batteries; the batteries were connected by switches so that the load could be transferred to any battery as required. A 12-volt system was charged by a separate generator driven off the transfer box, through two additional 6-volt batteries which powered the wireless and inter-communication sets, the two machine-gun cooling motors and the electrically operated Graviner fire extinguisher system. Finally, the turret traverse mechanism was driven by a 40-volt system charged directly by a generator off the transfer box; the starting of any engine immediately provided power, through the transfer box and the 40-volt generator, for the turret traverse motor.

The suspension was based on that of the M3 medium tank. However, due to unfavourable reports on the M3 design, the Hotchkiss type suspension was adopted with horizontal volute springs. The standard M3 rubber track was accepted initially as a temporary expedient (and most photographs show this type of track in use) but an Australian all-steel track was also made and fitted.

AUSTRALIAN CRUISER MARK 3

Production of the AC 3 in quantity was not achieved, although a number of hulls had been made when work on the tank was cancelled in July, 1943. The main and obvious difference from the AC 1 was the 25-pdr. gun, mounted in a similar but larger turret carried on a turret ring which had been increased in diameter from 54 to 64 inches; the hull angles were modified to accept this change. The Vickers ·303 machine-gun was retained as co-axial armament with the 25-pdr., but the hull gun was removed and the front armour was sloped back sharply. The space vacated by the front gunner was used for ammunition stowage.

Internally, an improved engine lay-out offering greater power in less space was achieved with the three Cadillac engines arranged radially on a steel frame around a common crankcase, transmitting power to a

In the turret section of the assembly plant at Chullora, operated by the New South Wales Government Railways.
(Photo: R.A.A.C. A.F.V. Museum)

An AC3 hull in the assembly plant. When Bradford Kendall Ltd., of Sydney, developed the techniques in 1941 of casting the AC1 hull as a single piece, this method of tank manufacture had not previously been used in so large and complex a unit.
(Photo: R.A.A.C. A.F.V. Museum)

transfer case which was incorporated in that unit. Credit for much of this work must go to Mr. R. Perrier, a French tank designer whose name is linked with this engine lay-out; he had been in Japan in 1940, on loan from the French government, and had made his way during the war to Australia.

AUSTRALIAN CRUISER MARK 4

The AC 4, as planned, was essentially a modified version of the AC 3, mounting the 17-pdr. gun and with an increased weight at 31 tons.

In order to test the Australian cruiser's ability to withstand the recoil of the high velocity 17-pdr. gun, tests were carried out in March 1943 with two 25-pdrs. mounted together in a special turret. The tank stood up to these tests in which the twin 25-pdrs., fired simultaneously, gave a recoil approximately 20% greater than that of the 17-pdr. and subsequent firing tests with the 17-pdr. in a turret were satisfactory. The new turret ring had a diameter increased yet again to 70 inches, and the Vickers machine-gun was retained in the co-axial mounting.

Although designs specified the Perrier-Cadillac power unit of the AC 3, another and more powerful unit was tested, consisting of four Gipsy Major engines built in Australia by General Motors—Holdens.

COMMENTARY

In any history of armour the Australian Cruiser tank, or Sentinel, is easily overlooked, or even dismissed, as having no influence on the development of other vehicles. That may be true, for it was unique in its own development and the project was killed before any significant number had been produced. Nevertheless, it is an interesting tank and its very existence was a remarkable achievement for a limited engineering industry, owing much to the determination, ingenuity and improvisations of the designers and manufacturers

Front view of AC1, Sentinel.

(Photo: R.A.A.C. A.F.V. Museum)

Side view of AC1, Sentinel. (Photo: R.A.A.C. A.F.V. Museum)

Note the wire screen which extends all the way behind the tool box on the track guard of the Sentinel. Behind the tool box (on both sides of the tank) air is vented or drawn in beneath an armoured cowl. The wire prevents litter getting packed behind the tool box. Side lights were fitted inside the metal protective loops on the hull sides above the track guards.
(Photo: R.A.A.C. A.F.V. Museum)

who were forced by circumstances to find and adopt some novel features.

In its cast hull, for a tank of this size, the Sentinel preceded the American M48 by about 10 years, and this work on development of cast armour was acknowledged at the time as a "real contribution". The development of AC 4 with the 17-pdr. gun was contemporary with similar work in Britain for this new weapon in a tank mounting and, whereas Sentinel was shown to be capable of accepting the 17-pdr., British designers had to go to new hulls (Challenger, Avenger) and, later, the Sherman.

As the Sentinel never went into action it is pure conjecture as to whether it would have been a reliable and battleworthy tank. There are justifiable criticisms on that score. Certainly, the AC 1 was obsolescent in terms of firepower before it was produced—a weakness shared with other tanks of the period. Mechanically, the Sentinel gave the performance required and it stood up to the rigours of training. It was not until 1956 that the tank was declared obsolete for this purpose.

SPECIFICATION—AUSTRALIAN CRUISER MARK 1, SENTINEL

General
Crew: 5—Commander, gunner, loader/operator, driver, hull gunner. (AC 3 crew—4).
Weight, laden: 28 tons.
Power/weight ratio: 12 to 1 b.h.p./ton.
Ground pressure: 13·4 lbs./sq. in.

Dimensions
Length overall: 20 ft. 9 ins.
Height overall: 8 ft. 4¾ ins.
Width overall: 9 ft. 1 in.
Track centres: 7 ft. 6½ ins.
Track width: 16½ ins.

Armament
Main: QF 2-pdr. (AC 3—25-pdr.).
Auxiliary: Two Vickers ·303 machine-guns, water-cooled, one co-axially mounted and one in forward hull mounting (AC 3—one co-axial Vickers). Bren ·303 light machine-gun.

Fire control
2-pdr. and Vickers: shoulder controlled in free elevation.
Traverse by hand or electric motor powered directly by 40 volt generator (110 volt in AC 3). Rate of traverse 18°/second.

Ammunition
2-pdr.: 130.
Vickers: 4,250.

Sighting and Vision
Commander: Two periscopes in revolving cupola. Porthole in turret side.
Gunner: 2-pdr. Telescope type 24 B, and porthole.
Loader: Porthole.
Driver and Hull Gunner (each): Revolving periscope, armoured visor in front and porthole at side.

Communications
Wireless Set No. 19 Mk. 2. Intercommunication between all crew by wireless set circuits.

Armour
Hull: One-piece casting to which the cast nose and power unit cover plate are bolted.
Armour basis 65 mm. Front; 45 mm. Sides and Rear; 25 mm. Top.
Turret: One piece casting, 65 mm. all round and 25 mm. Top.

Engine
Three Cadillac "75" engines arranged in "clover-leaf" pattern, transmitting power through clutch drives to transfer box and main clutch. 90° V-8 cylinder engines, water-cooled. Combined power 330 b.h.p. at 3,050 r.p.m. Fuel—140 gallons, plus 44 gallon jettison tank. (AC 3—Three Perrier-Cadillac 41-75 engines radially mounted.)

Transmission
Main clutch: Multi-plate dry.,
Gearbox: Constant mesh "crash" type. Five forward gears, one reverse.
Steering: Controlled differential with epicyclic gear train in front axle assembly.
Brakes: External contracting, operated by steering levers and assisted by compressed air.

Suspension
Australian Hotchkiss type, with horizontal volute springs. Three sets of bogies on each side, each of two wheels and a return roller on top.
Rubber tracks: 86 links each side, 6 in. pitch.
Steel tracks: 129 links each side, 4 in. pitch.

Electrical System
6 volt system, with three 6 volt batteries charged by engine generators, for lights, starting, ignition.
12 volt system, with two 6 volt batteries charged by separate generator, for MG cooling water pumps, wireless, fire extinguisher equipment.
40 volt system, charged directly by separate generator, for turret traverse. (AC 3—110 volt.)

Performance
Maximum speed: 30 m.p.h.
Trench spanned: 8 ft.
Road range: 200 miles.

The Australian Cruiser was a unique development, which was a blend of British ideas on armour shape with American automotive practice, but it was Australian in concept and manufacture, relying very little on imported assemblies. The Australian Cruiser Mark 1, Sentinel, mounted a 2-pdr. gun and was taken into use for training after the whole project was stopped in 1943, when American tanks became available in large numbers. At that time trials and designs were far advanced towards production of two further Marks mounting a 25-pdr. or a 17-pdr. gun. This tank bears the camouflage colours matched to suit conditions in Australia.

M. Trim © *Profile Publications Ltd.*

0   5′

The Australian Matilda Frog was a standard Matilda 4 modified to carry flamethrowing equipment in the turret. It went into action against the Japanese in the assault landings on Borneo in July 1945, operated by the 2/1st Armoured Brigade Reconnaissance Squadron. This tank bears the unit markings and the sign of 4 Australian Armoured Brigade, which was formed specifically for operations in tropical areas. It is painted the dark green that was best for jungle warfare.

Local modifications, which could be of varied design, were fitted to most Matildas for this fighting at close quarters, and two of these are shown; an armoured shield on the hull top to protect the turret ring, and anti-magnetic mine screens over the engine louvres.

T. Hadler © *Profile Publications Ltd.*

0   5′

Landing near Finschhafen, November 1943, before the first battle with Matilda tanks. Shipping was at a premium, and movement up the coast by landing craft was liable to be slow and laborious.
(Photo: Australian War Memorial)

Australian Matildas

by Major James Bingham

SOON after the Japanese entered the War, in December 1941, Australian forces were deployed for the defence of the mainland and the territories in New Guinea. Armoured units were equipped during 1942 mainly with the American M3 Medium and M3 Light tanks, but some Matildas were also issued. (The Australian Cruiser Mark 1 was in production in small numbers, but that project was to be dropped in the following year.)

The M3 Lights (General Stuarts) went into action in December 1942 in New Guinea during operations on the Buna Track and, despite the lack of proper training for infantry/tank co-operation, the tanks showed that they could effectively be used in "rooting the Jap out of his foxholes and rabbit warrens". As a result, the 4th Armoured Brigade was raised in 1943 on a scale suitable for operations in tropical areas, and one of its units was equipped with Matildas (as an Army Tank Battalion). The brigade was the parent formation for armoured units going to New Guinea and, in preparing for the jungle fighting ahead, the Matilda was selected as the most suitable tank available for the task. It was a rôle for which the tank had originally been designed, as a heavily armoured Infantry Tank, although the conditions would be

vastly different from those in which the tank had already proved itself in France and the Middle East.

In the close conditions on the islands of the South-West Pacific there would never be opportunities for armoured manoeuvre and the battalion/regiments of 4th Armoured Brigade were organised as self-supporting groups with their own detachments of engineers, signals, army service corps, workshops, ordnance field park and ambulance. In practice, when committed to operations, the regiments were normally split into separate, self-supporting squadron groups, sometimes hundreds of miles apart, with inadequate transport for stores and at the end of an intermittent supply line by landing craft and jungle track.

JUNGLE FIGHTING

In battle the squadron advance would, more often than not, be along a single track where the Troop Commander (3-in. Howitzer) took the lead, followed by the second tank (2-pdr.) and the leading infantry platoon, and then the third tank (2-pdr.). The closest co-operation was essential between infantry and tanks, whose crews were blinded by the jungle growth, and tank fire was normally controlled by an officer of the squadron who moved on foot with the leading

Side view of Matilda Frog, the tank-mounted flamethrower developed by the Australians specifically for operations in the South-West Pacific area.
(Photo: R.A.A.C. A.F.V. Museum)

infantry, using a Walkie Talkie set. Tank fire was brought to bear on any opposition in range, and bunkers were engaged and destroyed at ranges of 10-30 yards. The 2-pdrs., as well as the 3-in. Howitzers, fired High Explosive shell. The first Matilda action on November 17, 1943 was to become typical.

"The first tank was unable to see (the machine-gun post) because of the upgrade and the dense jungle, but after some of the jungle had been blown away by 3-inch Howitzers and 2-pounders, the third tank put the gun out of action. Actually most of the tanks' firing was more or less blind. The infantry platoon commander supporting the tanks would give the order, 'Rake with Besa between (this tree and that).' The attack continued in a series of short bounds with the tanks firing rapidly on both sides of the road at enemy defences, mainly pill-boxes and

foxholes all with strong overhead cover and sited in depth along the track."
(D. Dexter, Australia in the War of 1939-45. The New Guinea Offensives.)

The landing of Matilda tanks in New Guinea, at Milne Bay, in August 1943 was a well kept secret in preparation for their use against the Japanese, but it was some time before a suitable opportunity was presented for the Matildas to come forward in support of the infantry in jungle fighting. Only two squadrons of 1st Australian Tank Battalion were landed and moved to the forward areas, and it was by dint of much hard work in "selling" the tank idea that the tanks were eventually used. Indeed, the fact that the tanks

A Matilda (3in How) of 1st Tank Battalion moving with infantry in thick undergrowth during the assault on the Sattelberg Road, November 17, 1943—the first Australian Matilda action.
(Photo: Australian War Memorial)

reached New Guinea at all was the result of much preliminary "selling" by Brigadier Macarthur-Onslow, the commander of 4th Australian Armoured Brigade, for the infantry had an innate mistrust of armour, born of experiences in the Middle East, and needed to be convinced that the tanks would not be more trouble than they were worth in the restricted jungle conditions. Eventually, "C" Squadron was given the chance on November 17, 1943 in the assault on the Sattelberg Road in support of the 9th Division on the Huon Peninsula.

The operations proved convincingly that, properly handled, the Matilda was a powerful weapon in jungle fighting. After the opening engagement:

"morale in the squadron was high; . . . and all were happy about the Matildas which had proved to be powerful and successful weapons and undoubtedly saved the infantry many casualties while allowing a steady progress to be maintained, although this had been somewhat impeded by the difficulties of terrain. The performance of the tanks had amazed even their own crews."

(The Royal New South Wales Lancers. 1885-1960).

The successful use of the Matildas on the Huon Peninsula was not, however, the signal for more tanks to be deployed at once. Operations ended for the 1st Australian Tank Battalion in this campaign in February 1944 and the unit returned to the mainland in May, to be replaced by 2/4th Armoured Regiment in August. The offensives of 1943-44, in which the Australian Army had been the spearhead in the land battle against the Japanese, had strained the resources of the nation, and during the latter part of 1944 most of the army was preparing for the final effort in 1945.

The Japanese had quickly introduced anti-tank measures after the first encounter with the Matildas, and they made increasing use of mines to protect their positions, supplemented by aircraft bombs and explosives fired by remote control. They had no effective anti-tank gun against the Matilda, however, and their 75-mm. gun could cause little more than superficial damage. Even so, it was not uncommon in 1945 to find this weapon sited in the jungle for anti-tank defence. This account of an engagement in May illustrates those battles at close quarters.

"A log across the track caused the point tank to halt and search the neighbouring ground. The gunner Dick Allen was looking at a large lily leaf when it swayed to one side disclosing the muzzle of a 75 mm. 20 yards away. The gun fired immediately, missing the tank. Without more ado, Dick let fly with 2-pounder, disabling the gun and crew of three. . . . Behind the gun position there was approximately a company of Nips, dug in and with heavy bunker positions. 8 Troop played a merry tune on their Besas and 2-pounders and the Nip very wisely 'scrambled'."

(Tank Tracks. The War History of the 2/4th Australian Armoured Regimental Group).

Landing from an American LST (Landing Ship, Tanks) at Tarakan, April 30, 1945—2/9th Armoured Regiment. This tank carries considerable extra armour in the form of spare track plates, as well as metal tracking for the anti-magnetic mine screen.

(Photo: Australian War Memorial)

Tanks of 1st Armoured Regiment advancing inland at Balikpapan, July 1945. The wire mesh screen over engine louvres can be seen on the tank, as well as canvas water-proofing (already blown away) hanging from the side. (Photo: Australian War Memorial)

Special bridges had to be built to enable the tanks to move forward. The armoured shield to protect the turret ring, and the anti-magnetic mine screen over the engine louvres are fitted to this tank on Bougainville. (Photo: Australian War Memorial)

Closed down for immediate action, a Matilda of 2/4th Armoured Regiment moves forward to Slater's Knoll, Bougainville, supported by infantry, April 1945. A spotlight has been mounted beside the driver's hatch. (Photo: Australian War Memorial)

Matilda Frog "flaming". (Photo: Australian Official)

The Matilda Frog at Puckapunyal, Victoria. Clearly seen here is the armoured shield fitted on the hull top to protect the turret ring, fitted to many Matildas in action at the end of the War. (Photo: R.A.A.C. A.F.V. Museum)

Knocking down a coconut palm after landing at Balikpapan, July 1945, where the tanks waded through 3 ft. 6 in. surf with ease. On this tank the canvas water-proofing screens over the gun mantlet and sides of the engine compartment have not yet been blown away.

(Photo: Australian War Memorial)

Experience led to modifications on the Matilda and to the development of new equipments. Screens of wire mesh or metal tracking were fitted over engine/air louvres as a protection against magnetic mines, and the turret ring was protected by an armoured shield on the hull top; improvised fittings of microphone and headset were made at the rear as an emergency tank telephone to the crew, until an official modification with a telephone in an armoured box was issued; waterproofing equipment was designed to permit deep wading; a tank dozer, a flamethrowing tank and one which could project a salvo of bombs were developed.

Some of these were ready, in action, during the final stages of the War.

From January 1945 until the end of the War in August the 2/4th Armoured Regiment had three squadrons of Matildas taking part in the campaigns from Aitape to Wewak, and on Bougainville Island. Just as the tanks had shown a year before, they proved their worth again and saved many casualties, converting most of their remaining critics to the need for armour in that type of warfare. Tanks are apt to be cumbersome beasts, however, when facilities for movement are restricted, and throughout the campaigns the

Matilda Frog of 2/1st Armoured Brigade Reconnaissance Squadron moving with infantry towards the oil refineries at Balikpapan.

(Photo: Australian War Memorial)

Matilda Frog in action at Balikpapan, July 1945. Ranges of engagement were normally 15–30 yards. with occasional shots up to 90 yards.
(Photo: Australian War Memorial)

Australian Matilda Dozer No. 3. The blade and push poles could be jettisoned without exposing the crew, and the tank could then fight as a normal gun tank.
(Photo: R.A.A.C. A.F.V. Museum)

The Hedgehog projector raised, showing the containers for seven bombs which were fired over the turret. The projector was raised and lowered by a hydraulic ram at each side.
(Photo: R.A.A.C. A.F.V. Museum)

The Hedgehog projector raised in the firing position. When lowered, metal projections through the bottom of the shield held the bombs steady, to protect the fuzes.
(Photo: R.A.A.C. A.F.V. Museum)

tanks were liable to be left behind when the going was difficult, inactive (except for any job to which the Matilda could be put as a heavy, tracked vehicle), waiting for landing craft or struggling to find a way forward through impossible country. Tank crews became adept at rapid waterproofing and improvisations, with their engineer detachments, in dealing with obstacles, through creeks and along jungle tracks, in their determination to get forward.

During the final campaign in Borneo, May—July 1945, the 2/9th Armoured Regiment provided squadrons for the assault landings at Tarakan, at Brunei and at Labuan. The 1st Armoured Regiment, returning under a new name, came into action again in the landings at Balikpapan, where there was fierce fighting for the heavily fortified town and oil refinery.

Matilda Hedgehog with the projector, over the rear of the engine compartment, lowered in the travelling position. The Hedgehog bomb, standing at the side, weighed 63 lb.
(Photo: R.A.A.C. A.F.V. Museum)

CIRCUS EQUIPMENT

The specialised equipments which were being developed in Australia, or intended for use in the South-West Pacific operations, acquired their own descriptive title as the "circus equipment", similar to the "Funnies" of the British 79th Armoured Division. They included the flamethrowing Matilda Frog, the Matilda Dozer, the bomb-launching Matilda Hedgehog and the Covenanter Bridgelayer. Work in developing and testing the "circus equipment" was carried out in units of 4th Armoured Brigade equipped with the Matilda, but for operational purposes in Borneo the Matilda equipments were taken over by 2/1st Armoured Brigade Reconnaissance Squadron. Detachments of the squadron accompanied and went into action with the armoured regiments which carried out the assault landings in Borneo in June/July 1945, but other equipments which were sent to New Guinea and Bougainville arrived too late to take part in any fighting.

MATILDA FROG

The Australian Matilda Frog was developed specifically for operations against Japanese bunkers and pillboxes in the South-West Pacific area, and the demand for a tank-mounted flamethrower was initiated soon after the New Guinea operations of December 1942. There were, however, considerable problems affecting research and development, using locally available materials, and it was not until 1945 that the Matilda Frog was ready for action in the closing stages of the War.

Automotively, the tank was identical with the normal Matilda, and superficially it resembled the gun tank in having the flame projector nozzle extended forward of the gun mantlet inside a mild steel tube. In appearance this was like the 3-in. Howitzer barrel, except for the counter-weight at the muzzle.

The 7·92-mm. Besa co-axial machine-gun was retained, but it was awkward to handle because of the other equipment which was introduced in the turret. An 80 gallon fuel tank was fitted inside the turret basket, filling most of the forward and right sections up to the level of the turret ring (a jettison tank at the rear provided another 40 gallons, the fuel being transferred to the main tank by electric pump). A compressed air tank, behind the fuel tank and to the right of the commander, provided pressure for fuel supply to the projector. Traverse of the turret was by

the normal Matilda hand and powered systems, while elevation and depression of the coaxial Besa/flame projector mounting was obtained by a special sprocket and chain drive from a small handle suspended from the turret roof. A normal optical sight was used.

A maximum range of 145 yards has been quoted for the flamethrower but, when the Matilda Frog went into action, the normal range of engagement was 15-30 yards with occasional shots up to 90 yards.

A troop of Frogs went ashore with 2/9th Armoured Regiment in the landing at Labuan on June 10 and, during the battles that followed, had the distinction of being the first flamethrowing tanks to go into action with the Australian forces. Another troop of Frogs landed with 1st Armoured Regiment at Balikpapan on July 1 and was soon in action to burn out bunkers, tunnels and buildings. The Frogs worked closely with other Matildas in support of the infantry, the basic drill being for gun tanks to engage and blast open the bunker positions from the flanks, while the Frogs advanced frontally to close range.

MATILDA DOZER

The Matilda Dozer was an Australian development for use in clearing away obstacles when under fire and, although the bulldozer kit involved substantial fittings inside and out, the tank remained a gun tank with its normal armament.

The bulldozer blade assembly was attached to push poles riding on trunnions mounted to the skirting

The rear of the Matilda Hedgehog, with rear cover open.
(Photo: R.A.A.C. A.F.V. Museum)

Matilda Dozer in use in New Guinea. This is an early version in which the blade is controlled by winch and cable mounted on the hull front. (Photo: Australian War Memorial)

Watched by interested spectators, a Matilda 3-in Howitzer fires onto a distant pillbox, directed by telephone from a forward infantry position at Tarakan. (Photo: Australian War Memorial)

plates on each side. On an early version of the Dozer the blade was raised by cable and winch on the front of the hull, but the Matilda Dozer 3 incorporated two hydraulic jacks in armoured shields mounted on the sides of the tank, each operating through a pivot frame and connecting link to the push pole. Hydraulic power was provided by a gear type oil pump mounted low between the engines and chain-driven from the propeller shaft. The oil reservoir for the system was fitted in the hull within the fighting compartment.

All operations of the blade were controlled by the driver and, in Dozer 3, both the blade and push poles could be jettisoned without exposing the crew.

A troop of Matilda Dozers landed on the first day at Balikpapan but it was found that they were unable to help much in recovery of other tanks which had been bogged—hardly a fair task on which to judge a tank dozer—and the blades were dropped so that the tanks could be used in their rôle as gun tanks.

MATILDA HEDGEHOG

The Hedgehog projector was originally a Naval store designed as an anti-submarine weapon, and this was seen to have a value also in bunker-busting, as a means of delivering a heavy, High Explosive bomb at short range. As a result, and to give the weapon armoured mobility, the Matilda Hedgehog was developed to carry seven Hedgehog bombs, suitably modified, within a double shield of boiler plate over the rear of the engine compartment.

The bombs weighed 63 lbs. each (37 lbs. of Torpex explosive) and they were mounted on spigots on a rotatable shaft which was turned by two hydraulic rams; the rams were operated by a pump connected to an electric motor and control valve. The bombs were fired electrically, either singly or as a salvo, from a switch and plugboard on the hull side behind the gunner. The maximum range was normally 200 yards but, with a new propellant, a range of 330 yards was achieved.

In operation the tank took up position with the turret at 12 o'clock and the commander lined the tank onto the target by means of a sight on the turret top.

The driver operated the hydraulic control valve to raise and lower the projector, and he had two indicators from which he could tell the commander both the angle of elevation of the weapon and any error in the level of the tank sideways (which would mean a correction for line). The projector was set at an angle to suit the range and, after firing the first bomb, corrections of aim were effected either by moving the tank or raising/lowering the projector. Inter-locking safety switches were incorporated in the firing system so that bombs could only be fired between safe minimum and maximum elevations; to protect the wireless aerial, bomb No. 5 could only be fired with the turret at 1 o'clock and, for that position, the commander had another sight on the turret.

The Matilda Hedgehog remained a normal gun tank in other respects and the mounting of this additional armament was an ingenious arrangement. Many of the parts used were acquired from other equipments, the hydraulic rams having been designed for an aircraft under-carriage and the hydraulic control valve being taken from the M3 Medium tank. Though the tank lacked sophisticated methods of control, it incorporated proper safety devices and it was proved to have the accuracy to engage spot targets, with a powerful blast effect. However, it was never to be tried in battle. A troop of six Matilda Hedgehogs was formed in 4th Armoured Brigade and these were sent to Bougainville in 1945, but they arrived too late for action before the end of the War.

POST-WAR MATILDA

When the Citizen Military Force (equivalent to the British Territorial Army) was re-formed in 1948, the Matilda tank was issued for training in some of the armoured units, and in this capacity filled an important need during the next few years. However, age and deterioration made it increasingly difficult to keep the tanks on the road. In 1955 the Matilda was withdrawn from training in the C.M.F. and was generally replaced by the Centurion.

AFV Series Editor: DUNCAN CROW

The trio of Churchill IIIs sent to the African desert for testing under combat conditions with the 7th (Motor) Brigade at the time of Alamein. They were used for propaganda shots, as depicted here, and played no significant part in the Alamein battle. (Imp. War Mus.)

Churchill—British Infantry Tank Mk IV

By B. T. White

"THE Sqn. Ldr. was ordered, at all costs, to force a way past Steam Roller Farm and annihilate the enemy at the head of the Pass. Two tanks, commanded respectively by Capt. E. D. Hollands, D.C.M., and Lieut. J. G. Renton, succeeded in breaking through. Together they covered the 1,500 yards which separates Steam Roller Farm from the head of the Pass. To do this they had to advance down a narrow causeway from which no deployment was possible. This causeway was covered by an 88 mm. gun firing at a range of less than 200 yards. It fired two shots, which missed the leading tank, which charged, and the gun crew fled. The two tanks slowly wound their way to the top of the Pass, which was very steep and rocky. There, they had the shoot of their lives, but the remainder of the Sqn. and the Coldstreams were unable to force a passage and join them and they were finally ordered to withdraw. Before they did they accounted for two 88 mm., two 75 mm., and two 50 mm. anti-tank guns, four lesser anti-tank guns, 25 wheeled vehicles, two 3-inch mortars, two Mk. III Tanks and about 100 Germans.

"A wireless message from the commander of the German Bde. Group to General von Koch was intercepted. This was to the effect that he had been attacked by 'a mad tank battalion' which had scaled impossible heights and forced him to withdraw."

Some of the excellent qualities of the Churchill tank are brought out in this account of the first action in which the 51st Battalion Royal Tank Regiment took part—in Tunisia on February 28, 1943—when part of "A" Squadron was engaged in support of infantry of 2nd Battalion Coldstream Guards. It is further recorded in the *Short History of 51st Bn. Royal Tank Regiment*, from which the extract is taken, that for their part in this minor but vivid action, the two tank commanders were awarded respectively, a D.S.O. and an M.C., and members of their crews gained one D.C.M. and two M.M.'s.

The Churchill had had a somewhat unfortunate history up until this time: it was designed to a specification still influenced by memories of World War I and produced in haste under the invasion threat of 1940–41, which resulted at first in a great deal of mechanical unreliability. Sent into action for the first time in the Dieppe raid of August 1942 in an opposed landing, the majority of the tanks were not even able to get ashore, let alone have a chance of proving their value in battle.

By early 1943, however, a great deal of development work by the designers, reinforced by the practical experience of the regiments equipped with the Churchill tank, had eliminated most of the early faults so that one regiment (the 142nd Regiment R.A.C.) was able to say (referring to their tanks just after landing in North Africa)—

"The Churchill tank won its spurs for mechanical efficiency during this march southwards. Twenty-four tanks [all those involved in this particular operation] arrived at Sbiba without any mechanical breakdown. Some of these had come straight off their transporters without time for minor adjustments; while the few 'B' squadron tanks that had set out for the Bou Arada front moved on their tracks without a hitch a hundred miles in 24 hours."

The main armament of the Churchill had, by 1943,

been considerably improved by the substitution of the 6 pdr. gun for the 2 pdr. fitted in the early models. The 6 pdr. was a good gun capable of knocking out the German Tiger tank in favourable circumstances—as was demonstrated in Tunisia. The Churchill, designed to provide support in close co-operation with infantry across shell torn ground, was also shown in Tunisia to be capable of tackling difficult hill country—terrain probably not envisaged by the General Staff planners mindful of the Flanders battles of 1914–18.

CONCEPTION AND BIRTH

The history of the Churchill goes back to the General Staff specification A.20, for an infantry tank to supplement and replace the A.12 or Tank, Infantry Mark II—better known as Matilda. (The Infantry Mark III—Valentine—was designed by Vickers Armstrong without the benefit of a G. S. specification but was nevertheless accepted by the War Office for mass production.)

The French Maginot and German Siegfried lines of fortifications facing each other seemed in 1939 likely to bring about the same sort of stalemate on the Western Front as in World War I. Tank design to overcome this problem in support of the French ally followed two lines of thought. One was left to an independent committee under the chairmanship of Sir Albert Stern and composed, like himself, of men who had close associations with tanks in World War I. The alternative solution was sought through the more conventional means of a General Staff specification. The A.20 specification, put forward in September 1939, called for an infantry tank able to negotiate waterlogged ground cratered by shell fire; to overcome moderate vertical obstacles and gaps; and with frontal protection on a 60 mm. basis to give protection against 37 mm. anti-tank guns. A speed of only 10 m.p.h. was required. Various forms of armament were considered, the original proposal being a 2 pdr.

Rare view of A20/E1 pilot model built by Harland & Wolff to meet the original requirement for a 'shelled area' infantry tank, and subsequently sent to Vauxhall to become the basis for the Vauxhall-designed A22. Similar configurations to that used in the Churchill I is evident. (Peter Chamberlain Collection.)

gun with coaxial Besa machine gun in a sponson at each side and a Besa and a 2-inch bomb thrower beside the driver—armament very much on the lines of the World War I tanks. Other weapons given consideration were the 3-inch howitzer and the 3·7-inch howitzer (both rejected because of their low muzzle velocities); the Army 6 pdr.; the Naval 6 pdr.; the French short 75 mm.; and a combination of a turret-mounted 2 pdr. with a hull 6 pdr. between the front horns. The final choice was, however an infantry Tank Mark II pattern turret mounting a 2 pdr. gun and coaxial 7·92 mm. Besa machine gun; a 2 pdr. in the front of the hull and a 7·92 mm. Besa at either side of the hull.

The specification as finally decided was put into broad practical terms of design by the Chief Superintendent of Design at the Woolwich Royal Ordnance Factory, and the engineering and shipbuilding firm of Harland and Wolff Ltd. of Belfast were awarded a contract in December 1939 to design and supply four mild steel pilot models of the A.20, designated Tank, Infantry Mark IV. They were to be powered either by a 300 b.h.p. diesel engine being developed by Harland and Wolff or by a new Meadows flat 12 cylinder petrol engine. The final drive was to be of the type developed

His Majesty the late King George VI inspects the first production model of the Churchill I, then still known only as the Infantry Tank Mk. IV, in March, 1941. Ordered straight off the drawing board, this was also the 'pilot' model, and was made of mild steel. (Peter Chamberlain Collection.)

for the A.13 Mark III (later known as Covenanter) through a gearbox designed by Dr. H. E. Merritt. The four vehicles were known individually as A20E1, A20E2, A20E3 and A20E4.

Harland and Wolff Ltd. had the first A.20 pilot completed, except for the turret and armament by the middle of 1940 and ready for running trials. Its general appearance, despite the decision not to include side sponsons, was broadly suggestive of the heavy tanks of World War I: the long hull, necessary for good cross-country performance, had overall tracks with the top run level with the hull roof and a high prow for facility in mounting obstacles. The long pitch tracks and the suspension consisting of small independently sprung road wheels are said to have been inspired by the Char B1 bis, one of the best contemporary French heavy tanks.

The trials of the A.20 proved to be disappointing, for the gearbox gave trouble after only a short run, the Meadows DAV engine did not produce the required power and calculations showed that the front hull 2 pdr. would have to be sacrificed to maintain the planned performance and keep within reasonable distance of the specified weight of 37½ tons, already increased from the originally estimated 32 tons. Vauxhall Motors were asked to design a new engine for the A.20 and the result—a Bedford 12 cylinder side valve unit—produced the required 350 b.h.p. right from the start. Nevertheless it was decided to abandon the A.20 in June 1940, with two of the four pilot vehicles still unbuilt.

A revised specification for Tank, Infantry Mark IV —A.22, was then drawn up and Vauxhall Motors Ltd. of Luton, Bedfordshire, were invited to undertake the detail design, followed by production "off the drawing board" of the new vehicle. This was July 1940, when France had capitulated to the German armies and invasion of the United Kingdom was expected to follow at any moment.

The task was accepted by Vauxhall Motors. Dr. H. E. Merritt, Director of Tank Design, with a small staff of draughtsmen (who had already prepared some preliminary drawings for the A.22) moved to Luton. The drawings of the A.20 were used for guidance in layout and one of the two A.20 pilot vehicles (neither of which had the turrets or armament fitted) was sent to the Vauxhall factory, where it was test run to provide data on the Bedford engine designed for it by Vauxhalls and which was also to be used for the new tank.

The A.22 was, in a sense, designed around the Bedford 12 cylinder engine, although since this engine had originally been intended for the A.20 it was possible to use much of the configuration of the earlier tank.

A larger gun than the 2 pdr. was envisaged for the A.22, but since in 1940 the 2 pdr. was the only high velocity tank weapon available in production it had to be used. The 2 pdr., however, did not fire the high explosive ammunition so useful for infantry support and so provision was made for a 3-inch howitzer in the front of the hull beside the driver.

The first prototype A.22 was undergoing trials by the end of 1940 and the first batch of 14 completed Tanks, Infantry Mark IV came off the Vauxhall Motors production line in June 1941. It may be noted that the first of these vehicles still bore the "Caution Unarmoured" plate which denoted to the users that

Three views of one of the first production Infantry Tank, Mk. IV taken at Luton May 9, 1941, show the characteristics of the Churchill I, including the 3-in. howitzer in the hull front, small cast turret with pistol ports and 2 pdr. gun, brackets for long range fuel tank at rear, lack of track covers, unarmoured exhaust manifolds and the original type of intake louvre. (Imp. War Mus.)

mild steel had been used wholly or partially instead of armour plate. The new tank was named Churchill— because, as Mr. Winston Churchill is reputed to have said, it too was "a thick-skinned beast".

The remarkably short time in which the Churchill was designed and put into production by Vauxhall Motors Ltd.—a firm without previous experience of the design or construction of tanks—reflects great credit on it. At the same time as designing the tank and arranging to build the first vehicles, Vauxhall Motors also undertook the design and production "parentage" for the whole future programme planned for the Churchill. This entailed arranging sources of supply of materials from hundreds of sub-contractors for the ten other major firms in the production group as well as for Vauxhall's own output; planning the production operations; designing and obtaining the special equipment—jigs, machine tools etc.—needed for production; and passing on their newly acquired "know-how".

In the Churchill II, the 3-in. howitzer was replaced by a Besa machine gun. The front horns were also fitted with strengthening plates, added retrospectively also to the Mk. I. Note the fuel tank at rear. (Peter Chamberlain Collection.)

Fine view of the Churchill II in service in early 1942 shows all crew members at their respective hatches. (Peter Chamberlain Collection.)

The Churchill Tank Production Group consisted of the following firms (not all of which, however, remained on Churchill production throughout the War):—

The Birmingham Railway Carriage and Wagon Co. Ltd.
Beyer, Peacock and Co. Ltd. (Manchester)
Broom and Wade Ltd. (High Wycombe, Bucks.)
Dennis Bros. Ltd. (Guildford, Surrey)
The Gloucester Railway Carriage and Wagon Co. Ltd.
Harland and Wolff Ltd. (Belfast, Northern Ireland)
Leyland Motors Ltd. (Leyland, Lancs.)
Metropolitan-Cammell Carriage and Wagon Co. Ltd. (Wednesbury, Staffs.)
Newton Chambers and Co. Ltd. (Sheffield)
Charles Roberts and Co. Ltd. (Wakefield, Yorks.)

There were many problems in co-ordinating the work of such a variety of engineering firms spread throughout England and one in Northern Ireland. But the arrangements worked well considering the difficulties. For example, the first Leyland-assembled Churchill was completed in June 1941 (concurrently with the first production models produced by Vauxhall Motors themselves) and the first Metro-Cammell Churchill was delivered early in July 1941. The production of Churchill tanks continued until the War ended and in all 5,640 were built. In numerical importance the Churchill came second only to the Valentine.

A supply of completed tanks coming off the production lines was required by the Government within one year from the time Vauxhall Motors undertook the responsibility for the design and output of the Churchill tank in July 1940. It was expected that an entirely new tank built under these conditions would be likely to give trouble later on, but tanks that could run only a dozen or so miles, or even, acting as immobile but heavily armoured blockhouses, not run at all, might make all the difference were the country to be invaded, and the risk was accepted. (Much was made in wartime propaganda of the virtue of the Churchill's potential value as a static blockhouse. Fortunately, this need never arose for the defence of the United

Mr. Winston Churchill, the Prime Minister, paid a visit to Vauxhall in 1941 to see the tank which later took his name. He is seen here in the second production vehicle (nearest the camera) talking by R/T to General Sir John Dill, C-in-C Home Forces, in the first production machine. Note the triangular warning plate on the turrets indicating mild steel construction. (Imp. War Mus.)

Kingdom, but in Tunisia on one occasion a single Churchill, disabled on a minefield, continued to support the infantry against an enemy counter-attack by infantry with two tanks. For this action the tank commander was awarded the M.C.)

During trials and in the hands of the Army tank battalions to which the Churchills were issued as they came off the production lines many faults were revealed. A survey by the War Office showed in November 1941 that Churchills delivered up to the previous month were not fit for use in the Middle East or even for sustained operations in the United Kingdom unless 16 important modifications were incorporated. Ten of these modifications were to the transmission and steering and three to the suspension. Nearly 1,000 tanks had to be re-worked out of the first 1,200 built, and as late as July 1942 both reworked and new Churchills were failing their acceptance tests at mileages as low as 150. Some failures, at least, in Churchill tanks were probably caused by misunderstanding, in experienced units, of the degree of maintenance required. In one Army tank battalion (converted from an infantry unit) for example, only 30 tanks out of 54 were fit to go out on one exercise. Of these, a third did not return to camp afterwards. (It was recorded, however, that most of them seemed to have broken down near roadside cafes, leaving the suspicion that old soldiers were not above exaggerating, when convenient, the incapacity of their tanks!)

The clutch was one major source of trouble in the early days—the clutch cover showed a tendency to burst when only a slight excess over engine maximum permitted revolutions occurred. Apart from this and other less serious design faults which were corrected as quickly as possible in existing vehicles and eliminated, where practicable, in the production stage, trials and user experience indicated the need for modifications of various sorts. In order to ensure the maximum co-operation between the manufacturers and the customers Vauxhall Motors appointed their own engineers to each of the Army tank brigades equipped with

Close-up view of a Churchill II turret, with the vehicle commander studying his map. (Imp. War Mus.)

Churchill tanks. These men no doubt learned a few home-truths about the product for which they were responsible, but they were able both to give useful advice to the tank units and at the same time to help ensure close and immediate liaison with the manufacturers, so that early action could be taken to rectify faults and design modified components where necessary. This was one of the means whereby, after a long series of modifications had been introduced, the Churchill was eventually considered to be a very reliable and battleworthy tank.

THE CHURCHILL DESCRIBED

The Churchill was developed through eight different Marks and numerous sub-variants but the layout and main features, except for the armament and the armour thickness, remained fairly constant throughout,

Churchill IIs seen on a Southern Command exercise in October, 1942. (Imp. War Mus.)

although various improvements were introduced during the course of production and in re-working earlier Marks. In describing the Churchill, therefore, the details of the armament and armour will be left to be outlined in a summary of the Mark by Mark differences.

The hull of the Churchill was basically a box structure constructed of flat steel plates joined together by steel angles, to which they were riveted. To this inner shell of the hull structure the armour plates were bolted, the bolts being screwed into the armour plates from inside. Escape doors were provided in either side of the hull giving access to the tank via the driver's compartment. These doors (except in the later tanks, Marks VII and VIII) were fitted with quick opening revolver ports. In the roof of the hull, double-hinged doors were provided for the driver and front gunner; and in the hull floor six removable plates gave access to various components. The compact design of the suspension gave an almost uninterrupted "pannier" space at each side of the hull between the upper run of the track (which was level with the hull roof) and the lower run. This useful space was used for the stowage of equipment and ammunition and also carried the main right-hand and left-hand fuel tanks.

The interior of the hull was divided transversely into four compartments. The front compartment contained the driver's position and the driving controls for the tank and, on the driver's left, the hull gunner's seat, the hull armament being mounted in the same vertical plate as the driver's vision port.

The steering control was a centrally pivoted handle bar (rather like that of a bicycle) mounted just below the driver's vision door. This operated the steering brakes through a Lockheed hydraulic system and was equipped with air pressure servo-motors to make operation easy. The gear change lever was at the driver's right, and on the floor, from left to right, were

A Churchill II rears over a 'knife-edge' to show its hull top to the camera. Note the early small-type cast turret was not symmetrical. Commander's hatch (left) rotated. The cylindrical container on the turret side is a stowage for the signal flags. (Peter Chamberlain Collection.)

A typical III with the added features which became standard on all Churchills from mid-1942 onwards: full track covers, and the improved engine air intake louvres which had the opening on the top instead of the sides, so facilitating waterproofing for deep wading. (Peter Chamberlain Collection.)

the clutch pedal (connected to an air pressure servo-motor to make for light operation); the foot brake pedal (operating the main brakes through a Lockheed hydraulic system); and the accelerator pedal. The hand brake lever was mounted on the floor at the left of the driver. Except in the Churchill VII and VIII, a half handle bar steering control in the front gunner's position was linked to the main handle bar to enable the hull gunner to steer the tank in an emergency, and a duplicate ignition switch would allow him to switch off the tank's main engine.

The next division was the fighting compartment, with the turret mounted on a ball race on the hull roof. From the turret, and forming an integral part of it, was suspended the platform carrying the commander, gunner and wireless operator. The turret could be traversed when the engine was running by an electric motor carried in it and geared to a fixed toothed ring mounted in the hull roof. An alternative hand traverse system was available for use with the engine stopped. The power traverse was operated by means of a control handle which speeded up the turret rotation the farther left or right of centre the handle was moved. The ball race on which the turret rotated was $58\frac{1}{4}$ inches in diameter and consisted of 117 steel balls in a bronze cage. The platform which rotated with the turret and formed the floor for the three men in the fighting compartment was suspended from the turret at three points and was constructed of "Plymax"—a multiply wood faced each side with sheet metal.

The tank's wireless equipment was carried inside the turret on a shelf at the back. This consisted of a wireless transmission set providing both long range communications and also communications over short distances operated separately on a higher frequency. The aerial for the long range equipment was at the rear of the turret at the left-hand side and the shorter, short range aerial was at the right-hand side. A separate intercommunications system enabled the crew members to speak to each other.

Behind the fighting compartment, separated by a bulkhead, was the division containing the engine. On the outside of the hull each side at this point were the

A Churchill II leaves a LCT in May, 1942, during trials and exercises for the Dieppe landing. Note intake louvres have been removed to avoid fouling the sides of the LCT, and that this tank has the then new, full track covers. (Imp. War Mus.)

projecting heavy armoured louvres protecting the engine air intakes. These louvres were removable for rail transport. Finally, behind the engine in the rear of the tank was the compartment housing the gearbox; the steering brakes and the main brakes; the air compressor (a two cylinder Clayton Dewandre unit) for the assisted steering and clutch operation; the auxiliary charging set for the electrical system and the generator for the turret power traverse.

The Bedford horizontally opposed 12 cylinder engine drove the tracks through driving sprockets at the rear. The Borg and Beck clutch was of the single dry plate variety: operation was assisted by compressed air power through a hydraulic system. At one stage of the Churchill's development, incidentally, until new clutch facings were designed by Ferodo Ltd., it was thought that a twin-plate clutch would have to be substituted for the single plate type.

The gearbox was fitted transversely and parallel to the final drive to the driving sprockets. The Merritt-Brown gearbox was designed by Dr. H. E. Merritt and developed and built by David Brown Tractors Ltd. It combined the gears for regulating the engine power transmission with a steering unit working on the controlled differential principle. This adjusted the power during a turn between the inside and outside tracks (the inner track in a turn moving more slowly) and offered a greater degree of control than other contemporary steering systems in that a variety of turning radii were available, depending on the gear chosen. The lowest gear gave the sharpest turn and with the gear in neutral the tank swung on its pivot point. Five-speed gearboxes were fitted in the earliest production Churchills but these were soon replaced by a re-designed 4-speed model which gave approximately the same speed range over its four forward ratios. It is interesting to recall that a self-changing gear box, designed by the Fluidrive Engineering Co. Ltd., was tested in Churchill tanks (also, it is believed, another

make of automatic gear box) but the mechanical type was retained in all but the experimental vehicles.

The suspension of the Churchill was of a pattern not hitherto used in British tanks and comprised 11 small 10-inch diameter steel bogies (or road wheels) each side, mounted on short trailing arms and independently sprung on vertical coil springs. The idler wheels were at the front and the driving sprockets at the rear. The tracks used on the Churchill were of three types— a heavy cast steel type (the original design), a light cast steel type with improved shoe pattern and a final type

The Churchill III had a new, larger, welded turret and mounted the 6 pdr. gun. This is an early production vehicle still fitted with the original pattern engine air louvres. In the driver's position is Major D. Thorpe, 4th C.L.Y., at that time Chief Instructor, 56th Training Regiment, R.A.C. Catterick. The A.F.V. Series Editor, Duncan Crow, is at the front of the turret gunner's hatch. (Peter Chamberlain Collection.)

The Churchill's first and unhappiest action; Dieppe on the afternoon of August 19, 1942. Canadian Churchill III tanks, of the Calgary Regiment knocked out on the beaches. Note the exhaust pipe extensions for deep wading. See drawing on centre pages for finer detail. (Imp. War Mus.)

of similar profile to the light cast steel type but made of manganese steel. The Churchill VII and VIII were fitted only with the manganese tracks, although all three types could be used on all Marks.

THE BASIC MARKS

The first model of Churchill to be produced—known at first only as Tank, Infantry Mark IV—had a 3-inch howitzer in the front hull, and a 2 pdr. gun with coaxial Besa machine gun in the cast turret. The next model, Tank, Infantry Mark IVA, which was in production very shortly afterwards, was identical except for the Besa replacing the 3-inch howitzer in the hull and associated changes in ammunition stowage. Although already known unofficially as Churchill, this name was adopted for general use instead of the type mark numbers and suffixes following a minute (including, rather coyly, in its text "A.22 has an alias, I think") sent by the Prime Minister in June 1941 to the Secretary of State for War and the Chief of the Imperial General Staff. The first two models of Tank, Infantry Mark IV then became known as Churchill I and Churchill II respectively.

The next model, Churchill III was the first Churchill to be fitted with the 6 pdr. gun. Discussion on this question began in March 1941 and three different types of the 6 pdr. turret—welded, cast and bolted—

A Churchill I knocked out on the beach at Dieppe, August 19, 1942. (Imp. War Mus.)

were designed and tested, following which, in August 1941, Babcock and Wilcox Ltd. were given a contract for the production of welded turrets.

As well as being used in current production Churchill III's, earlier tanks were subsequently reworked and had their 2 pdr. turrets replaced with the new type equipped with the 6 pdr.

The Churchill III, together with some Churchill I's, was the type used by the Canadians at Dieppe on August 19, 1942, and these were the first Churchill tanks to be used in action against the enemy. The Prime Minister had been anxious to see the new tanks in action at the earliest opportunity and caused two Churchill tanks to be sent in September 1941 to the Middle East where they could be tested under desert conditions and any necessary modifications made to fit this type of tank for employment in the Libyan battles. They arrived in December 1941 but, through inadequate protection against the weather on the voyage, were in very bad condition. Later on, three Churchill III's were received by the 1st Armoured Division and allotted to 7th (Motor) Brigade for desert trials. During the battle of Alamein (October 1942) they were used as H.Q. vehicles by the Brigade commander and, later, in action, when one was knocked out by an 88 mm. gun and the guns jammed in the other two tanks.

A number of Churchill III's and earlier Marks were supplied in the latter half of 1942 under Lend Lease to the Russians who, though no doubt glad enough to receive them at that time, regarded them, like all British tanks, as under-armed.

The Tunisian campaign of First Army saw the first use in action of the Churchill IV, together with a greater quantity of Churchill III's and, for close support, a number of Churchill I's. The Churchill IV was identical to the Churchill III except for the turret, which was cast instead of welded. Two tank brigades (six regiments) of Churchill tanks were in Tunisia by the end of the campaign in May 1943. Their remarkable cross-country performance—the only form of transport other than mules to get up some hills in the "Longstop" area for example—and their good 6 pdr. gun earned the confidence of their crews. One fault, however, of the 6 pdr. was that although its armour-piercing performance was good (an infantry 6 pdr. knocked out the first Tiger tank encountered by the

A Churchill III of another Canadian tank unit, the 12th Canadian Tank Regiment (The Three Rivers Regiment) taking part in Exercise Spartan in Southern England, March 1943.
(Peter Chamberlain Collection)

British army), it was not designed for high explosive ammunition for use against other targets. To make up for this deficiency as quickly as possible for the forthcoming Italian campaign the complete gun mountings (with 75 mm. gun and coaxial 0·30 inch Browning machine-gun) including the external mantlets, were removed from Sherman tanks and installed in Churchills in place of the turret 6 pdr. and Besa. (The hull Besa machine-gun was also replaced, experimentally, by a Browning, but it was proved rather difficult to cover the hole left in the mounting, and the Besa was put back!) The American 75 mm. gun was a good all-round weapon, capable of firing all types of ammunition, although its anti-tank properties were inferior to the 6 pdr. 120 Churchill IV's (and one solitary Churchill III, which did not get far as it was accidentally driven into the sea over the edge of a quay) were converted in this way by the 21st Tank Brigade workshops in North Africa and became known as Churchill "N.A.75's".

In the meantime, back in Britain a programme of reworking earlier 2 pdr. models with new 6 pdr. turrets to bring them up to Churchill III standard had been undertaken from the end of 1942 onwards. These and other earlier improvements were in many cases introduced in stages so that some of the Churchills with the new armament still had, for instance, the old pattern of side air intake louvres. The policy of re-working Churchills to bring them up to approximately the same standards in armament and protection (as well as in the incorporation of improved mechanical components, where possible) as current production vehicles was continued throughout the War and in all 3,092 tanks were rebuilt.

A heavier close support weapon for tank use was designed to replace the 3-inch howitzer and this, the 95 mm. howitzer, was incorporated in the Churchill V, which apart from the main armament and associated ammunition stowage was almost identical to the Churchill IV. The Churchill V, together with the later Mark VIII, was used in the North-West Europe campaign but in Italy Churchill I's continued to be employed for close support work, although a modification was introduced in that the turret 2 pdr. was replaced by a 3-inch howitzer, so that the tank then carried two howitzers. An experimental development in the United Kingdom, known as Churchill IICS (i.e. close support), had a 3-inch howitzer in the turret and a 2 pdr. in the hull position, but this version was not used in action.

The first introduction into the Churchill of the British-built 75 mm. dual purpose gun (which was developed from a bored-out 6 pdr.) was in the Churchill VI—apart from some earlier experimental vehicles. This gun was fitted with geared elevation, unlike the 2 pdr. and the 6 pdr., and marked the final breakaway from the old Royal Tank Corps tradition of quick firing by tanks on the move. Churchill VI was identical to the Churchill IV except for this armament change. The 75 mm. gun had inferior penetrative ability to the 6 pdr., but fired a 13¾ lb. projectile. This had a muzzle velocity of 2,030 feet per second. For comparison with a weapon the Churchill frequently encountered, the Panther's KwK 42 (L/70) of the same calibre fired a 15 lb. shell at a muzzle velocity of 3,068 feet per second with getting on for twice the British gun's penetration at 500 yards.

The advance in the power of enemy tank and anti-tank weapons caused the armour protection of the Churchill to be increased. Supplementary armour—known as appliqué—was added to the hull sides (including the side doors) and to the hull nose plate. In addition, tank units in action, particularly during

"Ghosted" view of the Churchill IV clearly shows the interior layout and location of all the roof hatches used by the crew. Note ammunition stowage in the far pannier.
(Peter Chamberlain Collection)

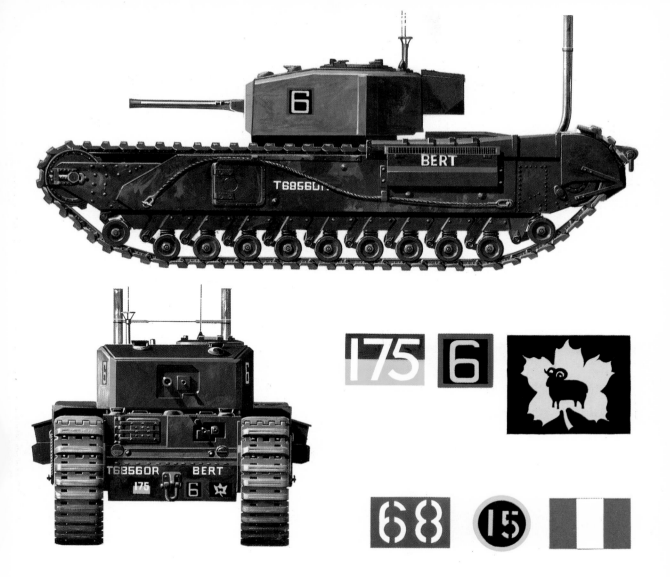

(Above) 'Bert', Churchill III of the Calgary Regiment, 1st Canadian Tank Brigade, equipped with exhaust extensions for deep wading, Dieppe, August 19, 1942.

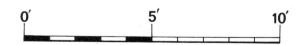

(Left) 'Cyclops', Churchill III of 51st Royal Tank Regiment, Tunisia 1943.

T. Hadler   © Profile Publications Ltd.

0'   5'   10'

the campaign following D-Day, often added further protection to the turret and frontal hull in the form of spare Churchill or Sherman track links. These were welded on (or sometimes just tied) and were of particular use for protection against shaped-charge projectiles. In some cases an external plate was added by unit workshops over the coaxial gun mounting.

The specification A22F (later A42) for a new model of Churchill provided for a basic six inches of frontal armour and this type, known as the Churchill VII, was developed and produced in time to form a fair proportion of the tank strength of the three Churchill tank brigades which fought in Normandy in 1944. The Churchill VII was also the basis of the Crocodile flamethrower with which a whole tank brigade in North-West Europe was eventually equipped. A rectangular hatch in the hull floor for the installation of Crocodile apparatus was included in all Churchill VII's and VIII's.

The incorporation of this extra protection in the Churchill VII involved fairly extensive redesigning since the idea of bolting the armour on to the hull shell was now dispensed with in favour of integral armour plating which actually formed the hull. Apart from round instead of square driver's ports and escape doors (to eliminate weaknesses in these features) and a rather different turret shape, however, the new Churchill remained essentially similar in appearance. But numerous detailed improvements were included, one of the most important being a new vision cupola for the tank commander which enabled him to command

A Churchill IV taking part in an exercise in Britain in November, 1942, marked with white crosses to indicate that it was an enemy vehicle. Censor had obliterated unit marks.
(Peter Chamberlain Collection)

Original restriction to within British rail loading gauge limits was one of the factors which later prohibited the fitting of the 17 pdr. gun to the Churchill, which was too narrow to take a large turret. Engine intake louvres were removable for rail transportation. Hammer and Sickle emblem on this Mk. III may indicate that it was one of the batch shipped to Russia.
(Imp. War Mus.)

the tank more effectively when it was closed down. This device consisting of eight episcopes incorporated in the commander's revolving turret hatch was introduced after the first Churchill VII's had been built, but was subsequently fitted in the early production tanks and also, later, to some tanks of previous Marks. The Churchill VII turret was of composite construction— the vertical part cast and the roof welded. With increased protection and the other refinements the Churchill VII was a better fighting vehicle than its predecessors, although unfortunately the size of the turret ring did not allow a larger gun to be fitted and the Q.F. 75 mm. was retained. The new features increased the weight of Churchill VII by about a ton and, to offset this, heavier suspension with stronger springs was fitted, and the gearbox was modified with slightly lower ratios and the governed top speed reduced from just under 16 m.p.h. to about 12¾ m.p.h. (It may be mentioned here that one regiment, at least, had discovered by trial that the Churchill with engine governor "sabotaged" could do 25 m.p.h. downhill— a practice certainly not recommended by the manufacturers or by the War Office!)

The final basic Mark of Churchill to go into production was the Churchill VIII, which was the close support version, armed with a 95 mm. howitzer, of the Churchill VII. Further Mark numbers IX, X and XI were, however, allotted near the end of the War to Churchills III, IV, V and VI officially reworked to approximately contemporary standards of protection by the addition of appliqué armour, although all retained their original armament. Churchill IX was the Marks III and IV with new turrets (earlier, the designation Churchill III* was given to tanks which had appliqué armour added in Normandy). Mark X was the Churchill VI reworked with new turrets and Mark XI was the corresponding modified Mark V. There also existed Churchill IX LT, X LT and XI LT in which the original turrets (LT signifying "light turret") had to be retained because of a shortage of the

*See AFV No. 16.

Close-up view of one of the three Churchill IIIs used at Alamein. Crew are re-ammunitioning. Note size of the 6 pdr. shells. (Peter Chamberlain Collection.)

heavy turrets, although the rest of the re-armouring was carried out.

Production of the Churchill ceased in October, 1945. As battle tanks they were replaced in the postwar British Army by the new Centurion series. Churchills continued in service, however, in some of the special roles in which they had made a name for themselves in the War*. The Churchill's roomy wellarmoured hull and good cross-country performance made it very suitable for adaptation for special purposes. Churchill Crocodiles were used in Korea in 1951 and the very last Churchill in service—a post-war A.V.R.E. (Armoured Vehicle Royal Engineers) modification—was retired only in 1965, 20 years after the War had ended.

THE 3 INCH GUN CARRIER AND THE BLACK PRINCE

Two further AFV designs stemmed directly from the Churchill during the war years and, while each was of great interest, both were victims of the policy changes
*See AFV No. 16.

and fluctuations which characterised British AFV development at this period. Paradoxically, however, both vehicles, the Churchill 3-inch Gun Carrier and the Black Prince (or "Super Churchill"), represented successive attempts to overcome one of the principal shortcomings of the basic Churchill design—the physical limitations, already noted, which prevented the installation of a 17 pdr. gun.

Development of the "Carrier, Churchill, 3-inch Gun, Mark I", dated from September 1941 when the General Staff asked the Tank Board to investigate the possibility of producing both cruiser and infantry tanks with high velocity guns, as a direct result of the generally poor showing of British tanks and tank guns against the Germans in the Western Desert fighting. The cruiser tank requirement eventually led to the design of the Challenger (which is outside the scope of this narrative) with the 17 pdr. gun. Neither of the existing infantry tank designs, the Churchill and the Valentine, could mount a gun bigger than a 6 pdr., but it was suggested that the 3-inch (21 cwt.) AA gun, could be fitted to the Churchill in a limited traverse mount. Stocks of 3-inch guns were then available as this weapon had by then been supplanted by the 3·7-inch gun as the army's standard heavy AA weapon.

One hundred 3-inch guns were therefore set aside for fitting to the Churchill, and Vauxhall Motors were asked to give priority to designing a suitably adapted vehicle and to be prepared to build 100 of them. Design work was in hand by December 1941, and the pilot model was ready for firing trials at Larkhill by February 1942. These proved satisfactory but the provisional order for 100 vehicles was reduced to only 24 since the War Office was by now anxious not to hold up output of Churchills with 6 pdr. guns and did not want to divert chassis into largely untried projects.

Since the manufacturers were geared up for quantity production however, with parts and armour plate

The approach to the action at 'Longstop Hill' in Tunis, January, 1943. These are Churchill IIIs of the 142nd (Suffolk) Regiment, RAC. (Imp. War Mus.)

ordered, they not unnaturally protested at this change of plan. The order for 100 vehicles was therefore reinstated, but almost immediately cut again, this time to 50. Production started in July 1942, but the programme was further delayed by inter-departmental bickering. Because the Churchill 3-inch Gun Carrier had no turret, there was argument as to whether it should be classed as a tank or as self-propelled artillery. Eventually it was decided to class it as a tank, but this immediately brought forth a request for many detail modifications from the Department of Tank Design. By this time, however, production was under way and the alterations could not be contemplated.

In late 1942 when production was complete, progress was being made with the Challenger design, and tactical requirements and policy had changed in favour of the 75 mm. "dual purpose" gun (able to fire HE and AP shot) for future production with a proportion of 17 pdr. gun tanks. The Churchill 3-inch Gun Carrier was thus abandoned and not used operationally. However, with the gun removed some of these vehicles were adapted in 1943–44 to carry "Snake" mine exploding equipment, though in this guise they were used only for experiments and training.

The Churchill 3-inch Gun Carrier was a quick and effective improvisation for getting an AFV with a powerful high velocity gun into service very swiftly when there was a definite need for a vehicle in this class. Though eventually stifled by indecision it remains specially interesting as the only official British attempt to use an AA gun in the anti-tank role—in contrast to the Germans whose adaptation of the 88 mm. AA gun for the anti-tank and tank roles played such a decisive part in their AFV policy.

The General Staff requirement of September 1941 for cruiser and infantry tanks with high velocity guns was framed specifically with the 17 pdr. gun in mind, design of which had started in Summer 1941. In the cruiser tank category the Cromwell design had to be lengthened and widened to take a 17 pdr. turret (resulting in the Challenger design), while, as we have seen, the Churchill was adapted to take the 3-inch gun in the infantry tank category, though consideration was given concurrently to modifying the design to take a 17 pdr. gun in a turret as a long term aim.

Four Churchills lined-up in Italy show clearly the difference between the Mk. IV (NA 75s) with 75 mm. gun from Sherman tanks, compared to a Churchill VII with 75 mm. gun, which is the second vehicle in the line. Note the commander's cupola in this later vehicle. This picture was taken in April, 1945, when NA 75s were still in service. (Imp. War Mus.)

Like its contemporaries, however, the Churchill was too narrow for this in its existing form. This was due to several factors, including War Office insistence that all tanks be designed within British railway loading gauge limits for transportation purposes, a restriction which was lifted for later designs.

Plans to terminate Churchill production were made in late 1942 once Cromwell production got into its stride and little or no progress was made with the idea of mounting a 17 pdr. gun, though the Churchill programme was reprieved in the following year as a result of its good performance in Tunis. It was not until the end of 1943 that Vauxhall were asked to go ahead with definite plans for a Churchill with a 17 pdr. as an interim design while requirements for an entirely new "universal chassis" vehicle were formulated, this latter, incidentally, eventually emerging as the A41 Centurion. Designated A43, Black Prince, the modified design was essentially a Churchill VII with a widened hull to take a 17 pdr. gun and turret,

A Churchill squadron (a mixture of Mks. III and IV) move forward towards the River Foglia during the Eighth Army attack on the Gothic Line, September, 1944. (Imp. War Mus.)

A Churchill VI, which was essentially a Mk. IV re-armed with a 75 mm. gun, seen in North-West France in October, 1944. Note the use of Sherman track shoes for added protection. (Imp. War Mus.)

and strengthened tracks and suspension to compensate for the extra weight which was now increased to 50 tons. Armour thicknesses remained the same, as did the power plant, but the extra weight meant that maximum speed now fell to only 11 m.p.h. Work on the Black Prince started in January 1944 and six pilot models were built, ready for troop testing in May 1945. By this time, however, the first Centurion pilot models were also ready and the war in Europe was at an end. Though full trials were carried out with the Black Prince no production order was placed and the Centurion subsequently became the main British battle tank of post-war years.

CHURCHILL IN SERVICE

From the time of their entry into service in 1941 until the end of World War II, Churchill tanks were employed in Army tank brigades—independent formations normally under direct Army command but allocated to corps or divisional commanders for training and operations as needed. In mid 1942 a new organisation was introduced in which six of the

Army tank brigades each replaced the third infantry brigade of an infantry division, so that the infantry would have their own integrated tank support.

The two Army tank brigades in the Tunisian campaign—both equipped with Churchills—formed part of "mixed" divisions, although they operated in the way envisaged only on rare occasions. It was found that the mixed divisions had insufficient infantry reserves and the establishment was abolished in 1943, although the policy remained for Army tank brigades to remain in support of infantry in close co-operation.

Churchill tank battalions (or regiments) consisted of a regimental headquarters and three fighting squadrons, together with supporting vehicles. The regimental headquarters had four Churchill tanks and in addition a reconnaissance troop of 11 carriers, replaced later by Stuart light tanks, and an inter-communications troop of nine scout cars. Each squadron comprised a headquarters of three Churchill close support tanks and five troops, each of three Churchill tanks, making a grand total of Churchills for the battalion of 58. This organisation was modified in Italy in 1944 when some regiments received Sherman tanks in place of Churchills in two troops in each squadron.

The employment of Churchill tank units in support of infantry naturally varied with the requirements of the action, but a typical attack in Italy (before the Gothic Line in September 1944) was described by the 142nd Regiment, R.A.C. as follows:—

"The tanks and the infantry advanced from fire position to fire position, one Churchill troop going forward, sometimes one tank at a time, supported by the fire of the others, the infantry and the tanks being within 100 yards of one another during most of the advance." The infantry company commanders and tank troop commanders kept in close touch with each other throughout, and when the attack was

An early Churchill IV with the original 6 pdr. gun Mk. 3 distinguished by its counter weight on the muzzle. (Imp. War Mus.)

The Churchill V was the same as the Churchill IV, complete with cast turret, but carried a 95 mm. howitzer for support fire in place of the 6 pdr. gun. (Peter Chamberlain Collection.)

successfully accomplished, the tanks remained to guard the flanks until the infantry had consolidated the position.

The Churchill was the final manifestation of the policy, formulated before World War II, which divided British tanks into two categories: cruiser tanks to equip the armoured divisions, mobile, relatively lightly armoured vehicles intended for employment in the "exploitation" role—the old task of the cavalry; and infantry tanks. The requirements for the latter called for heavy armour, but only modest speed. Unfortunately emphasis on the gun was lacking in both cruiser and infantry tanks, so that the fire power of British tanks lagged behind that of the Germans—their principal opponents—for nearly all of the War. The "two tank types" policy lapsed towards the end of the War, and armoured divisions and Army tank brigades alike were employed in less rigid concepts, although they remained hampered at times by their equipment and to an extent by the bias of their earlier training. The Churchill was the last type of British infantry tank to go into service—later designs reached prototype stage only—and although limited by its original specification was one of the most successful British tanks of World War II. It fought with distinction in the Mediterranean theatre from early 1943 onwards and in the North-West Europe campaign of 1944–45. (The end of the War put an end to plans for employment of Churchills in the Far East, although a few were attached to the Australians in the Pacific area for experimental purposes.) In these campaigns, the Tunisian mountains, the Gothic Line in Italy, the hard fighting before the breakout from the Normandy bridgehead, the reduction of Le Harve, and the final advance into Germany were all battles in which the Churchill proved its value.

Through the long refinement of its design the Churchill was turned into a reliable and battleworthy tank and, although never one of the easiest to maintain, a tank which had the liking and confidence of

its crews. The Churchill's gun lacked range and fire power compared with enemy tanks, but the protection of its thick armour to some extent made up for this. When hit, the Churchill had the good quality—absent in many of its contemporaries on both sides—of not burning quickly. The top speed of the Churchill was not great, but the tank was lively in response to the controls and in difficult cross-country running could put up a far better performance than the majority of other tanks of its time.

The achievement of the Churchill in difficult mountain terrain in its first major campaign formed our opening theme and its performance in very different country almost exactly two years later, near the end of World War II, will make a fitting conclusion.

Two Churchill tank battalions (9th Royal Tank Regiment and 147th (Hampshire) Regiment, R.A.C.) were given the task of supporting the infantry through

Churchill VII of the Scots Guards (6th Guards Armoured Brigade) crosses a bridge laid over a crater by a Churchill Bridgelayer during the advance on Celle, April, 1945. Note use of Sherman and Churchill track shoes for added armour protection. The track covers, incidentally, were made in three removable sections. On this vehicle, the centre section is removed, and some vehicles were seen with all sections removed giving them an appearance at first glance to the original Mk. 1 Churchill. (Imp. War Museum.)

the heart of the Reichswald Forest, part of the Siegfried Line. This was in February 1945 and with torrential rain falling special Churchills carrying extra equipment (such as A.V.R.E.s and Crocodiles) got bogged down, but many of the ordinary Churchill tanks managed to get through. Even so, some became bogged down to the level of their turret tops and others had their turret traverse mechanisms wrecked through the guns hitting trees. This is without mentioning the fanatical opposition of the enemy in defending their homeland: the conditions were well suited to snipers and camouflaged S.P. guns.

Nevertheless with their supporting infantry the tanks burst through to the Rhine and the heart of Germany beyond, with surprisingly few casualties, after six days spent in the permanent soggy gloom of the Reichswald. The forest had always been regarded as a complete tank obstacle. The success of the Churchills was summed up after his capture by an indignant German colonel—"Who but the British would think of using tanks in this forest? It's not fair."

A.F.V. Series Editor: DUNCAN CROW

SPECIFICATION: TANK, INFANTRY, MARK IV—CHURCHILL III

General

Crew: Five—commander, turret gunner, wireless operator, driver, hull gunner.
Battle weight: 39 tons.
Power/weight ratio: 8·33 bhp/ton.
Bridge classification: 40.

Dimensions

Length overall (also same as hull length): 25 ft. 2 in.
Height: 8 ft. 2 in.
Width: 10 ft. 8 in. (9 ft. 2 in. without side air louvres).
Width over tracks: 9 ft. 1 in.
Track centres: 12 ft. 6 in.
Track width: 14 in.

Two views of the Churchill VII show the new turret, the commander's cupola, the 75 mm. gun, the round escape hatches and armoured covers on the exhaust manifolds, all introduced on this mark. Note also the new side appearance, the bolts having 'disappeared' due to the integral armour plating on the hull. (Imp. War Mus.)

Two views of the Churchill VIII, the close-support variant of the Mk VII, which had a 95 mm. howitzer replacing the 75 mm. gun. Note the driver's periscope raised. (Imp. War Mus.)

Armament
Main—Ordnance, Q.F. 6 pdr. 7 cwt. Mark III (calibre 57 mm.—2·244 in.) 43 calibres long. The 6 pdr. Mark V with a longer and thinner barrel 50 calibres long was also fitted in some Churchill III's.
One 7·92 mm. Besa machine gun, mounted in turret, coaxially with the 6 pdr.
One 7·92 mm. Besa machine gun mounted in hull front plate.
Auxiliary—one 0·303 in. Bren light machine gun, mounted on collapsible mounting on turret roof for A.A. use, but normally carried stowed inside turret.
One 2 in. bomb thrower, mounted in turret roof. Verey pistol and Thompson machine carbine carried for crew use.

Fire Control
Free elevation (by means of shoulder piece) for 6 pdr. and Besa coaxial mounting—elevation maximum 20°, depression 12½°.
Traverse by electrical power: 360° rotation in 15 seconds; alternative manual operation. 6 pdr. and Besa fired (by means of pistol grips) mechanically, through cable.

Ammunition
6 pdr.: 84 rds., stowed in fighting compartment.
Besa: 42 boxes (each 225 rds.) stowed in fighting compartment and in front compartment.
Bren: 6 magazines (each 100 rds.) in turret.
2 in. bomb thrower: 30 bombs.
Verey pistol: 20 cartridges (green, red, illuminating).
Thompson m/c: 23 box magazines (each 20 rds.).
6 hand grenades also carried in the tank.

Sighting and Vision
Commander: 1 periscope on turret roof, 2 periscopes in turret hatch.
Turret gunner: 1 periscope on turret roof, 1 Telescope, Sighting, No. 39, Mk.I.S. in gun mounting.
Driver: vision door, incorporating small port protected by armoured glass block, periscope on hull roof.
Hull gunner: periscope on hull roof; Telescope, Sighting, No. 30, Mk.1 or 1A or No. 33 Mk. I.S. or II.S for Besa machine gun.

Communications
Wireless Set No. 19—incorporating 'A' set: long range, and 'B' set: short range. Also intercommunication for all crew members.

Armour
Turret: welded plate.
Hull: plates bolted on to frame.

Two views of the Gun Carrier, 3-inch Churchill Mk. 1, showing the new superstructure and the limited traverse mount for the 3-inch gun. This particular vehicle is the pilot model built by Vauxhall. Production vehicles were built by Beyer Peacock. (Peter Chamberlain Collection.)

The A43 Black Prince (sometimes known as the 'Super Churchill') was essentially similar to the Churchill VII, scaled-up to take a 17 pdr. gun. Note that the intake louvres were moved to the hull top, however, and the exhaust was led to the rear. Increased width of this vehicle to take the wider turret is noticeable. In the Black Prince, also, the commander's position was moved to the right as the gun was turned sideways for left-hand loading. Only six vehicles were built and the Black Prince never entered full production. (Peter Chamberlain Collection.)

Churchill, post-war—a Mk. VII, one of a small batch supplied to the Royal Jordanian Army in the mid-fifties. (Peter Chamberlain Collection.)

A Churchill X of the Irish Army, 1967. This is typical of the reworked models with appliqué armour, 75 mm. gun and added cupola among many other modifications. At the time this book was published, the Irish Army was the last force with the Churchill in full service. The tanks were acquired from Britain in the early 'fifties. (Hilary Doyle.)

Thicknesses in mm.:
Hull: Front nose plate 88 mm. at 20°. Front glacis plate 38 mm. at 70°. Driver's plate 88 mm. vertical. Sides 76 mm. vertical. Rear 50 mm. vertical. Roof 16 mm. horizontal. Floor 20 mm. horizontal.
Turret: Front 88 mm. vertical. Sides 76 mm. vertical.

Engine
Bedford Twin-six: petrol.
12 cylinders, horizontally opposed.
Capacity 1296 cubic inches.
350 bhp. at 2200 r.p.m.
Fuel: 182½ gallons (total). 75 gals. in 3 interconnected tanks of right hand fuel system, 75 gals. in 3 tanks of left hand system (mounted inside "panniers" on either side of vehicle); 32½ gals. in auxiliary tank (jettisonable) attached to hull rear plate.

Transmission
Merritt-Brown 4 speed gearbox, with steering epicyclic gear trains. Ratios: 1st 6·220:1, 2nd 2·263:1, 3rd 1·176:1, 4th 0·0703:1. Reverse, 10.658:1.

Suspension
Eleven steel 10 inch diameter road wheels each side, independently mounted on trailing arms and sprung on vertical coil springs. The front and rear road wheels on each side mounted higher than the others.
Idler wheels—toothed sprockets, at front of vehicle. Final drive sprockets at rear.
Tracks: Heavy cast steel type, pitch $8\frac{5}{16}$ in. 70 links per set (each side). Light cast steel and manganese steel types—pitch 7·96 in. 72 links per set.

Electrical System
Main dynamo 12 volt, mounted on top of engine. Turret traverse dynamo mounted on floor of gearbox compartment.
Auxiliary generator (Delco-Remy unit—dynamo driven by single cylinder 4 stroke aircooled petrol engine) carried behind hull gunner's seat.
Batteries: Two 6 volt, connected in series.

Performance
Maximum speed recommended: 15½ m.p.h.
Vertical obstacle: 2 ft. 6 in.
Trench: 10 ft. 0 in.
Wading depth (unprepared): 3 ft. 4 in.
Range: 120 miles approx. (with auxiliary fuel tank).

Sherman Crab flailing. (Photo: U.S. Official)

Churchill and Sherman Specials
by Peter Chamberlain & Chris Ellis

WHILE conceptions of the tactical uses and value of fighting tanks themselves changed radically in the six years of the Second World War, this same epoch saw the development of an entirely new breed of tracked fighting vehicles which was evolved to meet the conditions imposed by a war in which the tank was almost always the dominant battlefield weapon. War provides the greatest impetus to change and new ideas, and nowhere can this be more vividly demonstrated than in the vast range of so-called "funnies" which appeared during the years 1940-45. Just as Britain pioneered the tactical and technical development of tanks in the First World War, so it pioneered the "special purpose" tank in the Second World War. In 1915-16 there had been the need to find the answer to the stalemate of trench warfare—culminating in the tank itself; and in 1940-42 there was the need (initially) to find the sort of specialist tank needed to assist invading forces in forming any bridgehead for the proposed invasion of Europe. This—as was amply demonstrated by the sad failure of the Dieppe raid—provided the impetus to British endeavour. The Germans, faced from 1942 with a defensive war in "Fortress Europe", had little or no need to develop tanks for specialized rôles, and the Americans were late starters whose somewhat sophisticated special purpose designs saw relatively limited production or service before hostilities ceased. Significantly, the two special purpose versions of the Sherman used in greatest numbers by the U.S. Army were both British—the flail tank and the D.D. So here we concentrate on the wholly British developments in the field of special purpose tank designs, restricting coverage in the main to the vehicles developed for the

assault rôle. Most of these were operated by 79th Armoured Division. They fall into six main categories: The AVRE, Flame-Throwing Tanks, The Sherman D.D. Tank, Mine Clearing Devices, Bridging Expedients and Miscellaneous Types.

Churchills and Shermans were also converted to the rôle of Armoured Recovery Vehicles.

The Avre

Though the Dieppe raid of August 1942 had been unsuccessful, it led directly to the development of many specialized types of devices and equipment which were to be required in the invasion of Europe.

One particular item of equipment shown to be lacking was some form of protected vehicle for the engineers engaged on clearing obstacles; the Canadian engineers had sustained heavy casualties while trying to breach the sea wall and clear other obstacles on the Dieppe beaches. During the period when the lessons of Dieppe were being evaluated, Lieut. J. J. Donovan of the Royal Canadian Engineers, attached to the Special Devices Section, proposed a scheme for converting a tank into an armoured carrier for the use of engineers. It was felt that engineer personnel operating in conjunction with armoured formations and as assault engineers should be provided with an AFV to protect and carry their stores. The vehicle was to be provided with a weapon able to fire a heavy demolition charge to breach or destroy concrete obstacles.

Comparative trials carried out with the Sherman

Fully fitted Churchill AVRE (Mark IV with cast turret) showing the special standard attachment brackets for C.I.R.D. (Canadian Indestructible Roller Device) and other devices. Not all AVREs were so fitted. (Photo: Imperial War Museum)

Top left: *Ardeer Aggie, a converted Churchill III designed to try and improve on the power of the Petard mortar.* (Photo: Imperial War Museum)

Middle left: *The fascine carried on the AVRE presented navigation problems, solved by the commander riding in an exposed position atop the fascine. This was later remedied by the issue of a folding periscope which looked like a broomstick pushed out through the cupola. In practice, however, the periscope was rarely used. The fascine was released by a slip rope led through the cupola. The wooden cradle was usually dropped with the fascine.* (Photo: Imperial War Museum)

Bottom left: *Churchill AVRE with AVRE sledge and fascines—N.W. Europe, October 1944.* (Photo: Imperial War Museum)

Below: *AVRE with S.B.G. (small box girder) bridge in travelling position.* (Photo: Imperial War Museum)

and Ram tanks, experimentally fitted for the engineer rôle, showed the value of the Ram side doors for easy access and exit from this vehicle under fire. However, the Ram lacked the stowage space required for the necessary engineer stores, and the Sherman was much in demand as a gun tank, so the Churchill was considered as the most suitable vehicle for conversion. Its side (or pannier) escape doors were also at a more convenient height for access and the vehicle offered superior armour protection over the Ram and Sherman. In October 1942 it was decided that the 1st Canadian Mechanical Engineering Company, under the direction of the Special Devices Section, would begin work on a prototype vehicle incorporating all of Lieut. Donovan's proposals. By December 1942 the M.E. Coy. had completed the first prototype, converted from a Churchill II, in which all ammunition bins were removed as well as the co-driver's seat, the turret basket and main armament. New stowage compartments were arranged to accommodate 36 cu. ft. of engineers stores, demolition gear, and tools, etc. A mock-up of a spigot mortar was mounted in the turret front. Work on the actual mortar which was to arm this vehicle was commenced in September 1942. A preliminary experimental model was mounted and tested in a Covenanter tank. As this proved successful, arrangements were made in November 1942 with the firm of Messrs. Blacker Development Ltd. to design and make three prototypes of a spigot mortar. To be known as the "Petard", it was to be capable of fitment in the 2-pdr. mounting of the Churchill tank. The Petard's projectile was given the name of "Flying Dustbin". The actual manufacture of the production Petards was later sub-contracted to Messrs. J. Williamson & Sons, Lancaster.

As a result of the inspection of the first vehicle, it was decided that the 1st Canadian M.E. Coy. would make a second prototype engineers' vehicle, this time converting a 6-pdr. Churchill. This version, slightly modified and without armament, was ready by February 1943. Trials were carried out later that month and successfully demonstrated the transportation of six sappers and their explosive charges to the site of demolition. Trials also proved the vehicle's ability to give cover to the sappers as they disembarked to lay explosive charges under simulated fire.

At the same trials the first engineer vehicle fired a prototype Petard and successfully demolished reinforced concrete obstacles.

As a result of the demonstrations by these two vehicles it was decided in March 1943 that nine further Petard prototypes and 100 Flying Dustbins would be made for trials. It was also decided that drawings and instructions should be prepared to enable the 6-pdr. versions of the Churchill tanks to be modified to engineer vehicles, now known as A.V.R.E. (Armoured Vehicles Royal Engineers), either by R.E.M.E. workshops or by the manufacturers in the course of production. The first experimental conversion to these instructions was made by the 79th Armoured Division with certain modifications of their own, one of which was the retention of the turret basket. These amendments were later accepted in the finalized design. In December 1943 the prototype production vehicle was made ready by the firm of Messrs. Cockbridge & Co. Ltd. of Ipswich who had been appointed to prepare the necessary production drawings and to manufacture 475 AVRE conversion kits. The first 108 AVREs were to be converted by R.E.M.E. workshops.

The Cockbridge model, with a few minor modifications, was accepted for production and the vehicle was passed to M.G. Cars Ltd. of Abingdon who had been appointed design parents and were to handle the production order for AVRE conversions. A total of nearly 600 AVRE conversions were produced by M.G. Cars and in addition 108 vehicles were converted by the R.E.M.E. with 734 conversion kits being manufactured by Messrs. Cockbridge.

SPECIFICATION
AVRE (Churchill Mk. III or IV converted)

Crew: 6 (commander, demolition NCO, mortar gunner, wireless operator, co-driver/loader).
Weight: 38 tons (stowed).
Armament: 1 × Mortar, Recoiling, Spigot, 290 mm., Mk. I or II.
  Length of weapon: 7 ft. 2 in. overall.
  Loading trough: 3 ft. 9 in.
  Weight of projectile: 40 lb.
  Rate of fire: 2-3 rounds per minute.
  Effective range (with 40 lb. projectile): 80 yds.
  NB: 6-pdr. gun sight used with this weapon.
  1 × Besa MG in hull.
All other details as for Churchill III or IV, but with revised internal stowage arrangements.

Churchill with T.L.C. Carpet Laying Device. The wire which actuated the carpet release is clearly seen. This equipment fitted on the standard AVRE attachment points.
(Photo: Imperial War Museum)

Churchill with Twin Bobbins laid a double track of hessian and chespalings from a horizontal spindle. It also fitted the standard AVRE attachment points.
(Photo: Imperial War Museum)

Churchill with Snake being towed from a LCT to clear beaches of mines in a pre-Overlord exercise.
(Photo: Imperial War Museum)

Sherman with Snake. It was disconnected by the co-driver through the belly escape hatch. (Photo: Imperial War Museum)

Sherman with 18-inch C.I.R.D. and Flying Bangalore Torpedoes (mounted above C.I.R.D. arms). (Photo: Imperial War Museum)

Early in 1944 it was decided to form and equip three R.E. regiments as armoured assault regiments for participation in Operation Overlord, the Normandy landings. These regiments, each with an establishment of approximately 60 AVREs, formed the 1st Assault Brigade, R.E., of the 79th Armoured Division which had been formed to train and administer all special purpose armour taking part in the invasion. At the same time, it was decided that these tanks should be capable of being fitted with various devices such as fascines, bridges, mine ploughs, etc.

THE AVRE DESCRIBED

As put into production in early 1944, the AVRE consisted of a basic Churchill Mk. III or IV with the 6-pdr. gun, cradle, elevation gear, and recoil system removed. Also removed were the ammunition stowage bins and co-driver's seat. The flaps of the co-driver's seat were welded up and an aperture 13 in. by 12½ in. was cut immediately above the co-driver's position and fitted with a sliding flap. To load the Petard spigot mortar which was installed in the turret front, the turret was traversed to bring the weapon above this aperture, whereupon the loader pushed the flap forward and passed a projectile up into the loading trough of the mortar. Compartments for holding 26 projectiles were formed in the side panniers, fore and aft of the nearside escape door, and aft of the offside door, each of about 9 cu. ft. capacity. Other equipment carried included an electric cable which could be connected to the tank battery for firing the hand-placed explosive charges.

The Petard was bolted directly to the 6-pdr. mantlet and fitted with a screw elevation gear suspended from gimbals on a bracket welded to the turret roof. The lower splash plate was modified to accommodate the Petard, while the upper splash plate was completely redesigned. Brackets were fitted on the sides of the hull and front for the fitment of various devices such as anti-mine rollers and ploughs, mechanical charge placers, carpet bobbins, etc. For towing fascines, explosive and other engineer stores a simple dropside sledge known as the AVRE sledge with steel runners was produced.

CHURCHILL ARDEER AGGIE

To meet the demand for a more powerful demolition weapon than the Petard, the Ardeer Aggie was proposed. Originally called the Ardeer Projector, it was a recoilless gun in which the recoil momentum was neutralized by the firing of a dummy projectile to the rear simultaneous with the discharge of the main round through the barrel. Development was started in September 1943, the first prototype being mounted on a 6-pdr. field carriage. The second Ardeer prototype was mounted on a Churchill III in 1944. It weighed 9 cwt. and had a length of 10 ft. The projectile weighed 54 lb. and the sand-filled dummy counter-projectile weighed 48 lb. Range was 450 yd. and the rate of fire about three rounds in two minutes. Development of this interesting weapon was stopped as it was found to be unpractical under action conditions.

Churchill Carpet-Layer Type D, shown with wading trunking fitted, coming to the end of its "lay".
(Photo: Imperial War Museum)

WOODPECKER

This was another experimental version of the AVRE evolved during 1944 for the demolition of concrete fortifications and consisted of Flying Dustbins with rocket attachments mounted four each side of the vehicle. They could be fired in salvo or as single shots. This equipment was not developed to production stage.

AVRE SPECIAL DEVICES

Churchill AVREs equipped the 5th, 6th and the 42nd Assault Regts., R.E., these regiments forming the 1st Assault Brigade, R.E. As finalized, the AVRE design allowed for the fitting of various special devices and equipments for tackling the obstacles and defences likely to be encountered by the armoured units of 21 Army Group.

The following is a summary of the specialized equipment that was used and includes reference to the experimental devices that were developed but not used in action:

MARK II, S.B.G., AVRE (ASSAULT BRIDGE)

This device was evolved by the Canadian Army in April 1943, as a method for wall or ditch crossing in assault. It consisted of a small box girder bridge fitted to the front of the AVRE and adapted for quick release. The bridge weighed four tons, was 34 ft. long, was able to take a load of 40 tons, and was controlled by a winch mounted on the rear of the vehicle. The bridge could surmount a 15-ft. wall or span a 30-ft. gap. Fascines (brushwood bundles) were often used in conjunction with the S.B.G. bridge. To enable the AFV to climb over high obstacles the AVRE released its bridge at an angle against the obstacle and then withdrew; a second AVRE carrying fascines climbed to the top of the bridge and dropped its fascines over the wall. This broke the fall of the AVRE as it followed the fascines over the wall.

FASCINES

This method for crossing ditches by AFVs had first been introduced during World War I, being used by British tanks at Cambrai in November 1917 to enable

Churchill II with Light Carrot. (Photo: Imperial War Museum)

Churchill with Jones Onion device.
(Photo: Imperial War Museum)

them to cross the wide German trenches. The modern counterparts consisted of brushwood bundles of two types, 6 ft. and 8 ft. in diameter and 11 ft. long. They were carried on the front of the tank supported by a wooden or steel cradle and could be jettisoned by a quick release mechanism which operated by a line led inside the tank through the cupola. In most cases a crew member had to expose himself to give directions to the driver whose view was obscured by the fascine. So experiments were carried out with periscopes similar to those used with the D.D. tanks. These were 6 ft. and 8 ft. in length and were fitted to the commander's cupola to enable him to see over the fascines. These were later discarded with the appearance of new types of fascines which gave a better view ahead.

MAT LAYING DEVICES

These were designed for laying rapidly and, if necessary, under fire, a carpet in a lane over poor or bogged ground and over barbed wire obstacles for the rapid advancement of troops, trucks and AFVs.

T.L.C. Laying Device and Carpet (Type A) Mark I

This device was first tried out in March 1939 on a Cruiser Tank Mk. I, further trials being carried out on a Matilda II tank and a Universal Carrier. Development for fitment to the Churchill began in April 1942, the pilot model being tested in July. A similar device was also used during the Dieppe raid and consisted of a small carpet bobbin fitted between the

Churchill with Elevatable Goat. (Photo: Imperial War Museum)

front horns of a Churchill III. The Type A model consisted of a reinforced hessian carpet wound on to a horizontal reel and carried above ground across the front of the Churchill by fixed arms attached to the vehicle. Its primary object was to enable wheeled vehicles and infantry to cross barbed wire obstacles. On meeting such an obstacle the weighted free end of the carpet was dropped on to the ground whilst the tank ran on to the free end, and then the carpet automatically unwound itself, so that the vehicle ran over it across the obstacle. On completion of the crossing the spindle device could be jettisoned. Production of this model was completed by the end of 1944.

Carpet-Layer (Type B) Twin Bobbins

This device featured two small bobbins of hessian and chespaling on a horizontal spindle carried across the front of the vehicle by fixed side arms attached to the tank. When in motion the spindle unwound a separate carpet under each track.

Carpet-Layer (Type C) Mark II, and (Type D) Mark III

Prior to the invasion of Normandy, aerial reconnaissance had shown that some beaches had strips of blue clay in which vehicles would bog. A similar beach was found at Brancaster in Norfolk and a special trials wing of 79th Armoured Division was established. As a result of these trials various improved carpet equipments were developed.

Two of the types developed by the 79th Armoured Division at Brancaster were the Types C and D and these were used during the landings on the Normandy beaches. Fitted with side arms, and with variations in the carrying structure, Mark III mounted a larger bobbin with a longer length of carpet, though both marks of carpets were 9 ft. 11 in. in width. Operating speed was 2 m.p.h. and the bobbin could be jettisoned by a small charge. With these versions the bobbins were carried above the turret. The side arms of Type C were movable.

T.L.C. Laying Device and Carpet (Fascine Type)

Developed in 1940, this device was designed for rapidly laying a carpet over poor ground breached through a minefield. It was intended to be used for wheeled traffic only, but in emergency could be used by tracked vehicles. The carpet consisted of coirchespale with 2-in. tubular reinforcement 11 ft. wide and 100 ft. long. The carpet was tightly reeled in the shape of a fascine and mounted on a modified steel fascine cradle in a manner similar to a normal fascine. The carpet reel was held on the cradle by a set of travelling cables and a reel spindle securing cable. The reel when released rotated on an axle through which the spindle securing cable was threaded. The carpet skidded out from underneath and dropped under the tracks of the AVRE. Laying speed was 5 m.p.h.

Log Carpet Device
The carpet of this equipment consisted of 100 logs each 14 ft. long with an average diameter of 6 to 8 in. joined together by 2-in. wire rope. It was mounted on a steel frame on top of the AVRE. This frame consisted of Decauville track fitted in sockets on either side of the AVRE, and could be removed when not required. To release the log carpet a series of small charges were fired to cut the cables holding the mat on the frame. Laying speed was 2 m.p.h.

ANTI-MINE EXPLOSIVE DEVICES
To enable assault troops and armour to pass through cleared lanes in mine fields without waiting for the normal detecting and probing methods by R.E. sappers, various methods were developed whereby mines could be destroyed by explosive, or by the blast from the explosive creating sympathetic detonation. Some of these explosive mine devices were used with both Sherman and Churchill tanks, though the methods of attachment were generally different.

Churchill AVRE or Sherman with Conger 2 inch Mark I
Evolved in January 1944 for mine clearance in assault, this device consisted of an engineless Universal carrier containing a 5-in. Rocket No. 3 Mk. I and projector, air bottles and a tank of liquid explosive. Fitted to the rear of the carrier was a wooden box containing 330 yards of 2-in. woven hose. The explosive carrier was towed to the edge of the mine field and

released. The empty hose was attached to the rocket and fired over the mine field so that it lay extended across the field, one end of the hose still being connected to the carrier. The hose was then pumped full of explosive by compressed air. When sufficient explosive had been pumped into the hose the carrier was removed and the hose was detonated by a delay pull igniter, the blast creating a path through the mines. This equipment saw limited operational service.

Sherman C.I.R.D. with Tapeworm
Developed in March 1944 for mine clearance in assault, this was a trailer containing 500 yards of $2\frac{3}{4}$-in. canvas hose that had been filled with explosive. The trailer was towed by a Sherman C.I.R.D. (Canadian Indestructible Roller Device) to the edge of a mine field and then released. The Tapeworm was then pulled from the trailer by the Sherman as it advanced across the mine field. When the explosive hose was fully extended the hose was released and detonated, thereby blasting a path through the mines. The 50 ft. of hose nearest the tank was filled with sand to ensure the safety of the tank.

Sherman C.I.R.D. with Flying Bangalore Torpedoes
This device was developed in 1943 for wire clearance, and consisted of a Bangalore rocket projector mounted on both side arms of the roller assembly. Each projector held two Bangalore torpedoes fitted with small grapnels to catch the wire.

Churchill and Sherman with 3-inch Snake
Developed in August 1942 and used operationally, this simple device consisted of 20-ft. lengths of 3-in. water piping filled with explosive. The pipes were fitted together and pulled to the end of the mine field by the tank which then changed its position to the end of the Snake and pushed the piping into the mine field. It was then released and detonated, the

Churchill AVRE with Goat Mark III. Note covered Petard mortar.

(Photo: Imperial War Museum)

blast creating a path approximately 21 ft. wide. Maximum pushing length was 400 ft. and for towing 1,200 ft. (Sherman 700 ft.).

MECHANICAL CHARGE PLACERS

To enable obstacles to be breached or demolished, and at the same time give maximum protection to the demolition personnel, a series of Mechanical Charge Placers were evolved and experimented with. These methods suspended explosive charges on frames mounted in front of the tank for placing in front of or across the obstacles to be demolished. Because of its heavy armour, stable chassis, and adoption as the standard AVRE, the Churchill was the carrier vehicle used for almost all the British developed explosive charge devices.

The Light Carrot

Developed in July 1942, this was the code name given to an elongated rectangular explosive charge carried on an extension bracket fitted to the nose of the tank, so that it could be positioned against the object to be breached and fired without exposure of the tank crew. The weight of the charge varied from 12 lb. to a maximum of 25 lb. The project was abandoned in November 1943.

Onion (Jones Onion)

Developed in August 1942, this device consisted of a framework attached to the front of a tank so that various charges could be carried by it. The framework measured 9 ft. wide by 4 ft. 6 in. high. It was carried vertically by two side arms attached one each side of the vehicle. These could be jettisoned after the demolition had been completed. When the tank with the explosive device arrived at the obstacle to be attacked a mechanical release cable was pulled allowing the frame of charges to fall. A pair of

cranked legs pivoted to the frame met the ground first, so that the frame fell forward and was retained against the obstacle. The tank was then reversed away and the charges fired electrically by a trailing cable. A smaller similar device was known as the Single Onion.

Goat Mark III

A further development of the Carrot and Onion devices, this consisted of 1,800 lb. of explosive charges carried on a platform 10 ft. 6 in. wide by 6 ft. 6 in. long retained in a horizontal position above the nose of the AVRE by side arms, and so designed that contact with the wall or obstacle automatically released the explosive frame in a vertical position. The tank then pushed the frame up against the obstacle and backed off. When the tank was clear of the obstacle, the charges were fired either electrically or by pull igniter.

Elevatable Goat

This device was for use against high walls or obstacles, and consisted of a long braced frame carried on the nose of an AVRE in a similar manner to the Assault S.B.G. Fitted under the two main spars were a series of linked charges. On approaching the obstacle the complete assembly was placed against the wall and jettisoned from the vehicle. The linked charges were next released and these fell away from the spars to straddle the wall, the tank retiring to blow the charges.

Churchill with Bangalore Torpedoes

This was a simple device with two lengths of Snake piping fitted to an Onion frame assembly. The method of release was similar to the Onion device. It was developed for use against light obstacles and barbed wire.

Bottom left: *Churchill Oke from front. Note flame-projector pipe. Vehicle is a Churchill II.* (Photo: Imperial War Museum)

Below: *Crocodile flame projector in the Churchill VII bow machine-gun position.* (Photo: Imperial War Museum)

Above: *Churchill Crocodile, pilot model on Mark VII.*
(Photo: Imperial War Museum)

Churchill Crocodile in action on First Canadian Army front in Germany.

(Photo: Imperial War Museum)

Flame-throwing Tanks

The first General Staff specification for a flame-throwing tank, put forward in December 1938, was for a flame projector mounted in the turret of an Infantry Tank, replacing the main armament. The fuel was to be carried either in self-sealing tanks fitted outside of the vehicle, or in a two-wheeled towed trailer, that could be jettisoned from inside the tank. As a result of this General Staff requirement early research on flame-throwers was carried out at Woolwich under the Chief Superintendent of the Research Department during 1939 and early 1940.

In July 1940 under a directive from the Prime Minister, the Petroleum Warfare Department (P.W.D.) was established, its task being to develop the use of oil as a weapon. This resulted in the development of various flame devices that included the Flame Fougasses, Static Flame Barrages and other static equipments.

Parallel development was also at the same time being carried out by the Woolwich group (now under M.O.S.) who due to the blitz had moved to Langhurst in Sussex. Although both departments worked in co-operation, the P.W.D. concentrated mainly on pressure and pump-operated types of equipment, while the Langhurst group worked largely on cordite operated apparatus. In June 1942 the two groups were merged.

The first development by the P.W.D. was the Cockatrice. This was a pressure operated flame-thrower mounted on an armoured Bedford chassis. It was followed by a heavy pump unit mounted on an A.E.C. chassis. Research and experimental work on these types of equipment led to the development of a flame-thrower mounted on the Valentine tank which consisted of a trailer type of unit utilizing the flame gun of the heavy pump unit and compressed hydrogen bottles as in use with balloon barrages. In March 1942 this equipment was tried out side by side with the cordite operated device developed by the M.O.S. at Langhurst and which had also been mounted on a Valentine tank. As a result of this joint demonstration the pressure type equipment of

the P.W.D. was preferred; this led to a General Staff decision that a flame-thrower of this type should be developed for the Churchill tank. General Staff specifications for a flame-thrower tank were now amended from those laid down in 1938, namely that the main armament of the tank would be retained and the bow machine-gun replaced by the flame-projector.

A minimum effective range of 80 yards was requested with a duration of fire of not less than 60 seconds, the fuel to be carried in a jettisonable trailer. The 1938 specification had called for a range of 200 to 300 yards with an endurance of 30 minutes intermittently. The Churchill Mark IV was selected for the new flame-throwing equipment as it was reasoned that a specialized flame-throwing tank would be required for use mainly against enemy strongpoints and villages or against beach defences in conjunction with other arms. Twelve pilot models were ordered in July 1942.

In August 1942 came a change in the War Office flame-thrower policy. They had come to the conclusion that there was no requirement for a tank flame-thrower, the view being that these would be vulnerable to attack in close range work, and that the flame-throwing rôle could be undertaken by the man-pack and carrier-borne flame-throwers.

Even though there was no official demand for the tank flame-thrower, the P.W.D. continued the work of research and development of their trailer type equipment, which eventually became the Crocodile, arranging trials with military units for field tests. They also demonstrated the new type of thickened flame fuel that gave an increased range and better target effect. During April 1943 official opinion changed when it was realized that there was a definite rôle for this type of weapon. This really resulted from the better results achieved with the new type of flame fuel, the performance of the equipment on the unofficial trials, and the possibility of the adaptation of this equipment to the new methods of unorthodox armoured assault weapons that were being

Churchill Oke flame-thrower as used at Dieppe. Observe fuel tank at rear and flame pipe along the side.
(Photo: Imperial War Museum)

An unusual fitting to the Churchill Crocodile was the Cullin Hedgerow device (or 'prongs') more usually found on Shermans or cruiser tanks in the 1944 period. These Crocodiles are taking part in the American attack on Brest in September 1944.
(Photo: Imperial War Museum)

Sherman Ginandit was an experimental mat-laying version of the D.D. for crossing swampy ground.
(Photo: Imperial War Museum)

Sherman Crocodile—one of four converted in Britain and used by the U.S. Army. Note armoured fuel pipe on side.
(Photo: Imperial War Museum)

evolved and developed for the 79th Armoured Division, which had been formed under Major-General Hobart for the attack on German occupied Europe.

As the P.W.D. model fulfilled the requirements of the War Office the Crocodile was now officially adopted, tests by the Ministry of Supply showing that with minor modifications the model was suitable for production. The only major change was the installation of the flame projector that was already in use with the Wasp Mk. II Flame-throwing Carrier to replace the original flame gun. In August 1943 an order was placed for 250 Crocodiles in spite of the fact that the normal troop trials had not taken place with the prototype vehicles. This was due to the urgent need to make this new equipment available for Overlord, scheduled for the following spring. By October the production of six prototypes was going ahead. It was then decided to modify the design to enable it to be fitted to the now improved Churchill Mk. VII which was just in production. The flame-throwing equipment was now to be capable of fitting by unit personnel in the field to any Mk. IV or VII Churchill. These vehicles were to be permanently fitted during production with the necessary parts for the attachment of the Crocodile parts which would come as sets for fitment in the field when required. The Churchill Mk. IV was subsequently dropped from the scheme due to the difficulties of providing a universal Crocodile for both marks, and only the Mk. VII saw service in the rôle. Due to delays in the production of the Mk. VII prototypes, the first two did not reach the troops until January 1944 when trials revealed defects in the trailer link. This was rectified and production models began to reach the troops by April 1944, only just in time for training for the Overlord (D-Day) landings. The production order for Crocodile equipment was now for 750, to which later a further 250 sets were added for India and South-East Asia. By the time the war had finished a total of 800 sets had been built. The 141st Regiment R.A.C. was the first Crocodile-equipped unit.

CHURCHILL OKE

The first flame-thrower equipment fitted to the Churchill tank, however, was an unofficial one and had no direct part in the development of Crocodile equipment. Late in 1941 the P.W.D. had developed a flame-throwing equipment for use with the Universal Carrier. Called Ronson, this was a pressure operated projector with the flame fuel tanks carried outside at the rear of the vehicle. It was proposed by Major J. M. Oke that this equipment be adapted to fit a Churchill tank. This was achieved by attaching the flame projector in a fixed elevation to the inside of the front track guard, just in front of the hull machine-gun so that it had to be aimed by manoeuvring the tank. A large jettisonable and externally mounted flame fuel tank was carried at the rear of the vehicle. Normal armament was retained. The flame projector had a range of 40 to 50 yards.

Three of these units were made by P.W.D. and adapted to the Churchill Mk. II during the summer of 1942, by-passing the official channels that included the Director of AFVs, to have them ready to take part in the Combined Operations Dieppe raid in

Above: Sherman Badger flame-thrower. Projector is arrowed. Ram Badger was similar. (Photo: Imperial War Museum)

Right: Sherman Adder flame-thrower, showing armoured flame fuel tank at rear, armoured cover over supply pipe, and projector on co-driver's hatch. This vehicle has experimental skirt armour. (Photo: Imperial War Museum)

August 1942. Used by the Canadian Calgary Regt., they were either sunk or knocked out before they could be tested in action. One, however, was later retrieved and tested by the German Army. The firm of Lagonda, who built the Ronson equipment, carried out the modification and fitting to the tanks.

THE CROCODILE DESCRIBED

The Crocodile equipment consisted of an armoured two-wheeled trailer weighing 6½ tons and containing 400 gallons of flame fuel, plus controls, and five pressure bottles containing nitrogen. Connection from trailer to the flame projector in the tank hull was through the Link, a device through which the pressurized fuel could pass. A range of 120 yards was obtainable in favourable conditions, but the generally accepted range was 80 yards. The projector could fire 80 one-second bursts or continuous fire. If the trailer was hit or damaged it could be jettisoned by a quick release device and the tank which retained its main armament (75-mm. gun and Besa MG in turret) could revert to its normal rôle of gun tank. The flame projector took the place of the hull machine-gun and was operated by the hull gunner. The trailer could also be jettisoned when the flame fuel was exhausted and a detachable towbar was fitted to each trailer so that unit transport could collect empty or discarded trailers from the battle zone and take them in for replenishment or repair. The Churchill Crocodile weighed 41·2 tons.

Experiments were carried out with tracked and mono-trailers (one-wheelers) with increased armour protection but these projects were dropped; operational use proved that the lightly armoured trailer was adequate.

SHERMAN CROCODILE

Favourably impressed with the Churchill Crocodile, HQ European Theatre of Operations (E.T.O.U.S.A.) submitted a requirement for the fitting of Crocodile equipment to the Sherman tank, and this development was undertaken by P.W.D. on their behalf. Difficulties presented themselves with this conversion, particularly in relation to the flame projector which could not be installed in the hull machine-gun position at the expense of the Browning gun. As the main armament was to be retained, it was decided to mount the flame projector on a platform to the right

of the hull gunner's escape hatch. The flame liquid was obtained through a pipe which was connected to a towed trailer and ran along the side of the tank in an armoured cover to the flame gun that was fitted in an armoured housing.

A satisfactory prototype was produced between September 1943 and April 1944 and work was begun on six production models. Though mass production of these equipments was planned, with certain parts to be manufactured in the United States, this project lapsed in August 1944 due to the lack of interest in the U.S.A. and the non-requirement for Crocodiles in theatres of war other than Europe. Only four Sherman Crocodiles were delivered to H.Q. E.T.O.U.S.A. These four were issued to a platoon of the 739th Tank Battalion (Special) (Mine Exploder) and were the only large capacity flame-throwers used by the American Forces in Europe, though American forces received occasional support from British Crocodile squadrons.

ADDER/COBRA FLAME-THROWERS

The Adder and Cobra were flame-throwing devices that could be rapidly produced and easily fitted to the vehicle by unit fitters in the field. The Adder was for fitment to the Sherman and was later designated "F.T. Transportable No. 6, Mk. I". The Cobra, formerly known as the Mamba, was for fitment to the Churchill tank. Both these equipments were to have as many interchangeable parts as possible. Priority, however, was given to the Sherman equipment due to the demand for the Sherman tank in South-East Asia. The war with Japan ended before the Adder project was completed. Adder was subsequently introduced to India for the Sherman Mks. III and V under the above designation. The equipment consisted of an armoured container fitted outside on the rear plate of the vehicle, containing one 80-gallon fuel tank, pressure bottles and control valves, etc. The flame fuel was piped from the rear through a flow pipe which was sheaved in an armoured cover that ran along the offside of the vehicle and was connected to the flame projector mounted on a turntable base plate fitted to a re-designed co-driver's hatch and protected by an armoured hatch. The projector displaced the standard periscope, but had built into it a periscope telescope mounted co-axially. A limited number of Adders saw service after the war.

Top Churchill Mk VII Crocodile of 7th Royal Tank Regiment, May 1949

Centre Churchill AVRE of 16th Assault Squadron, 42nd Armoured Regiment, Royal Engineers 1944

Bottom Sherman Crab Mk II of the 1st Lothians & Border Horse, September 1944

Bottom right Formation sign of 79th Armoured Division, carried front and rear

Martin Lee © Profile Publications Limited.

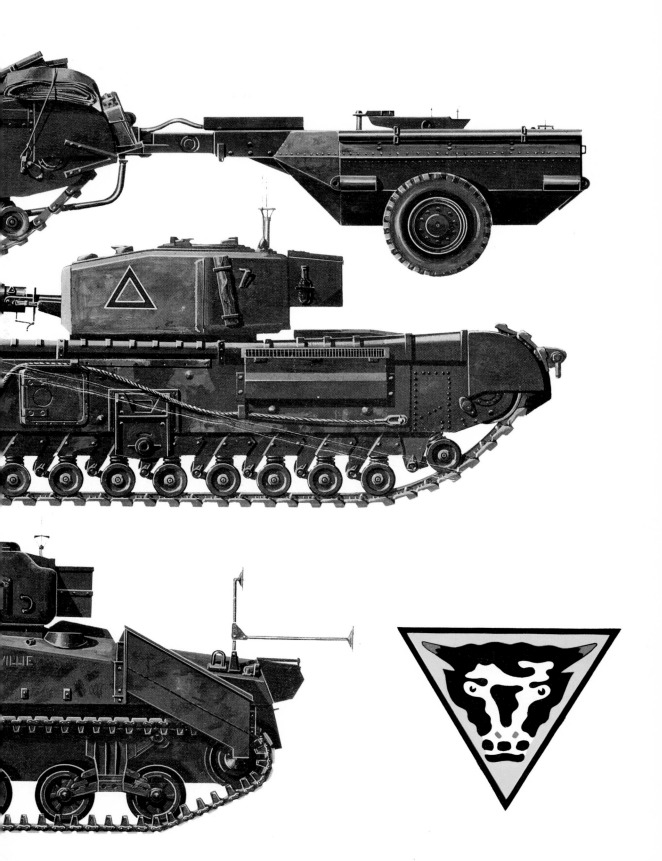

Churchill Crocodile in post-war exercises on Salisbury Plain, May 1949, passes through smoke from its own flame gun. Tank is from 7th RTR who later used Crocodiles again in Korea. The old 79th Armoured Division formation sign (the bull's head) was used post-war by the engineer assault training wing at Bovington.

SALAMANDER FLAME-THROWER

Reports from the Far East in 1943 indicated that a mechanized flame-thrower would prove of great value. However, the value of the carrier-borne flame equipment in jungle conditions was limited due to its restricted mobility and lack of overhead cover, and the trailer type flame-thrower was vulnerable in close jungle conditions. A requirement was therefore put forward by the General Staff in late 1943 for a flame-thrower unit to be mounted in a light tank. But early in 1944 this project was dropped due to this type of vehicle being insufficiently armoured against Japanese anti-tank weapons, and it was realized that a heavier vehicle was essential. To meet the extreme conditions of jungle war, it was decided after much research that the only type of device to fit these requirements adequately would be a permanently built-in flame-throwing equipment for the Churchill or Sherman tank in which the main armament was replaced by the flame gun with an all-round traverse and good elevation and depression. The fuel and pressure equipment were to be stowed internally. A range of 100 yards with a fuel capacity of 200 gallons was specified, and the tank was to be capable of wading in 6 feet of water. Various prototype models were built and there were in all eight Salamander projects designed from 1944. These are summarized below:

Salamander No. 1, P.W.D.: British Sherman, or Churchill fitted with Wasp Mk. IIA flame projector in armoured sheaf below dummy 75-mm. gun.

Salamander No. 2, Lagonda: British Sherman fitted with Wasp flame projector with extended barrel inside dummy 75-mm. gun. It could also be fitted with flame projector in gun loader's periscope.

Salamander No. 3, Lagonda: This equipment was fitted to the British Sherman and consisted of a Wasp flame projector with extended barrel inside a dummy 75-mm. gun.

Salamander No. 4, P.W.D.: Fitted to a British Sherman, this consisted of a Wasp IIA flame projector in the mantlet below a dummy gun.

Salamander No. 5, P.W.D.: Again fitted to a British Sherman, this equipment had the flame projector co-axial with the main gun.

Salamanders Nos. 6, 7 and 8 were variations of No. 5 retaining the 75-mm. gun, with the flame device mounted on the wireless base, the co-driver's seat, or on the turret side.

BADGER FLAME-THROWER

This was a development which arose from the need felt for increased armour protection for the Wasp carrier, and was developed by the Canadian Army in the United Kingdom at the request of the First Canadian Army. The basic vehicle consisted of a Ram Kangaroo, a turretless Ram tank that had been converted to a personnel carrier. The Wasp flame projector was installed in the front ball mount, replacing the machine-gun, two fuel tanks (the 40 and 60 gallon units of the Wasp Mk. II) and pressure bottles were fitted inside the vehicle. A crew of two was carried. The Badger became available in February 1945, and was used successfully by the Lake Superior Regt. (Motorized) with the 4th Canadian Armoured Brigade on several occasions.

SHERMAN BADGER

During 1947 the Canadians converted three turretless M4A2 Shermans to flame throwers for experimental and training purposes. These were also known as Badgers and were essentially similar to the Ram Badger.

Sherman with AMRCR equipment.
(Photo: Imperial War Museum)

Sherman Scorpion IV was used operationally in Italy. Note twin motors in armoured housings to drive rotor arm.
(Photo: Imperial War Museum)

Sherman Marquis. Note armoured box superstructure.
(Photo: Imperial War Museum)

Sherman Pram was an experimental prototype not chosen for production.
(Photo: Imperial War Museum)

frame, with leaf springs on each bogie to ensure that the rollers maintained constant ground contact whatever the contours. The Obstacle Assault Centre developed the AMRCR and in its No. 1 Mk. I form it was designed for attachment to the Sherman, and in No. 1 Mk. IA form it was for use with the Churchill. The AMRCR device was cumbersome and heavy, however, and it was not used operationally.

CIRD

A much more successful development was the Canadian Indestructible Roller Device (CIRD or C.I.R.D.) which, as its name implies, was of Canadian Army origin. Designed in September 1943, it consisted essentially of two heavy armoured rollers attached to projecting side arms in front of the vehicle, and the CIRD proved most effective on trials. The rollers were arranged so that when either one passed over a mine, exploding it by pressure, the blast caused the roller to jump up in an arc over the side arm so that the motion caused the spade end of the roller arm to dig into the ground. By a mechanical arrangement, plus the motion of the tank, the roller subsequently returned to its travelling position.

Two sizes of roller were put into production from several tested, these being of $15\frac{1}{2}$ and 18 inches diameter respectively. The latter was intended for the Churchill. The CIRD could be used with either the Sherman or the Churchill tank, and was put into production for both. Sherman CIRDs were intended to support Sherman Crabs (see below) in flail regiments, though they were not in fact used operationally: the CIRD was among the equipment which could be

attached to the special fittings on the side of the Churchill AVRE. Though issued, however, the CIRD does not appear to have been used in action by 79th Armoured Division. There were several experimental equipments developed which involved the use of the CIRD and one or two of these have previously been mentioned in connection with explosive mine clearing devices.

LULU

A further roller device was the Lulu, designed and developed in 1943-44. Physically it resembled the other roller devices, but this was not in fact a pressure-detonating equipment. It consisted of light wooden rollers arranged tricycle fashion, two ahead and one behind, to be pushed and trailed on light girder arms by a Sherman tank. The rollers were detectors only, each carrying electrical detector coils which signalled the presence of buried metallic objects (i.e., mines) as the rollers passed over the ground. A light and aural signal indicated the presence of a mine on equipment inside the tank, and the position was plotted so that follow-up units could uncover and render the mine safe. The Lulu was both cumbersome and fragile, however, and it was not put into production.

SCORPION

The most effective of all mine exploding devices— and the most important—was the flail in which the mine was exploded by pressure from beating the ground above it. First suggested by a South African engineer officer, Major A. S. du Toit, flails in various forms were developed for Matilda, Valentine and Grant tanks before being produced for the Sherman. In the Middle East du Toit's original ideas were developed into the Scorpion, first used at Alamein, in which a rotor arm fitted with heavy chains was driven by auxiliary engines to beat the ground immediately ahead of the tank. The rotor was carried on girder arms. In the Sherman Scorpion there were two auxiliary Dodge engines driving the rotor, these engines being mounted in armoured compartments on the hull rear. Developed in 1943, a few Sherman Scorpions were used in Italy. Most Scorpions, however, were based on the Matilda, Grant, or Valentine.

MARQUIS

The first flail tank based on the Sherman and developed in Britain was the Marquis which had its rotor arms arranged so that they could be raised hydraulically to lift the flails clear of the ground and reduce the overall length of the vehicle. In the Marquis, designed by AEC Ltd., twin Ford engines were mounted in a box-like fixed superstructure, driving the rotor by shafts and universal joints. The rotor arms were simple girder-like structures, much simpler than those used on the Scorpion. The Marquis was completed in late 1943.

CRAB

Meanwhile another development was taking place in which the rotor was driven from the tank's main engine rather than from auxiliary motors. This greatly simplified operation, and the first vehicle with this feature was the Sherman Pram Scorpion, produced in mid-1943. Here the rotor arms and flails were retained but the rotor was driven by chains from extra sprockets geared to the front sprockets of the tank. Gearing compensated for changing speeds on the sprockets as the tank was steered, so that the rotor speed stayed constant. Following the Marquis, AEC produced a vehicle with similar flailing attachments, but now with drive from the main engine.

Known as the Crab, this had shaft drive to the rotors, the shaft being driven by chains from the main drive shaft of the tank. The rotor shaft drive was taken out through the right side of the hull. Like the Marquis, the Crab had rotor arms which could be lifted hydraulically.

Of the three prototypes, Pram Scorpion, Marquis and Crab, the Crab was the most satisfactory, and this vehicle, based on the Sherman V (M4A4) was ordered on the basis of conversions from existing stocks of Shermans. Initially, 300 vehicles were ordered but the requirement was later doubled.

The Sherman Crab thus became the standard British mine clearing vehicle, and by far the simplest and most effective of all designs of this type evolved in World War II. 30th Armoured Brigade, part of 79th Armoured Division, was wholly equipped with Crabs from late 1943 onwards and took part in the Normandy landings and subsequent operations in N.W. Europe. A number of Crabs were also delivered to the U.S. Army after D-Day. The Crabs retained their main armament, so being able to defend themselves or even act as normal gun tanks if needs be. By 1945 an improved model had been developed, the Crab II, which had an automatic contouring device enabling the rotor to be kept at constant height above the ground whatever the undulations in the surface. This overcame the one failing of the original Crab, its tendency to "miss" the ground momentarily when flailing if a sudden small undulation was encountered.

An improved design, known as the Lobster, was also produced, incorporating a rotor of larger diameter and open construction based on that of the Matilda Baron, one of the earliest of the flail tank designs. It was thought that this rotor would give a longer flailing life. However, in practice the Crab was satisfactory and production of the Lobster was not proceeded with.

A number of special devices were produced for Crabs to assist in the actual process of minesweeping. These included station keeping lights on the rear of the vehicle which shone dimly to the rear so that the

View of a Sherman Crab Mark II shows the station keeping lights and the lane marking device, a hopper full of powdered chalk on each rear quarter of the vehicle.

(Photo: Imperial War Museum)

Sherman Lobster—designed to succeed the Crab but not put into production. (Photo: Imperial War Museum)

tanks of a flailing team (operating in staggered line) kept on station and in line relative to each other. To indicate the extent of "swept" lanes there was a lane marking device consisting of a hopper of powdered chalk which was allowed to trickle out on to the ground as the vehicle flailed its way forward. Later a more sophisticated lane marking device was used (the Whyman) which consisted of flagged pickets "fired" into the ground at intervals and controlled by the vehicle commander. Fitted in the tank was a "yardometer" for measuring precisely the distance covered while flailing, and gyro and magnetic compasses for following pre-arranged flailing lanes and directions.

Sherman Crab Mark I in Normandy with the flail arms raised for road travelling. Note station keeping lights which showed to the rear. (Photo: Imperial War Museum)

Bridging Expedients

Experiments with bridges or ramps to be carried by tanks were first undertaken during the latter part of World War 1 when trials took place with a Mark V** tank carrying a girder structure mounted on its nose which could be laid to span a 20-ft. gap. Further trials of bridging devices were made in the mid-1920s, the carrying vehicle being a Dragon Mk. I (gun towing vehicle) with a 30-ft. bridge mounted on its modified structure. This bridge was launched by a pulley system. The Vickers Medium Tank Mk. II was also adapted, and this version carried two 18-ft. ramps on either side of the hull, these being hinged and folded back and supported by brackets fixed on the hull side. When required the ramps were man-handled into position. Interest in self-propelled bridging equipment then seems to have waned until the outbreak of World War 2.

As reports had indicated that the Germans had constructed a large number of wide and deep anti-tank obstacles in depth on their borders, work was begun in 1940 on various devices that would enable tanks to breach these obstacles. Among the various devices developed were the following:

ROLLER FASCINE

This consisted of two cable drums 6 ft. 6 in. in diameter running on an axle to which was attached a pair of short ramps. Attached to the front of the tanks by the ramps, the roller fascine was pushed to the ditch to be crossed. A quick release hook enabled the fascine to be dropped into the ditch and so form a causeway for tanks up to 25 tons, the ramps enabling the vehicles to climb up on and over the drums.

A second pilot model of this equipment was developed with slightly longer ramps, which could be folded for towing. This model was put into limited production.

MOBILE BRIDGE

This was a further development and consisted of a light bridge 25 ft. long mounted on a pair of cable drums. This again was pushed in front of the tank to the gap to be crossed and released into it, thus spanning the gap.

BRIDGE, SELF-PROPELLED (TRACK)

Projected in 1940, this tracked bridge was constructed on a Dragon Mark IV (gun towing vehicle) that had been fitted with a top platform and rear trailing ramps. The initial object of this device was that the vehicle would drive up to a vertical object and allow other vehicles to climb it and so surmount the obstacle. In addition the Dragon bridge was capable of performing the function of a large fascine by ditching itself in a gap and allowing following vehicles to cross on its back. As the possibility was foreseen of using this type of device as a means of surmounting the special steel rail obstacles of the Siegfried Line, a pair of ramps 23 ft. long were attached to the front of the Dragon; these could be launched mechanically. It was intended that the vehicle would approach the sloping steel rails and project the front ramps over the top of the obstacle, thus enabling following vehicles to cross over its body.

Another tracked mobile bridge that was built and tested in 1941 was 30 ft. long and was based on Loyd Carrier components. It was intended to serve as a mobile bridge for tanks up to 25 tons and for wheeled vehicles by ditching in large gaps and allowing the

Sherman Fascine Carriers of 2nd New Zealand Division in Italy— Senio, April 1945. They were also used by 79th Armoured Division in N.W. Europe. (Photo: Imperial War Museum)

Roller fascine being crossed by a Light Tank Mark VIB.
(Photo: Imperial War Museum)

Churchill ARK Mark I in position on one of the sea walls built on the 79th Armoured Division training area at Orford. These were exact reproductions of parts of the German anti-invasion defences.
(Photo: Imperial War Museum)

Above: *Churchill ARK Mark II, Italian Pattern.*
(Photo: Imperial War Museum)

Above: *Churchill AVRE (left) pushing Mobile Dalton Bridge with Churchill ARK as main carrier.*
(Photo: Imperial War Museum)

Left, Above: *Churchill ARK Mark II, U.K. Pattern with ramps raised.*
(Photo: Imperial War Museum)

Bottom right: *Sherman Octopus with special lattice type ramps. Another type had ramps made from girder sections.*
(Photo: Imperial War Museum)

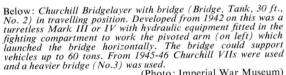

Below: *Churchill Bridgelayer with bridge (Bridge, Tank, 30 ft., No. 2) in travelling position. Developed from 1942 on this was a turretless Mark III or IV with hydraulic equipment fitted in the fighting compartment to work the pivoted arm (on left) which launched the bridge horizontally. The bridge could support vehicles up to 60 tons. From 1945-46 Churchill VIIs were used and a heavier bridge (No.3) was used.*
(Photo: Imperial War Museum)

Below: *Mobile Bridge consisting of a 25 ft. light bridge mounted on drums.*
(Photo: Imperial War Museum)

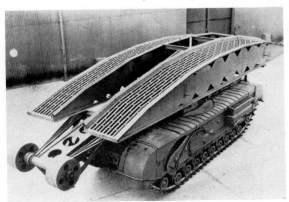

following vehicles to cross on the deckway built on its chassis.

Though much valuable experience was gained with these early devices they did not go into production, the course of the war in 1940 removing much of the object of this type of equipment.

ARK MK. I

It was not until after the Dieppe raid of 1942 that it was again realized that there was a requirement for an armoured bridge-carrying vehicle able to lay ramps across sea walls or span defence ditches for the assault on German-occupied Europe.

Experiments by the 79th Armoured Division during late 1943 led to the construction of a pilot model of such a device in January 1944. Such was the promise shown by the pilot model that requirements were put forward for 50 similar vehicles, arrangements being made in February 1944 for the firm of Messrs. R. Boby of Bury St. Edmunds to prepare a production design and two prototype vehicles. Design work was completed two weeks later and the production of the superstructure was undertaken by Messrs. T. C. Jones of Shepherd's Bush. The fitting of the superstructure on the Churchill hulls was shared by R.E.M.E. and M.G. Car Co. Ltd. The hulls used for these conversions were Churchills III and IV that had originally been earmarked for conversion to Canal Defence Lights.

This vehicle, known as the ARK (Armoured Ramp Carrier), consisted of a turretless Churchill tank with a 14 mm. B.P. blanking plate welded over the turret aperture. The plate incorporated a double flap hatch. On top of the hull was mounted a raised superstructure providing two timbered trackways along the length of the tank, one immediately above each track. Hinged to the front transom were two ramps 3 ft. 5¼ in. long, each in line with either trackway, the front ends of these ramps on the tracks above the front idler wheels. Two 5 ft. 8 in. long ramps were also hinged to the rear transom so that when the vehicle was on level ground they hung vertically with their ends clear of the ground.

The ARK was intended to be driven up against a vertical wall with its nose held against it as high as possible, so that following vehicles could then climb up its rear ramps on to the trackway, and then on to and over the wall. Alternatively, the vehicle could be driven into a ditch so that other tanks could be driven over it.

ARK MK. II

In July 1944 modifications were made to an ARK by the 79th Armoured Division and as a result of the successful trials of this modified vehicle arrangements were made for the production of 50 sets of parts for converting all existing ARKs to the Mark II pattern.

This consisted of various alterations to the trackway superstructure and included the widening of the left-hand trackway from 2 ft. to 4 ft.; the right-hand trackway remained 2 ft. wide. Hinged to the front transoms were two short 3 ft. 7½ in. ramps, in line with each runway, to which in turn were hinged two

ramps each 12 ft. 6 in. long. Two ramps, each 12 ft. 6 in. long were hinged to the rear end of the runway, all the ramps corresponding in width to the runways to which they were linked. The construction of the ramps was similar to that of the runway except that in the case of the wide left-hand ramps, where three longitudinals were provided to accommodate the increased width.

The ramps were initially raised from the stowed position and erected with the aid of a second vehicle and crane. In the erected position each rear ramp was supported by a ¾-in. diameter tie rod with eyes at both ends, connected to 2-in. diameter pins welded on the outside near end of the ramp. The other ends of the tie rods were held by plugs which formed the tongues of the quick release locks welded to the vehicle. The plugs could be withdrawn simultaneously by means of a quick release assembly operated from within the vehicle.

To support the front ramps in the erected position a 12 ft. long kingpost was fitted, and this was mounted on a pin passing through the existing front tow eye and an additional similar eye, welded on the nose plate adjacent to it. Welded at the upper end of the kingpost were brackets to which were shackled two 8 ft. long, ⅝ in. diameter steel hawsers secured by shackles to brackets welded to the inside of the forward end of each front ramp. To secure the front ramps in the erected position a 31 ft. long, ⅝ in. diameter steel hawser with a length of chain shackled to it at each end, was passed round a 5-ton snatch block mounted at the upper end of the kingpost. One of the chains was passed through a 'U' bracket welded near the centre of the second transom from the front of the runway, and secured by a shackle. The other was held by a Covenanter quick release hook mounted centrally on the roof plate at the rear. The quick release hook was operated by a Bowden cable mechanism from within the vehicle.

The turret aperture in the hull roof was covered by a 14 mm. thick blanking plate welded in position. This plate incorporated a double flap hatch cover giving access to the centre compartment. A rectangular conning tower was welded into position around the hatch and half the left-hand runway was removable to give access to the engine and transmission compartments. Some vehicles were fitted with independent release gear for each rear ramp. A wireless No. 19 set was fitted in the right-hand pannier aft of the side door. Basic vehicles used for the ARK II conversions were Churchills III and IV. Crew was four, and weight 38 tons 10 cwt. Trials were later carried out using 20 ft. long ramps.

ARK MK. II (ITALIAN PATTERN)

During November and December 1944 a limited number of Churchill tanks were converted to ARKs by the workshops of the Eighth Army in Italy. These became known as ARK II Italian pattern and differed from the ARK built in the United Kingdom by the lack of wooden trackways, the vehicles' own tracks serving as trackways, crossing vehicles making direct contact with the tracks and roofplates. The gap between the front of the vehicle and the front ramps was covered by a platform extension instead

Above: *Churchill Great Eastern Ramp—rear view with rear ramp in raised travelling position. Note magazine for rockets stowed at the rear.* (Photo: Imperial War Museum)

Left: *Sherman ARK II with twin kingpost at the front and track fitted with Platypus grousers.* (Photo: Imperial War Museum)

of articulated short ramps as on the U.K. pattern. The front and rear ramps were the standard U.S. pattern bridging ramps modified for this purpose and were interchangeable. Two types of ramps were used: the M.1 which was 15 ft. long and 2 ft. 9 in. wide, and the M.2, 12 ft. 3½ long and 3 ft. 9½ in. wide. Two kingposts, one at either end, supported the ramps in the raised position and the quick release mechanism was mounted on the turret blanking plate which was circular in shape. The external exhaust system was modified and flash eliminators were fitted. A wireless No. 19 set was fitted in the left-hand pannier aft of the side door. Weight of this version was 39 tons and a crew of four was carried.

OCTOPUS

Based on the Churchill IV this version was similar to the ARK II Italian pattern but each ramp consisted of three hinged sections that could be folded for better stowage on top of the ARK.

SHERMAN ARK II

Also converted by the Eighth Army workshops were a small number of Sherman tanks, similar in construction to the ARK II U.K. pattern, having a trackway built on a raised superstructure. Variations existed in the type of ramp used and the method of retaining them in the raised position.

One model was fitted with specially constructed ramps with a twin kingpost at the front and a single kingpost at the rear. An Octopus version also existed.

CHURCHILL GE RAMP (GREAT EASTERN)

Evolved for wall and ditch crossing in assault, trials of this device took place in May 1944, the basic vehicle being a Churchill I. As these trials proved successful a further ten prototypes were made, this time the basic vehicles being Churchill IVs with Churchill VII suspension.

During 1945 these ten vehicles were sent to 21 Army Group for user trials, but due to the lack of requirements for this type of device, the Great Eastern project was dropped.

The GE Ramp was basically similar to the ARK and consisted of a 27 ft. long superstructure built on to a turretless Churchill IV. Hinged to and folded back on to the superstructure was a 5-ton, 25 ft. long ramp, which was raised and propelled into position by two groups of 3-in. electrically fired rockets that were fitted to the ramp's free ends. Also fitted were two concertina shock absorber boxes to absorb the impact of the falling ramps. The rear 13-ft. ramp of 2 tons was set into the dropping position and released by means of electrically operated blow-out pins. Following vehicles could then mount the rear ramp and cross the operating vehicle. Weight was 46 tons. Overall length of bridge erected with end of bridge and tail ramp resting on ground was 60 ft. 5 in.

LAKEMAN ARK (GUN CHURCHILL)

Evolved in 1944 for wall crossing, this experimental device consisted of a combat Churchill with a sloping superstructure built on its hull. Attached to the rear of the superstructure which sloped down to the back of the vehicle was a hinged ramp. The vehicle approached its position in front of the wall, dropped its ramp, and the following vehicles climbed on to the ramp, crossed the built-up superstructure and on to the wall.

CHURCHILL HUDNOTT ARK

This was another device which incorporated rocket operating ramps. The ramps were mounted one on top of the other, with guide ways along the side, through which the ramps could be pulled by rockets. This existed as a project model only.

CHURCHILL WOODLARK

This consisted of a turretless Churchill tank upon which was mounted a girder superstructure and trackway similar to the ARKs. On top of the trackway were four folded ramps, each ramp being hinged in three places. The object of the hinging was to allow the ramps to articulate in their working position and follow the contours of the obstacle. The ramps were operated by rockets placed near the main hinges and at the end of the top sections. A set of quick burning rockets were also placed in each ramp assembly so that the shock of impact would be reduced as the ramps were falling.

CHURCHILL BRIDGELAYER (BRIDGE, TANK, 30 Ft., No. 2)

Evolved for ditch crossing in assault during 1942, this device consisted of a 30 ft. bridge carried on top of a turretless Churchill. When required the 4·8-ton bridge was lifted hydraulically on a pivot arm and placed forward across the gap to be bridged. The tank could also recover its bridge by the same process. The bridge was designed to carry a 60-ton tracked vehicle or Class 40 wheeled vehicles, and consisted of two tracks of welded construction joined together by cross pieces. The laying mechanism was operated by the driver. Basic vehicles used were Churchills III and IV. Crew was two men only, a driver and commander, and a special cupola was provided for the commander which was fitted with doors to provide entry into the tank. Weight of complete vehicle and device was 40·8 tons.

SKID BAILEY

Used in operations in Europe, this device consisted of a Bailey Bridge of certain length (depending on gap to be bridged) assembled on skids near the site of operations. When erected the bridge was pushed or skidded (hence its name) by one or two Churchill AVREs fitted with nose attachments. As the bridge was built longer than the gap to be bridged, the gap was spanned by the main section of the bridge before the point of balance was reached. Typical use was for bridging large craters in roads under fire.

CHURCHILL MOBILE BAILEY

This equipment was developed in the United Kingdom in 1943 and first used operationally in Italy in April 1945 at the crossing of the River Senio. The Bailey Mobile Bridge was designed to be pushed as a complete class 40 bridge to a 70 or 80 ft. wide gap, where it could be launched and opened to traffic within minutes. It was assembled a considerable distance from the site to be bridged to give protection to the bridge-building R.E. Unit. The bridge consisted of 150-ft. span of Bailey Bridge fitted with 10-ft. hinged ramps at either end. When erected the centre of the bridge was mounted on two Orolo caterpillar tracks, which were tracked rollers but provided no power. An early type of this bridge used a turretless Churchill as the carrying vehicle instead of caterpillar units. The tail end of the bridge was connected to the nose of a Churchill AVRE by a pusher frame. The assembled bridge was pushed up to and over the gap until the Orolo tracks had reached the edge and the main span of 90 ft. of bridging protruding in front of these tracks was placed across the gap, the pusher

tank then withdrew, dropping the hinged ramp. An additional AVRE towed from the front on the approach to the site.

CHURCHILL MOBILE BROWN BRIDGE

Developed by Captain B. S. Brown, Royal Canadian Engineers, of the Eighth Army in Italy, this bridge was based on an early improvisation that had been used for the assault crossing of the River Rapido in May 1944. The bridge consisted of 140 ft. of Bailey Bridge transported by two Churchill tanks, one of which had its turret removed. This, the carrier tank, was positioned slightly in front of the point of balance of the bridge taking the bulk of the load, this position being maintained while in transit. Fitted to the top of the carrier tank were a series of launching rollers upon which lay the bridge. The pusher tank fitted with attachments for holding and releasing the bridge was positioned below the rear transom where a skeleton 30-ft. tail was attached. This false tail was designed to act as a counter weight.

To launch the bridge, the vehicles carrying the bridge advanced towards the 80-ft. gap to be spanned. The carrier tank halted when the edge of the gap was reached, and the pusher tank continued to advance, and in doing so pushed the bridge over the rollers that were fitted on the carrier tank. As the pusher tank closed up to the carrier tank, the gap was spanned and the pusher tank and the skeleton tail was then disengaged from the bridge and reversed away, being in turn followed by the carrier tank, the bridge sliding down the carrier rollers as it moved back.

CHURCHILL MOBILE DALTON BRIDGE

This device was developed by Major T. R. Dalton, R.E., as an improvement on the Brown Bridge but was not used operationally. The 140 ft. of Bailey Bridge was carried on two tanks. The carrier tank, a Churchill ARK, was fitted with four transoms clamped laterally across the top deck, upon which were mounted rocking rollers and guide rollers. The ARK was positioned a little forward of mid-point of the bridge to take about two-thirds of the total load, this portion of the bridge resting on the rollers. The pusher tank, a Churchill AVRE, was fitted with two special frames upon which were mounted winches. These were connected by tackle to the last trunnion of the bridge. The pusher frames were bolted to existing fittings at each side of the tank, and were arranged to form a tray, the horizontal members of which supported the bridge. Also attached to the rear of the bridge was a skeleton tail to act as a counter weight.

To launch the bridge, the two vehicles carrying the bridge advanced towards the site, and the carrying tank halted at the edge of the gap, while the pusher tank continued to move forward. In doing so, it pushed the bridge over the stationary carrier rollers until the nose of the bridge had reached the far side. The nose of the bridge was then lowered to the ground by means of the winches on the pusher tank, which then disengaged by blowing with a small charge the links connecting the winch cables to the bridge. This vehicle then withdrew, followed by the carrier tank which backed out from under the bridge, lowering it to the ground as it passed from underneath.

Sherman Crib Carrier. Note how platform is held on with hawsers; and the traversed turret.
(Photo: Imperial War Museum)

Sherman Kangaroo APC (converted M4A2) in Italy, April 1945.
(Photo: Imperial War Museum)

Miscellaneous Types

C.D.L. (CANAL DEFENCE LIGHTS)

A few Churchills and at least one Sherman tank were fitted with a specially designed armoured turret housing a searchlight. It was originally planned to convert numbers of Churchill tanks to CDL vehicles, but this was cancelled and the hulls that had been earmarked for this conversion were subsequently converted to Arks. Most CDL conversions involved Matildas or Grants.

CHURCHILL AND SHERMAN WITH ARMOURED SLEDGES

This was an experimental project for transporting assault troops in armoured one-man sledges towed behind a Churchill or Sherman tank in units of four.

SHERMAN TANKDOZER

This was the British term for the normal M1 or M1A1 dozer blade fitted to the standard combat vehicle. Shermans so fitted were allocated to most Sherman regiments for clearing rubble, filling craters, or dozing emplacements.

SHERMAN FASCINE CARRIER

A limited number of turretless Shermans were fitted with a rail frame for the carriage of brushwood fascines as an aid to wall or ditch crossing. A few of these Sherman Fascine Carriers were used by 79th Armoured Division in N.W. Europe, 1944-45, on those occasions when there was a big requirement for fascines—for instance when filling in anti-tank ditches. The Sherman Fascine Carrier could hold two or three fascines on its built-up frame carrying structure.

SHERMAN CRIB CARRIER

This vehicle had a platform mounted on the front of the tank, the turret being traversed aft. A wooden crib was carried on the platform and could be dropped in a similar manner to a fascine. So far as is known, this device was experimental only and no record has been traced of the Sherman Crib Carrier being used in action. It was designed, however, to make any variant of a Sherman capable of carrying a crib, for the platform could be discarded after the crib was dropped and the tank could revert to its normal fighting rôle.

SHERMAN KANGAROO

The Sherman Kangaroo (armoured personnel carrier) was unique to the Eighth Army in Italy only. Kangaroos, based on old M7 Priests and Ram tanks, had been developed by 21 Army Group in France in the summer of 1944. This led to the adoption of a similar idea in Eighth Army, again utilizing old Priests. There were no Rams in Italy, however, so the Priest Kangaroos were supplemented by converting old "war weary" Shermans of the diesel-engined M4A2 model, one of the major types used by the British armoured divisions in Italy. To save time, the Kangaroo conversions were carried out by field workshops and 75 Sherman IIIs (M4A2) (plus 102 Priests) were so altered between October 1944 and April 1945. Turret and main armament of the Sherman was removed and the radio was re-sited in the sponson. Ten men and a crew of two could be carried. The first 25 Sherman Kangaroos were ready in nine days. 9th Armoured Brigade Workshops and 664 and 684 Tank Troop Workshops, plus a South African field workshop, carried out most of the conversion work, all in the Ancona area.

SHERMAN OP

The OP version of the Sherman was a British conversion to make the vehicle suitable for the command rôle, either for armoured unit commanders or for self-propelled artillery units. Various models were used, and the main physical features were not altered externally. The main armament was, however, removed and a dummy gun barrel was fixed in the original mantlet. This was to conceal the vehicle's purpose from the enemy for it retained the outward appearance of a gun tank. The co-axial and hull machine-guns were, however, retained. Inside the turret was fitted a map table, lockers, and extra wireless equipment according to the rôle in which the vehicle was employed.

A.F.V. Series Editor: DUNCAN CROW

AVRE of 79th Armoured Division in the attack on Le Havre, September 1944.

The 79th Armoured Division
by Nigel Duncan

THE 79th Armoured Division was a unique formation. It was the largest armoured formation in 21 Army Group and while it never fought on its own it was the only armoured formation whose units fought with every brigade, division, and corps in both the British and Canadian armies in France and North-West Europe from June 1944 onwards. Commanders of all formations paid tribute to the value of the specialised equipment handled by the division and Field Marshal Viscount Montgomery has stated "in any future Expeditionary Force one such formation should be included directly under command."

The success of the division was primarily due to one man, its commander Major-General Sir Percy Hobart who transferred to the Royal Tank Corps in 1923 and subsequently raised from nothing no less than four armoured formations all of which he brought to a high state of training: he was responsible for the 1st Tank Brigade, the 7th Armoured Division in Egypt, from command of which he was removed in the desert in 1940—unjustly. He then raised and trained the 11th

Armoured Division and finally the 79th where he was responsible for the evolution of new machines and original techniques to meet specialised conditions. He was utterly fearless, a devoted patriot and a man of high principles with a great sense of urgency. His divisions admired him, respected him, and either feared or loved him. He was a constant inspiration, and irritation, to all his subordinates; a fount of new ideas and new thoughts and a leader who drove those under him as fast and furiously as he drove himself.

The 79th Armoured Division formed as a normal armoured formation at Leeds in September 1942. Everything was short from experienced officers and men to the normal housekeeping necessities, tables and beds and cooking materials, to say nothing of armoured equipment. Somehow or other these difficulties were overcome, but just as the division was getting into its stride its rôle was abruptly changed.

By 1943 American opinion had hardened in favour of a direct blow against Germany through France and Belgium as the only certain method of ending the war.

Major-General Sir Percy Hobart, K.B.E., C.B., D.S.O., M.C., commander of the 79th Armoured Division, in the uniform of a Colonel-Commandant of the Royal Tank Regiment.

Dieppe—the key to invasion. The raid on August 19, 1942 was carried out by 2nd Canadian Infantry Division with attached troops including the Calgary Tank Regiment equipped with Churchills. Note exhaust extensions for deep wading.

Valentine DD tank afloat on Fritton Decoy.   (Imperial War Museum)

Successful though the Italian campaign might be, the under-belly of the Axis held no attraction for the United States who were determined to invade Europe across the Channel in 1944. Agreement on this point was reached between the Allies—the only problem was to put it into execution. The direct assault on a fortified coast held by the enemy was a formidable task, the nature of which had been underlined by the alarming experiences of the raid on Dieppe in 1942. Speed in the penetration of the enemy defences was essential, and speed in the subsequent build-up following the initial assault even more vital. Translated into 1944 the problem was even more acute for enemy defences, obstacles above and below the tide-mark, gun emplacements and mine-fields, increased day-by-day as the Germans strove to make good the deficiencies in the West Wall which had been disclosed by a recent survey. With every twenty-four hours that passed the task of the attackers became more formidable.

This defensive crust could only be penetrated by armoured machines specially constructed to deal with this particular problem. There would never be enough of this specialised armour to meet requirements: it would always be in short supply like landing craft. Thus, if the butter was to be spread evenly over the bread, some form of centralised control was plainly necessary.

To meet this problem the CIGS charged the Commander of the 79th Armoured Division with the evolution, development, training and operational control of the specialized armour needed by the invading troops to land successfully in face of enemy opposition.

THE COMPOSITION OF THE DIVISION
General Hobart had as part of the original 79th Armoured Division, 27 Armoured Brigade. This stayed with him and was the nucleus of the formation in its new rôle. The Assault Brigade Royal Engineers called into being as a result of the Dieppe lessons joined the division in the summer of 1943. 35 Tank Brigade, which had been trained to handle CDL tanks which carried armoured searchlights, also came under command in the summer of 1943, but was replaced by 1st Tank Brigade, also in the CDL rôle, in March 1944. In November 1943 30 Armoured Brigade joined the division specifically for the task of mine-sweeping.

THE AVAILABLE MATERIAL
Specialized armour had been developed to some extent during and immediately after the First World War. At Cambrai tanks had carried fascines to fill up trenches too wide and deep for other tanks to cross without assistance. A tank had been adapted to carry a bridge which could be dropped under fire to span a gap of twenty feet, while rollers slung from booms projecting

Valentine DD at Stokes Bay. The air pillars and side struts can be seen.
(RAC Tank Musuem)

slender nucleus of thought on the subject of specialized armour which had been reinforced by work on the subject carried out by DDSD (AFV) in the War Office from 1937 onwards, comprising both theoretical studies and practical experiments, which proved of considerable value although they were not originally conceived with the 79th Armoured Division problems in view.

DD TANKS (DUPLEX DRIVE)

Mr Nicholas Straussler, who was responsible for the design of the Straussler armoured car which had been tested for acceptance before the war, had invented a means of making a conventional tank swim. He reinforced the track guards and erected on them a screen made of canvas. This was reinforced by horizontal rails and locked into place by mechanical struts. The screen was raised by air pillars, tubes whose bases, secured to the track guard, carried a high pressure air line which caused them to straighten and so lift up the upper rail of the screen. The purpose of the screen was to displace enough water to give the tank buoyancy and so make it swim. Propulsion was effected by steerable propellors driven off the the tank's gearbox which gave a sea speed of four knots. The device was seaworthy up to seas of force 5 and its great advantage was that the swimming tank landed as a fully operational battle tank and not an under-armoured and under-gunned machine whose buoyancy was only achieved at the cost of all its fighting qualities. For the first time assaulting infantry could count on immediate armour support, as or before they landed on hostile shores, in the fire fight for superiority at the water's edge.

beyond the front of the tracks had served to detonate mines which never became anything like the menace they were in World War II*. There was therefore a

*This tank, a Mark V** which was known as the R.E. Tank, could also carry out demolitions under fire. It was in fact, the prototype of the AVRE and was developed by the experimental establishment at Christchurch, commanded by Major Martel. —Editor.

Sherman DD II. View from turret looking forward to erected screen.
(Imperial War Museum)

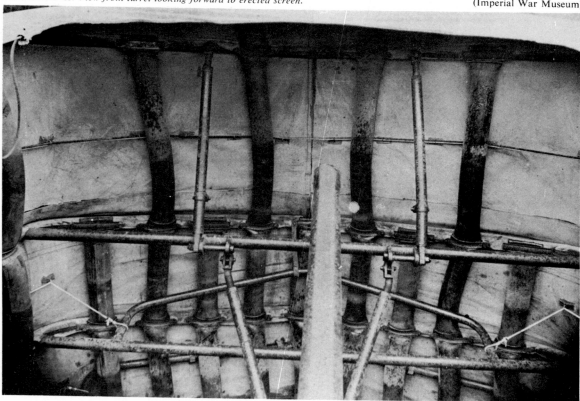

Sherman DD II showing twin propellors and the apron at the top of the screen, which could be raised on touching down to avoid being "pooped" during the fire fight to gain supremacy on the beach.
(RAC Tank Museum)

Sherman III AY, DD III, was U.S.-built model of the DD tank based on the British design and delivered to the British in late 1945. This model had HVSS and the 76-mm. gun; it was used by the British Army post-war.
(Imperial War Museum)

Sherman DD III tank leaving the ramp of an LCT. This is a post-war photograph of a late type LCT with new pattern of doors.

THE CDL (CANAL DEFENCE LIGHT) TANK

Night operations have always offered the enterprising commander great prizes but to achieve them a very high standard of training is required to compensate for darkness. The rights of the Thoren light, a particularly brilliant searchlight, were acquired before the war and this eventually appeared in Service form as the CDL tank. Originally the searchlight was installed in a special turret which replaced the 2-pdr gun version on the Matilda tank. An additional dynamo provided the necessary current for the light which occupied half the turret. The operator in the other half could maintain the light and could control its elevation and direction by operating hand wheel controls. The light was so arranged that its rays passed through a 2-in.

vertical slit in the armour of the searchlight compartment. An armoured shutter moved by power could open and close this slit and so give a "flicker" effect which made accurate aiming at the source of light a matter of some difficulty. Originally it was hoped to blind the enemy by making his eyes continually adapt themselves to alternate light and darkness but the differing rate of nigrescence of the human eye made this impossible. The device was rightly regarded as Most Secret, but in the hope of using it in a worthwhile operation it was never deployed for action, although a brigade in the U.K. and a regiment in the Middle East were equipped and trained in its use. It was eventually decided to use it to help the Canadians in their break-out from Caen. Ironically enough it proved impossible to move 1st Tank Brigade up in time to take part in the operation.

Sherman DD afloat in the Solent.

(RAC Tank Museum)

MINESWEEPING

Innumerable experiments had been carried out with every type of minesweeping roller, plain, spiked and jagged. They all suffered from one defect; they were liable to bridge the mine by consolidating ground on either side of it thereby preventing the roller from making contact with the mine. To overcome this the Middle East devised the Scorpion. Originally this was a Matilda tank with a box turret on it and no gun. Two booms projected in front of the tank carrying a drum or roller to which lengths of chain or wire rope were attached. The chains reached to about four inches below ground level. The roller could be revolved by an auxiliary engine, mounted behind the turret and operating the drum by a shaft running up one of the

booms. The booms were not adjustable for height but on level ground they ploughed up the ground to a depth of three or four inches and detonated any mine that they struck. Flailing speed was slow—1 to 1½ m.p.h.—and the machines were only used singly, making a track about 8–9 feet wide.

Every available tank gun was wanted in the assault and the 79th Armoured Division's minesweeping tank was the Crab. This used the roller and chains of the Scorpion but the drive to the roller came from the main engine and the tank gun was retained. When the tank was not flailing it could be handled as a normal gun tank and could therefore support other Crabs in the hazardous and dangerous task of sweeping. The speed was the same—about 1¼ m.p.h.—and the dust

The DD tanks debut in action. A Royal Navy LCT(4) heaves to in order to launch its load of Sherman DD tanks for the assault landing on the Normandy beaches in the early morning of June 6, 1944. The craft's ramp is already lowered and the first tank is about to enter the water. In the background LCAs from the infantry landing ships are forming up for the run in to the beaches.

(Imperial War Museum)

Sherman DD with canvas float screen folded. When the tank landed it was a fully operational battle tank. (Imperial War Museum)

"For the first time assaulting infantry could count on immediate armour support." DD tanks with screens folded in close support fighting. (Imperial War Museum)

The R.E. Tank, 1919, the prototype of the AVRE, laying a 21 foot bridge.

attracted hostile fire. Teller mines could be detonated to a depth of 4–5 inches, each mine accounting for one chain. Provided that the angle of attack was coincident with the angles between mines a Crab could explode up to 12 or 14 mines before having to re-dress the roller with new chains.

THE ARMOURED VEHICLE ROYAL ENGINEERS (AVRE)

The need for an assault vehicle which could be handled by Royal Engineers had been brought out by experiences at Dieppe. The AVRE was a Churchill Mark IV with a spigot mortar in place of the main armament. This fired a demolition projectile to a range of about 90 yards. Fittings were devised which allowed the AVRE to carry a fascine, or a 20-ft. assault bridge; either of these could be dropped from inside the tank. Racks were provided for the carriage of explosive charges specially shaped for maximum effect against concrete or armour plate. A frame of these charges could be carried in front of the AVRE and placed in position against an obstacle without the need to expose any of the crew. The AVRE could also push a Snake— a 4-in. iron tube filled with explosive that could be assembled in lengths up to 400 ft. With a special head to prevent it digging into the ground, this could be pushed across an enemy minefield and then detonated, when the blast was supposed to explode any mines either side of the Snake to a width of 16 ft. A variation was the Ark; also on a Churchill IV chassis this was a deturreted tank with runways over its own tracks. It could be driven into a gap, let down ramps which it carried, and other tanks could then drive over its trackways.

FLAMETHROWERS (CROCODILES)

Much research work on flame installations had been carried out by the Petroleum Warfare Board. Urged on by General Hobart a tank flamethrower was designed and tested and a satisfactory fuel was invented. This required a multitude of experiments to devise the gun, to determine the best methods of propelling and igniting the fuel which must have enough consistency to obtain the operational range and the requisite intensity of burning on reaching the target. Neither range nor flame present any problem by themselves: the combination is something that would drive a computer demented and this problem was solved before they were even invented.

The Crocodile flame gun had an operational range of 90 yd. and was installed in place of the bow gun in a Churchill VII. The tank towed a trailer with 400 gallons of fuel and nitrogen bottles to provide the necessary propulsive power for the fuel. The gas under high pressure was apt to leak and it was therefore essential not to pressure up too soon before an action if effective flame fire was to be available.

The original flame regiment, 141 R.A.C. (the Buffs) was not part of 79th Armoured Division but came under command in France when the armoured brigade of which it formed part found difficulty in arranging its operational deployment. It was later joined by the 1st Fife and Forfar Yeomanry, and the 7th R.T.R.

FORMATIONS AND TASKS

With this assault equipment that was or would shortly be available, the division faced the next problem of deciding who should handle what; to evolve the most economical and effective method of using these

AVRE with Small Box Girder bridge (SBG) mounted ready to drop over gap. Note similarity to R.E. tank carrying out similar task.
(RAC Tank Museum)

Churchill AVRE with elevatable Goat for placing explosive charges on high obstacles.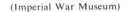(Imperial War Museum)

Churchill AVRE was a Churchill IV with a spigot mortar in place of the main armament. (Imperial War Museum)

specialist devices, to train units and formations within the division to handle them, and to educate commanders outside the formation who would have these machines operating in their support in the way that they should be handled and what they could and could not do.

27 Armoured Brigade formed part of the division before it was allotted its special rôle: they stayed with it and were selected to man and operate the DD tanks.

This involved the mastery of a new enemy—the sea, and then the actual assault on the beach against static enemy gun positions and defences, and after that the advance inland as a normal armoured brigade to make good as much ground as possible. This was a formidable task, studied in detail as far as land operations were concerned, but nothing could then be done at sea because the DD tanks were not yet available.

5, 6, and 42 Assault Regiments Royal Engineers

Churchill AVRE with Goat Mark III equipment for placing explosive charges against obstacles. The tank pushed the frame up against the obstacle where it was automatically released in a vertical position. The tank then backed off and the charges were fired either electrically or by pull igniter. (Imperial War Museum)

Front view of Churchill AVRE with fascine mounted.

140

Churchill AVRE with SBG bridge, three-quarter rear view. Churchill AVRE on right.

(Imperial War Museum)

formed the 1st Assault Brigade Royal Engineers and commenced their training in May 1943. They had a difficult rôle because they had to learn to handle their special equipment behind armour, to accustom themselves to working on wireless orders in conjunction with other units, and to change many of the techniques that they had learned as normal Sappers.

R.E.M.E. workshops began to reach the division early in 1943. They were concerned with maintaining the tanks and vehicles already on charge but even more

with the modifications, inventions and ideas which flowed and eddied within the formation in a never-ending stream. Because the task set was more difficult and more complex than anything that had ever been previously undertaken suggestions on procedure and equipment were canvassed throughout the formation. From trooper to brigadier anyone's ideas were considered, examined in minute detail from every angle, and if they made sense were embodied as standard procedure. The whole formation became one vast

Carpet-Layer (Bobbin) Mark II showing carpet on ground and the wire-cutting blades on the edge of the drum. This was one of the devices for facilitating the passage of troops, AFVs, and transport over boggy ground and barbed wire obstacles. The equipment is mounted on a gun Churchill Mark IV, probably during development trials.

(RAC Tank Museum)

"think tank" and with the willing co-operation of all hands the complicated sea procedure and the drill for operations inland, penetrating minefields, crossing obstacles and capturing enemy positions and redoubts was beaten into shape.

By November 1943, 30 Armoured Brigade who were to undertake the minesweeping task joined the division and the detailed procedure of the gapping teams, whose task was to sweep a path 24 ft. wide clear of mines, could be worked out. Two of these paths were needed on each battalion front and a third reserve path was also required. This automatically shaped the mine-sweeping squadrons into three troops, each of five Crabs; three to sweep a path 24 ft. wide with two Crabs in reserve in case of casualties.

THE INSTRUCTIONAL WINGS

Revolutionary techniques demanded a high standard of instruction and closely controlled development if unnecessary time-wasting experiments were to be avoided. The divisional procedure was to establish an instructional wing manned by the best available instructors and to use this to disseminate approved divisional instructions and procedures to the troops who were to use the equipment concerned. The wings also carried out experiments and devised and modified equipments with which they were concerned.

A Wing was the first to be formed at Fritton Decoy near Lowestoft and was concerned with the fresh water training for the DD tank. Valentines were the first to be modified as DD tanks and sea trials had been

The problem of navigating the tank with the fascine mounted was often solved by the commander riding on top of it.
(Imperial War Museum)

Churchill Carpet-Layer Mark III (left) comes ashore with a flail tank in the assault stage of Overlord—the Normandy landings—early morning, June 6, 1944.

(Imperial War Museum)

Sherman coming ashore on chespaling carpet at Arromanches, Normandy.

(Imperial War Museum)

Churchill AVRE with AVRE sledge, hauling ammunition in the Reichswald during Operation "Veritable" to breach the Siegfried Line south-east of Nijmegen, February 1945.
(Imperial War Museum)

carried out with them. They had proved seaworthy and difficult targets to hit when afloat. Little was known about launching them from landing craft and tentative ideas on their employment, often based on unsatisfactory presentations and trials had clouded the true potential of this weapon. To evaluate their worth Fritton Decoy was transformed. Tank parks and workshops grew like magic, while on the edge of this sheet of inland water structures which resembled the ramp of a Landing Craft Tank were built out of Bailey bridge components. Tank hulls were placed at the bottom of twenty foot deep tanks which could be flooded so that crews could practice evacuation if the tank sank. Escape drills were perfected and the method of launching when at sea was tentatively established.

While all this was going on the land training of the division went on without cessation. Units practised their tasks from the moment that the DD tanks touched down on the enemy shore, through the fire fight at the water's edge, and then to the advance inland. It was obvious that survival depended on accurate shooting and since the 75 mm. would not penetrate concrete the only solution was fire of such accuracy that the actual gun could be knocked out where it protruded from its armoured emplacement. Constant practice achieved this standard and when the division moved down to Linney Head in Wales in the summer of 1943 a very

high standard of individual training had been achieved. Battle practices were fired here and they formed the framework for a series of exercises covering lane gapping techniques and the necessary covering fire by day and by night when the CDL tanks were brought into the picture. Everyone took part, the DD tank brigade, the Assault Engineers, the CDL tanks and Scorpions, and for the first time the formation saw itself as a complete whole and was able to realise how closely interdependent each part was on the rest. The drill was tried out, altered, changed and retried until out of orderly chaos something emerged which would work and which could be adopted as standard procedure within the division—and outside too.

The importance of the visit to Linney Head in the story of the division cannot be overestimated: for the first time all the component parts saw themselves in action as part of a connected whole and outside commanders were given an inkling of the support they could expect from units of the 79th Armoured Division operating with them. The whole division were 21 Army Group troops and were to be available where required. They were never under command of other formations and misunderstandings on this point caused difficulties with other formation commanders after D-Day when units were being brought back under divisional control.

As soon as Linney Head was over another wing, B

144

DIV. HQ.

CDL

35th Tank Bde

- 49 RTR
- 152 RAC } (CDL)
- 155 RAC

(under comd till early 1944)

replaced in 1944 by

1st Tank Bde

- 11 RTR
- 42 RTR } (CDL)
- 49 RTR

DD

27th Armd Bde

- 4/7 R.I.Dn Gds
- 13/18 R. Hussars } (DD)
- 1 East Riding Yeo

CRABS

30th Armd Bde (came under, comd Nov 1943)

- 22nd Dragoons
- 1st Lothians and Border Yeo } (Crabs)
- Westminster Dns

141 RAC (Crocodiles) from June 1944 - Sept 1944

AVRE

1st Assault Bde RE

- 5th Assault Regt RE
- 6th " "
- 42nd " " } (AVRE)

43 RTR (Div Expt'l Regt till March 1944. Converted to CDL for S.E. Asia in May 1945)

Delivery Sqns

Signals

RASC

RAMC
RAOC
REME

CROCODILES & APCs

31st Tank Bde

141 RAC (from 30th Armd Bde - Sept 1944)
1st Fife and Forfar Yeo (Crocodiles)
7 RTR

+

49 RTR (ex-CDL) } APCs
1 Canadian Armoured Personnel Carrier Regt.

BUFFALOES

5 ARRE

11 RTR (from 1st Tank Bde Oct '44)

and

DD

4th Armd Bde

Staffordshire Yeo *
44 RTR (Under comd for training early 45)

33rd Armd Bde

4 RTR formerly 144 RAC
1 Northants Yeo
1 East Riding Yeo from 27 Armd Bde.

(Bde under comd for training Jan - Mar '45)

NOTE: *Joined 4th Armd Bde for Rhine crossing having previously been DD-equipped for South Beveland operation. Staffs.Yeo at that time in 8th Armd Bde, exchanged bdes. with 4/7 R.I. Dn. Gds. in Jan. '44.

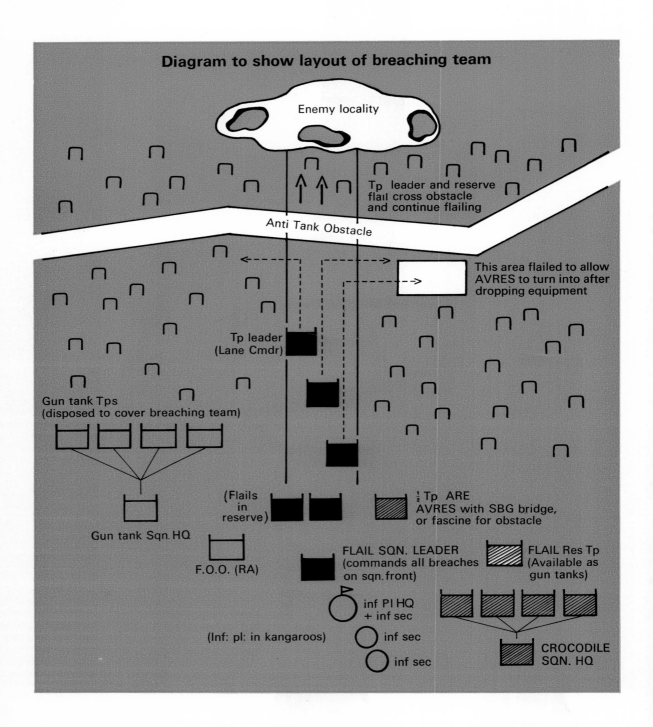

Diagram to show layout of breaching team

Enemy locality

Tp leader and reserve flail cross obstacle and continue flailing

Anti Tank Obstacle

This area flailed to allow AVRES to turn into after dropping equipment

Tp leader (Lane Cmdr)

Gun tank Tps (disposed to cover breaching team)

Gun tank Sqn. HQ.

(Flails in reserve)

½ Tp ARE AVRES with SBG bridge, or fascine for obstacle

F.O.O. (RA)

FLAIL SQN. LEADER (commands all breaches on sqn. front)

FLAIL Res Tp (Available as gun tanks)

inf Pl HQ + inf sec

(Inf: pl: in kangaroos)

inf sec

inf sec

CROCODILE SQN. HQ

Canadian wounded wait in the shelter of the captured beach defences to be transferred to a Casualty Clearing Station.

A German machine-gun nest in the Normandy beach defences knocked out on June 6.

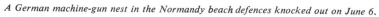

Exact reproductions of the German coastal defences were built on the 79th Armoured Division's training area at Orford in Suffolk. A Churchill ARK (Armoured Ramp Carrier) Mark I on a "rehearsal" sea-wall.
(RAC Tank Museum)

Wing was started on the Solent at Stokes Bay. Within a week a camp had been conjured out of nothing and DD tanks and allied equipment poured in for the sea training of the instructors who were to man the wing. A flotilla of Landing Ships Tanks were supplied by the Navy and together tanks and landing craft set out to establish launching procedures. Five tanks took two hours to become waterborne on the occasion of the first launch and of these two were sunk; yet within a week an LCT was regularly discharging its seven tanks in two minutes. The training of the instructors was completed by the end of October and the first units of 27 Armoured Brigade came down to do their sea training. Valentines were the first tanks used but these were changed for Shermans with a more robust propellor drive, a better screen, and above all a better gun

Churchill ARK Mark II in snow. The left-hand trackway was widened from the Mark I, and the front ramps were supported by a kingpost.
(Imperial War Museum)

Bullshorn plough for minesweeping mounted on a Sherman V on trial in the Orford battle area. (Imperial War Museum)

in the shape of the 75 mm. for use when the enemy shore had been reached. Training at B Wing went on continuously; as soon as 27 Armoured Brigade's had been completed two Canadian regiments* were trained and subsequently three American tank battalions.† The DDs were the only item of specialised equipment that United States forces elected to use for their landings.

Production of the Crab began in earnest in November 1943 and 30 Armoured Brigade were soon deep in every kind of experiment to determine the best kind of flail chain. The chain-making industry in England is a relatively small one: to meet the Brigade's requirements for a set of chains on each Crab and two spare sets would have meant, as they were forcibly told, "That none of His Majesty's ships would have an anchor chain at all." An alternative pattern using short straight links proved satisfactory and the chain industry was left to get on with its normal tasks.

Several types of anti-mine rollers were tested but they were all liable to "bridge" the detonator of a mine and were not 100% reliable. Ploughs of all types were also tested: the Bullshorn in particular, the GOC's pet, built in the divisional workshops and intended to turn mines bodily out of soft ground, occupied much time before its limitations were finally recognised.

On the Orford training area in Suffolk several full scale replicas of German coastal redoubts had been

built, complete with minefields, barbed wire entanglements and ditches. They were assaulted from every angle and the results were analyzed and dissected to finalize the technique for the assault between flails, AVREs and the infantry battalions who came to the area in increasing numbers for training. This was the fruition of the work done at Linney Head and here procedure was finally settled.

INVASION PLANS

Plans for the invasion grew firmer in the spring of 1944: 27 Armoured Brigade left the division to join infantry formations taking part in the assault; 35 Tank Brigade also left and 1st Tank Brigade with Grant CDL tanks joined in their place. Planning arrangements became more precise, down to the detailed composition of the loads of the leading landing craft who would come in under the cover of fire from the DD tanks. Each beach required something different depending on the slope and angle of the shore and the obstacles that the enemy had erected. The permutations were endless and for this operation the assault team organisation was broken down to ensure that whatever was needed, AVREs, Crabs, bulldozers, bridges and so on was to hand. Planning was greatly assisted by the wonderful low level photographs obtained by the R.A.F. which showed the beach defences in the greatest detail.

A dramatic incident was the discovery, after a daring beach reconnaissance, of patches of soft blue clay which would not carry the weight of a tracked

*1st Hussars (6 Canadian Armoured Regt.) Fort Garry Horse (10 Canadian Armoured Regt.)
†70, 741, and 743 Tank Battalions.

147

Anti-mine rollers mounted on a Mark IV of World War I being tested in 1918. Note the beams constructed of wood and the swivels on which the rollers are mounted. The device was no more successful than the rollers which were tried in World War II.
(Illustrated London News)

Snake being pushed by a Sherman tank on trial at Orford. This equipment was normally handled by a Churchill AVRE.
(RAC Tank Museum)

R.E. Tank 1919 minesweeping with a heavy roller.

vehicle. The problem of crossing this was given to the 79th Armoured Division with the information that similar patches of clay were to be found on the Wash. Within 36 hours E Wing had been established at Brancaster and 24 hours later a workable solution had been devised. This consisted of a gigantic bobbin, suspended between two beams built out in front of an AVRE. This carried a carpet consisting of hessian reinforced by lateral pipes two inches in diameter. As the tank went forward the carpet was unrolled by the tracks providing a pathway that would carry both tracks and wheels. The bobbins were made up in the divisional workshops and carpet-laying AVREs were included in the assault teams where the blue clay had

to be crossed. At Brancaster a tank driven on to the clay sank rapidly out of sight but on the invasion beaches the storm that caused postponement of the landing had covered the clay with a layer of sand that greatly reduced the potential menace.

The timing of the sea-borne assault had always been a matter of difficulty. The DD tanks were supposed to launch 10,000 yards out and their water speed was four knots or less if the weather conditions were bad. The LCTs carrying the assault teams came in to the shore at ten knots and the problem of ensuring that they landed after the DD tanks had had a chance to overcome the beach defences was always a difficult one. The launching distance was reduced but even so the

Sherman with 2in. Conger towing the gutted Universal Carrier which acted as a trailer for the hose and explosives. Note rocket for launching the hose on the carrier side. It was fired over the mine field and, with one end still connected to the carrier, was pumped full of explosive. The carrier was then removed and the hose fired, the blast creating a path through the mines. This equipment was also used with the Churchill.

Conger towed by Churchill AVRE. (Nigel Duncan)

actual landings on the British assault beaches showed many variations from the theoretical pattern.

THE LANDINGS

The drill worked perfectly on the eastern beach where the 13th/18th Hussars launched 5,000 yards out and swam ashore to cover the disembarkation of the assault teams and their subsequent advance inland under the most difficult conditions and against strong opposition until the open country was gained.

In the centre on the Canadian front DD tanks swam in from short range—1,000 yards. On one sector the assault teams encountered great difficulty in clearing the lanes and exploitation was consequently slow. On the other both DDs and the assault teams were delayed on the way in and the initial lodgement was effected by the gallantry of the Canadian infantry. Subsequently

the lanes were cleared to allow their armour to penetrate inland.

On the western sector the sea was so rough that it was not possible to launch the DD tanks and the 4th/7th Dragoon Guards and Sherwood Rangers were brought ashore in their landing craft: the assault teams had to assist in overcoming hostile fire, to open the gaps and to help the infantry forward as best they could, improvising local tactics to meet entirely unexpected circumstances. They succeeded magnificently and by nightfall the 50th Division were six miles inland. The moral of this is that skill and a high standard of training will allow troops to overcome unforeseen difficulties and by determination and drive reach their objectives.

The success of the landing has tended to belittle the achievement. For the first time a sea-borne assault had

Conger fired. (Nigel Duncan)

Matilda Scorpion flailing. Note rigid booms, wire ropes and bob weights on the rollers and the side superstructure housing the auxiliary engines driving the roller.
(RAC Tank Museum)

Close-up of Crab roller and chains now in R.A.C. Tank Museum, Bovington.
(Duncan Crow)

Side view of Sherman Crab Mark II. (Imperial War Museum)

Sherman Crab Mark I with station keeping discs folded down. Note the hydraulic cylinder which was fitted on both sides of the Mark I but on the right side only of the Mark II. (Imperial War Museum)

been preceded by armour in such strength that it was able to win the fire fight on the beaches and open a way for the infantry to reach their objectives at relatively low cost. By contrast the Americans' landing at the base of the Cherbourg peninsular on two main beaches, using only DD tanks and no specialized armour, managed to penetrate three miles inland on one sector and two miles on another at a cost of 3,000 casualties. They were hampered by rough seas and bad weather but they were held up by minefields and obstacles which were not more numerous or severe than those on the British front. 79th Armoured Divisional troops suffered a total of 179 casualties killed, wounded, and missing from the 22nd Dragoons, the Westminster Dragoons, and the 5th and 6th Assault Regiments RE —an incredibly low figure for a difficult and hazardous operation. The Assault Engineers deployed a total of 120 AVREs and lost 22 by enemy action while 30 Armoured Brigade troops who had 50 Crabs involved lost 12.

THE BRIDGEHEAD

The bridgehead, having been won, had to be enlarged and consolidated to resist enemy attacks and to make room for the build-up troops who were arriving in a continuous stream. This meant a series of minor actions in which the troops of the 79th Armoured Division played a full part and were often misemployed by the commanders of the formations in whose support they were still operating. The AVREs in particular were regarded as normal tanks in spite of the fact that the Petard only had a range of 90 yards: handled with the utmost gallantry by their crews they usually gained their objectives despite the unnecessary casualties they incurred through their misemployment.

79th Armoured Division's first task was to collect the scattered units which were ashore and to bring

Close-up of hydraulic cylinder on Sherman Crab.

(Duncan Crow)

Sherman Crab Mark II, showing the link pattern chains, the wire cutters on the end of the roller, the special hoods over the periscopes to overcome dust and mud, and the two discs at the rear which were devised for accurate station keeping while flailing. The box sloping downwards at the back of the tank held powdered chalk for lane marking.

(Imperial War Museum)

View from Sherman Crab turret of roller. In the centre background of this picture taken in the Tank Museum is a Locust M22 airportable Light Tank used by 6th Airborne Division in the Rhine crossing, 1945.
(Duncan Crow)

"Wandering Willie", Sherman Crab of 30 Armoured Brigade, passing a shell-shattered barn south of Caen, August 1944.
(Imperial War Museum)

Operation "Totalize", August 1944—the drive for Falaise. A flail tank of 79th Armoured Division (left) with Shermans of First Canadian Army. "Totalize" and its successor "Tractable" was the left arm of the pincers that formed the Falaise pocket.

(Canadian Official)

them under divisional control. It was not an easy business, only a small tactical div HQ was ashore and the divisional commander perforce was often in England. However it was accomplished in the face of the reluctance of formation commanders who had come to look on flails and AVREs as part of their command and were loath to let them go. Once collected it was possible to re-establish the 79th Armoured procedure, to make sure that machines were not wastefully deployed and that the utmost value was obtained from all specialised armour used in action.

To achieve this a 79th Armoured Division adviser was appointed for all operations where specialised armour was to be employed. He was responsible for advising the formation commander concerned on the types of equipment that were required, the quantity required and the outline plan. Once requirements had been determined, allocation of troops was made by Divisional HQ. The original adviser nominated other advisers at lower levels of command who were responsible for advising on the employment and planning the tasks of specialised armour with the subordinate formation commanders to whom they were accredited. All advisers were responsible for getting specialised armour released as soon as its task had been completed

so that it would be available for the next operation that might require its services.

The Crocodiles story is typical of the problems that had to be faced. They had taken part in the landing and had been used in the follow-up without any great success because the peculiarities of the equipment were not understood.

The flame gun had a long narrow pattern with a range of 90 yards; the high pressure gas system of the trailer was liable to small leaks: if pressured up too soon before action the drop might be so great that no flame was available and the fire of other tanks was essential while the Crocodiles closed to effective distance. When 141 RAC came under 79th Armoured Division it was possible to establish all these points and to plan operations so that the trailers were only pressured up within 30 minutes of the time they were to be in action. Success came in an attack on a German strong-point after joint consultation between the 79th's adviser and the formation commander concerned. The objective was captured with negligible casualties, the highlight being the remark of a captured German officer who said that he did not think that English troops would stoop to use such an un-British weapon as a flame gun!

Situated within the bridgehead was a German radar

155

Assault troops of 152 Inf. Bde., 51st (Highland) Division, forming up for Phase II of the attack on Le Havre, September 11, 1944.
Supporting them can be seen Sherman Crabs of B Squadron, 1st Lothians and Border Horse, and two AVREs, one with SBG bridge.
(Imperial War Museum)

Sherman Crab Mark I of A Squadron, Lothians and Border Horse, comes ashore at Walcheren, November 1, 1944. A second Crab
can be seen about to leave the LCT on the right. This landing, on the west of island, was carried out by three Royal Marine Com-
mandos and a detachment of 79th Armoured Division. The landing was strongly resisted.
(RAC Tank Museum)

Churchill VII adapted for use as a Crocodile. The flame gun can be seen between the horns of the tank with the fuel trailer being towed behind. (RAC Tank Museum)

station at Douvres of classical pattern with ditches, minefields and anti-tank guns to defend it. It was essential that the station be put out of action; distances were short and assault teams were slightly modified for the operation which proved to be a complete success. Thanks to careful planning casualties were very light, the assault teams overcame all the obstacles and the station surrendered after an attack which only lasted forty minutes from start to finish.

THE BREAK-OUT AND THE PORTS

The divisional technique which had been worked out in England was perfected in the operations that established the bridgehead ready for the break-out. Units of the division took part in the break-out, in the attack on Caen, and the subsequent advance from there to the Falaise pocket. After this the division continued the advance with the main body of Second British Army less a part which was diverted to deal

The assault landing in Normandy, June 6, 1944, showing some of the underwater obstacles. A Crocodile is in action on the beach at the top of the picture. (Imperial War Museum)

Men of 141st Regiment R.A.C. (The Buffs), the original flame regiment, loading a cylinder of nitrogen gas into the trailer of a Crocodile. The hand-wheels which controlled the pressure are immediately above the hinge of the trailer door.

(RAC Tank Museum)

with the Channel ports, Le Havre and later Boulogne and Calais in the hope that one or other of these might be captured in workable condition and so shorten the long supply haul from the invasion port.

All three towns in turn fell to assault teams of the 79th Armoured Division and in all three, minefields had to be swept, obstacles crossed and concrete emplacements destroyed: these tasks were accomplished with a minimum of casualties to the accompanying infantry. Boulogne actually fell to armoured columns largely composed of units of the division which passed through the leading infantry to strike at the defences. The attack was carried out at great speed and casualties were very light. The story at Calais was the same, although the technique of the attack was slightly different. The port installations had been so damaged

by the Germans that the amount of tonnage that could be handled through them was negligible.

Before the Channel ports had been captured the division had acquired a new weapon, the Armoured Personnel Carrier, known colloquially as the Kangaroo. This stemmed from the Canadian advance south of Caen when assaulting infantry were carried forward in Priests, de-gunned SP artillery, and disembarked at the scene of action, avoiding the long approach march which fatigued the troops and caused unnecessary casualties. The device proved so successful that two regiments were converted to this rôle and joined the division as part of their extensive armoury, 49th Royal Tank Regiment and the 1st Canadian Armoured Personnel Carrier Regiment. They were equipped with de-gunned and de-turreted Ram tanks and

Crocodile firing its flame gun.

(Imperial War Museum)

Churchill Crocodile in action in support of U.S. troops in the attack on Brest, September 1944.   (Imperial War Museum)

although they were uneconomical in that they only held a section of infantry, they covered the ground to the objectives speedily, gave cover to the infantry on the way and were able to fight their way forward under the fire of their own machine-guns. These regiments retained the normal sub-unit organisation of an armoured regiment and were able to co-operate very closely with the normal gun tanks who accompanied their advance.

It had early become obvious that water obstacles and their crossing would present acute problems.

Before the break-out from the bridgehead the three Assault Regiments RE carried out a period of water training on the Orne canal, 5th ARRE concentrating on the handling of the 50/60 ton raft. New amphibious vehicles were becoming available, the Terrapin which was the British equivalent of the DUKW and which could carry some three tons of stores on a 6-wheeled chassis, and the Landing Vehicle Tracked, an American amphibious tracked load carrier, one version of which could carry up to four tons of stores. The two types complemented each other: the Terrapin was better on

Invasion beaches 6 June 1944

To show assaulting divisions and 79 Armoured Div troops

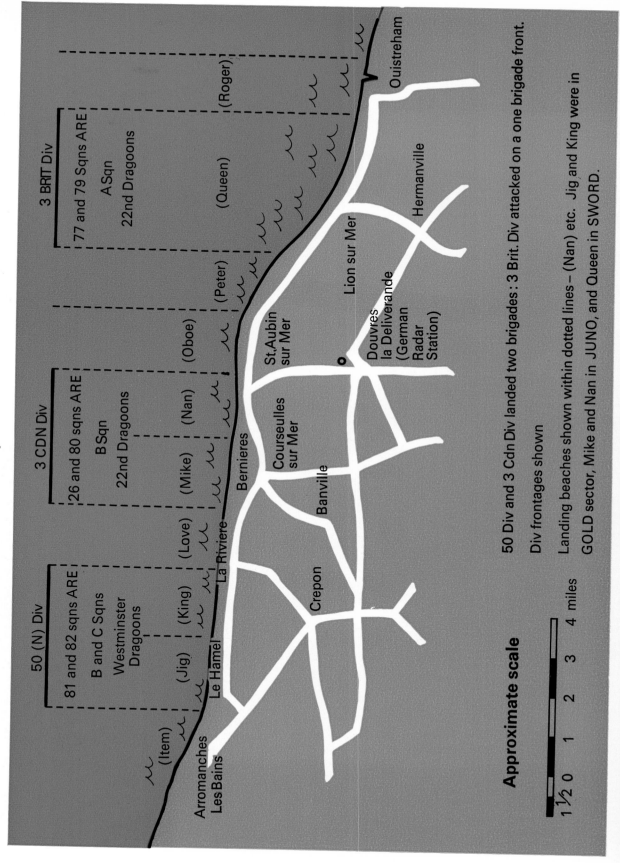

50 (N) Div

81 and 82 sqns ARE

B and C Sqns

Westminster Dragoons

3 CDN Div

26 and 80 sqns ARE

B Sqn

22nd Dragoons

3 BRIT Div

77 and 79 Sqns ARE

A Sqn

22nd Dragoons

(Item) (Jig) (King) (Love) (Mike) (Nan) (Oboe) (Peter) (Queen) (Roger)

Arromanches Les Bains

Le Hamel

La Riviere

Bernieres

St.Aubin sur Mer

Courseulles sur Mer

Banville

Crepon

Douvres la Deliverande (German Radar Station)

Lion sur Mer

Hermanville

Ouistreham

Approximate scale

1 ½ 0   1   2   3   4 miles

50 Div and 3 Cdn Div landed two brigades : 3 Brit. Div attacked on a one brigade front.

Div frontages shown

Landing beaches shown within dotted lines – (Nan) etc.   Jig and King were in GOLD sector, Mike and Nan in JUNO, and Queen in SWORD.

iii

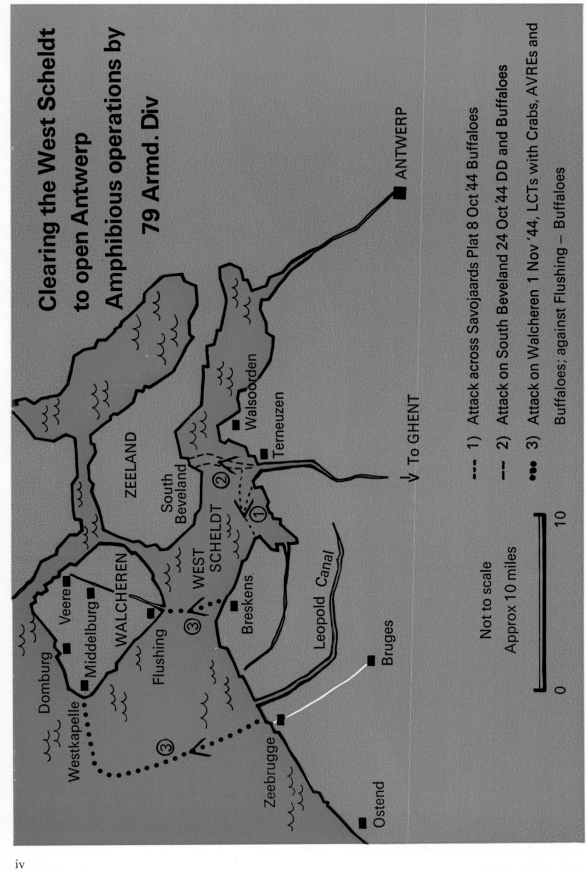

Clearing the West Scheldt to open Antwerp

Amphibious operations by 79 Armd. Div

--- 1) Attack across Savojaards Plat 8 Oct '44 Buffaloes

- - 2) Attack on South Beveland 24 Oct '44 DD and Buffaloes

••• 3) Attack on Walcheren 1 Nov '44, LCTs with Crabs, AVREs and Buffaloes; against Flushing – Buffaloes

Not to scale
Approx 10 miles

0   10

To GHENT

ANTWERP

Terneuzen

Walsoorden

ZEELAND

South Beveland

WEST SCHELDT

Breskens

Leopold Canal

Bruges

Zeebrugge

Ostend

Flushing

WALCHEREN

Middelburg

Veere

Domburg

Westkapelle

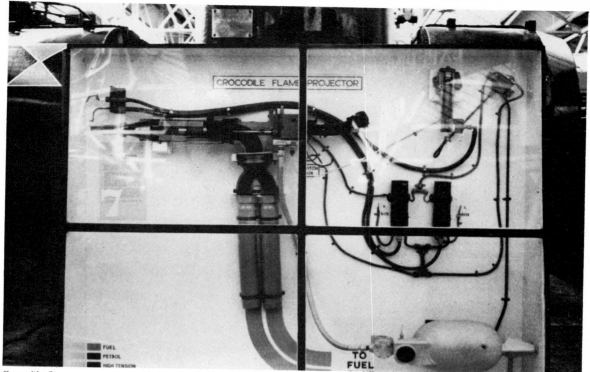

Crocodile flame projector assembly in a show-case at the RAC Tank Museum.

(Duncan Crow)

Crocodiles in snow camouflage pass through Hingen, Germany, in January 1945.

(Imperial War Museum)

Crocodile in action in the snow, supporting infantry attack.

(Imperial War Museum)

hard going but found difficulty in getting out of soft mud on the water's edge, while the LVT (Buffalo) could not run any distance on hard ground because the track grousers on which it depended for propulsion when water-borne became damaged. Five squadrons of 1st Assault Brigade were trained to use these vehicles while the advance into Belgium was continuing.

· Antwerp fell to the 11th Armoured Division early in September but although the port was virtually undamaged it could not be used for supply purposes because the Germans controlled both banks of the Scheldt and also held the island of Walcheren situated at the mouth of the estuary. The south bank was cleared by an attack which turned the German flank and was only made possible by the use of Buffaloes.

2nd Canadian Corps started to clear the north bank working west from Antwerp but encountered strong opposition on South Beveland. To overcome this an assaulting force crossed the Scheldt in Buffaloes with a squadron of DD tanks and cleared the opposition. The third phase was the capture of Walcheren which was accomplished by a full-scale assault carried in LCTs after a preliminary operation by the R.A.F. to breach the dyke at the western end of the island. Buffaloes, Crabs, and AVREs were landed and gave invaluable support to the Royal Marine Commandos who came ashore with them. 52nd Division were carried across the water from Breskens to Flushing to capture the town and the principal town, Middleburg, was captured by a Buffalo force from 11 RTR who

Ram Kangaroo, an armoured personnel carrier made by removing the turret from a Ram tank. 79th Armoured Division had two regiments in this role—1st Canadian A.P.C. and 49th Royal Tanks.

(Imperial War Museum)

Buffalo about to come ashore. These American LVTs (Landing Vehicles Tracked) were used by the British Army in the Mark 2 and Mark 4 versions. The LVT4 was the LVT2 with the engine moved forward and with a stern ramp for loading. (RAC Tank Museum)

had been converted to LVTs to reinforce the original Assault Engineer squadrons. Without specialised armour Walcheren would have been a more lengthy and costly operation, but the invaluable support offered by units of the division is often overlooked. A few days after this the minesweepers started to sweep the Scheldt and Antwerp was opened for normal working on November 28.

WINTER 1944-45

October, November and December saw many small operations east and south of Antwerp as the Allied forces pushed onwards towards the Maas. They are too numerous to record here, suffice it to say that units of the division, which was scattered over a very wide front, worked with First Canadian Army, Second British Army, First and Ninth American Armies. Action succeeded action involving Flails, AVREs, Crocodiles (141st RAC had been reinforced in the flame rôle by 1st Fife and Forfar Yeomanry and were later joined by 7th RTR) and Buffaloes. Operations were carried out in the most difficult conditions, deep

mud, flooded country and frozen ground—this last a barrier to the use of the Flails which were unable to break up the hard surface to get down to the mine. Among many other actions Blerick fell to a full-scale assault where Crabs flailed through the minefield. The AVREs laid six SBG bridges which the Crabs crossed to continue flailing, and infantry in Kangaroos passed through to capture the town. Before this Crabs of 1st Lothian and Border Yeomanry had been the first troops in the division to enter Germany in the assault on Geilenkirchen which was actually captured by two AVREs who reported the town clear of the enemy.

There followed then von Runstedt's offensive through the Ardennes. The division was not heavily involved in this; some Kangaroos worked in support of 6th British Airborne Division and some LVTs were available for 53rd Division but were hardly used. The German attack delayed operations for the advance to the Rhine by a matter of two months or so but otherwise had little effect on the campaign. A series of small operations cleared the ground up to the Maas leaving 30 Corps poised for the attack up to the Rhine, which had originally been planned for frozen ground;

Front view of the top of the LVT4 (Buffalo Mark IV) on display in the RAC Tank Museum, Bovington. The wire mesh is a Museum addition.
(Duncan Crow)

79th Armoured Division Sherman crews replenishing their ammunition from a Buffalo (left) on Walcheren, November 1944.
(Nigel Duncan)

Men of the Royal Dragoons (an armoured car regiment) carrying out the duties of bank control at the Rhine crossing near Rees. A 50/60 raft can be seen in midstream and a Buffalo on the near bank.
(Major K. G. Balfour, M.C.)

The two keys to the Buffalo's efficiency in water were: one . . . the "buffer" in front of the first roller which kept the track from being pushed inwards .(Note the track grousers which gave propulsion)

now that a thaw had set in it had to be considerably modified. Five divisions were to be deployed for the attack and all of them had 79th Armoured Division troops operating in their support. On the northern sector the flooded valley of the Rhine meant much work for Buffaloes which carried out miniature naval operations against various enemy-held strong-points which had to be secured to ensure the safety of the attacks due to take place on the higher ground to the south. These operations were difficult and dangerous—stray mines had been scattered over the area and the water tamped these when detonated, greatly increasing their effect. Ground conditions were bad and were made no better by continuous rain. 30 Corps, who were responsible for the operation, had first to clear the Siegfried Line, then to clear two subsidiary lines through thickly wooded country including the Reichswald forest and to exploit success up to the west bank of the Rhine. The ground east of Nijmegen was low lying and promised heavy going.

Operation "Veritable" began on February 8. Lanes were opened by Crabs and AVREs under most difficult conditions in which tanks became bogged and routes were only cleared with great difficulty. The Canadians operating on the northern flank carried out a series of amphibious attacks against German positions situated on ground high enough to avoid flooding. Some were carried out in LVTs while others involved the use of assault boats covered on to their objectives by the fire from LVTs of the ARRE and 11 RTR. The opportunities for water-borne operations were almost an epitome of full-scale naval assaults in miniature and without the LVTs it would have been impossible to have cleared the Germans from the locations that they were holding and which in enemy

Buffaloes cross the Rhine, March 1945.

(Imperial War Museum)

. . . and two the "squashed honeycomb" at the rear through which the tracks' wash was ejected. (Duncan Crow)

The Terrapin was the British equivalent of the American DUKW.

Grant CDL with dummy gun barrel on turret. (Imperial War Museum)

CDL equipment on a Grant chassis illuminating farm buildings about 400 yards away.

(RAC Tank Museum)

hands menaced the advance on the higher ground to the south.

The Siegfried line gave less trouble than was expected but the Reichswald forest proved very difficult. Operations were hampered by the paucity of roads in the area: to overcome this the Canadians built a superb corduroy road through the forest to ease the supply problem. The day that this was opened one lone AVRE which had lost its way and was unable to decide in which direction to go, turned through 540 degrees on the road where it had no business to be. He was undetected, but the full blame fell on the head of the divisional representative who knew nothing of the event until he received the full wrath of the Canadian Army Chief Engineer who was threatening all and sundry with death, preferably by one of the axes used to build the road! The damage was very considerable and the road was not opened for another thirty-six hours.

By March 9 Operation "Veritable" was over: it had been a complicated battle but when it was finished British and Canadian troops were in control of the ground up to the west bank of the Rhine and flail squadrons of the division working with the Ninth American Army had in three days cleared minefields on their front allowing their armour to sweep north and east up and across the Rhine. Crabs, AVREs, Crocodiles, Buffaloes and Kangaroos of the 79th had all played their part in operations on land and on the water and had materially assisted the advance. Improvisation had often been necessary but the basic techniques had once again proved themselves sound. Despite the extent of the front on which units had

been operating, touch had always been maintained and it had proved possible to meet all demands for specialised armour throughout this long drawn out battle.

79th ARMOURED DIVISION WINGS IN EUROPE

The divisional practice of establishing specialist wings to meet special problems continued throughout the

T10E1 Shop Tractor (a description adopted for security reasons) was an experimental CDL tank built by the Americans on a Sherman chassis. It was similar to the British type.

(U.S. Official)

Crocodile in action.

campaign. HQ Second Army passed the problem of the anti-personnel mine to the GOC and F Wing was formed at Gheel in Belgium to find a solution. Two types were involved, the Schu mine, made of wood and undetectable, and the jumping mine which threw a canister into the air where it burst scattering its charge of shot far and wide. Both were dangerous, very frightening and when encountered slowed up any movement. Many trials to defeat this menace were

carried out, and ultimately Centipede, a frame carrying a number of small rollers each with considerable vertical movement, proved successful. Centipede could be towed behind a Weasel, a tracked vehicle with such a low ground pressure that the mine would not be set off by the tracks, or behind the tracks of an ordinary tank to give accompanying infantry immunity from the threat. The advantage of this device lay in its speed: any A/P mines laid in the flailed path of a Crab would be destroyed but sweeping was a slow operation normally only undertaken where a minefield had been located. The Centipede gave a high degree of immunity at towing speeds of 5–6 m.p.h. Experiments were carried out to destroy these mines with flame or mortar bombs but they were not successful.

G Wing opened north of Maastricht in December to work out the technique for the Rhine crossing in conjunction with HQ 12 Corps. who were responsible for the operation. Discussion was followed by practical experiments and new equipment was devised to meet the particular conditions of this operation. Among others this included the development of a carpet-laying Buffalo to overcome the difficulties experienced by DD tanks on soft river banks. The carpet, basically hessian reinforced by iron pipes, was laid from rails running fore and aft on the Buffalo which came ashore on it leaving relatively good going for the tanks in succeeding waves. The Buffalo was also adapted to take a 17-pdr. anti-tank gun—a peculiarly awkward load since the gun was too long

Sherman Fascine Carrier was a turretless vehicle modified by 79th Armoured Division.   (Imperial War Museum)

AVRE with fascine and AVRE with SGB in Operation "Veritable".

to go into the cargo hold and had to be perched on a staging built inside the landing vehicle.

33 Armoured Brigade came under command for training in January 1945 although their subsequent operations were outside the control of the division. They were converted from Shermans to Buffaloes by 11 RTR who joined the brigade for later operations. The Staffordshire Yeomanry who had converted to DD tanks for the South Beveland operations moved to G Wing and were joined by 44 RTR who were trained in the amphibious rôle and were later joined by a squadron from 736 U.S. Tank Battalion. 7 RTR who were converting to Crocodiles from ordinary Churchills were also trained in their new rôle in the vicinity of the Wing.

H Wing was opened by the ARRE at Nijmegen on the banks of the Rhine to train Assault Squadrons in heavy rafting over a wide river. By March it had trained six squadrons in this technique and their mastery of the Class 50/60 raft proved invaluable in the early stages of the Rhine Crossing.

The last of the European Wings was J, devoted to navigational training. Buffaloes or DD tanks might have to work at night or in conditions of reduced visibility due to smoke by day. Accurate direction keeping was obviously a prime necessity if objectives were to be reached. After preliminary investigations attention was concentrated on the use of the magnetic and gyro compasses, radio direction-keeping equipment and the use of infra beacons. The radio direction-keeping equipment was devised by the division and involved the use of two 19 sets which by the use of suitable ground aerials allowed tanks or Buffaloes to "ride the beam" to their destination. DD and Buffalo squadron commanders attended a short course at the Wing in the use of these devices and by March 21,

G, H and J wings having completed their tasks were disbanded, the personnel returning to their own units.

THE CROSSING OF THE RHINE

Second British Army once across the Rhine were to push forward in conjunction with operations by the American forces further south who already had a small bridgehead across the river at Remagen: the Russian advance would start a few days later and they

Crabs of 1st Troop, B Squadron, 22nd Dragoons flailing a path at Groesbeek in Operation "Veritable".

(Nigel Duncan)

DD tank training at G Wing on the River Meuse.

and the Western Allies expected to meet each other roughly on the line of the Elbe.

The technique worked out by 12 Corps and 79th Armoured Division which was based on D-Day operations was accepted by HQ Second Army who deployed two Corps for the attack, 12 on the right and 30 Corps on the left. The assault was to be carried out by DD tanks and Buffaloes. Eight 50/60 rafts were to be built and since the defences were not established in great depth there was no immediate requirement for the other special equipment of the division in the assault, although Flails, Crocodiles and AVREs were to be ferried across the river as speedily as possible in case they were required later.

Once the assaulting divisions had established a bridgehead and consolidated their position, 12 Corps on the right were to enlarge it with another infantry division and pass 7th Armoured Division through in an exploitation rôle. On 30 Corps front the bridgehead was to be enlarged by 43rd Infantry Division and 3rd Canadian Infantry Division who were then to turn westwards towards Emmerich.

In 1918 the first British flag to cross the Rhine was a Tank Corps flag worn by the 17th Armoured Car Bn. of the Tank Corps. This precious relic was brought out from Bovington and was planted on the east bank of the Rhine by the CO 4 RTR whose Buffalo was the first to touch down on the opposite bank at 2104 hours on March 23. The leading troops encountered some enemy MG and mortar fire particularly from Rees. This town was stoutly defended and proved troublesome, preventing the assembly of one of the

50/60 rafts scheduled for 30 Corps front. However despite this the build-up of assault vehicles and stores continued throughout the night. The Staffordshire Yeomanry with DD tanks had the misfortune to have the inflation area shelled and had some of their tanks hit, but in spite of these and other casualties from enemy fire when they were afloat and trouble with sand-banks, the regiment was ashore by 0700 hours and in action thirty minutes later.

On the southern flank the 12 Corps attack launched at 0200 hours on March 24 encountered surprisingly little opposition and by 0800 hours 44 RTR had 59 DD tanks across the river and in action with the leading infantry. At 1000 hours an airborne attack by XVIII U.S. Airborne Corps, consisting of 6 British Airborne Division and 19 U.S. Airborne Division, was launched. They made an impressive spectacle with over 4,000 aircraft flying so low that troops waiting to drop could be seen standing at the gaping holes in the sides of the aircraft where the doors had been removed. The task of the Airborne Corps was to seize bridges over the Ijssel and to link up with advancing units of Second British Army. Both tasks were successfully accomplished and by nightfall on the 24th a bridgehead thirty miles long and seven miles deep was in Allied hands, with the exception of Rees which, troublesome to the last, held out until next day.

One other 79th Armoured Divisional unit deserves mention. A CDL squadron was re-formed from 1st Tank Brigade to provide light for the crossing. They were positioned on the upstream side of the areas selected for the crossing of both 12 and 30 Corps:

G Wing, River Meuse: Buffalo with 6-pdr.　　(Nigel Duncan)

G Wing, River Meuse: Buffalo with 17-pdr.　　(Nigel Duncan)

their instructions were to keep the water illuminated, to provide movement light for the Buffaloes and to open fire on any suspicious objects seen in the stream. Intensely disliked by troops in their immediate vicinity because of the enemy fire that they attracted, they destroyed many floating objects in the river, 35 of which blew up with a loud bang. They could have been frogmen, floating mines, miniature submarines—the fact remains that neither rafts, Buffaloes, DD tanks or bridging operations were interrupted by enemy water-borne action.

There is much more to tell, of small individual actions and some major assaults: after the Rhine crossing the division was continually in action on both Second Army front in Germany and on First Canadian Army front in Holland. Defences were sketchy and the principal requirement was for Crocodiles, Buffaloes and APCs. It is difficult to single out particular actions, but units of the 79th working with 49th Infantry Division were responsible for the capture of Arnhem. After the glorious failure of 1st Airborne Division to capture the town in September 1944, a German broadcaster set herself up as Mary of Arnhem. Her epitaph was written in chalk on a blackboard outside Royal Naval Control established on Arnhem quay. "Jack of Arnhem—Mary's gone!!!"

Bremen was attacked by 30 Corps on April 25 and was in our hands by the 27th: Buffaloes, Crocodiles and AVREs were all involved. Bremerhaven further north had a most unpleasant minefield—naval 11-in. shells with a pressure plate on the nose. They did great damage to the Crabs since the body of the shell acted as a fougasse, concentrating the effect of the charge. One AVRE was unlucky enough to hit a buried naval mine which put it out of action and all those connected

Buffalo with carpet at G Wing on the River Meuse
(Nigel Duncan)

with mine clearance were deeply thankful when this particular assault was over.

The advance continued up to and across the River Elbe with 79th Armoured Divisional units continually to the fore. The CDL tanks were again in action providing movement light across the river. Hamburg was strongly defended but 6 Airborne Division and 11 Armoured Division reached the Baltic shore by May 3 and on May 4 surrender terms were signed by the Germans at 21 Army Group Tactical HQ on Luneburg Heath.

Buffalo laying carpet.

(Nigel Duncan)

AVREs at H Wing, Nijmegen.

(Nigel Duncan)

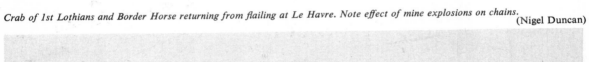

Crab of 1st Lothians and Border Horse returning from flailing at Le Havre. Note effect of mine explosions on chains.

(Nigel Duncan)

Over the limit! Two Shermans are too much for a 50/60 raft on the Rhine.
(Nigel Duncan)

Buffalo of 11th RTR blown up by a mine during Operation "Veritable".
(Nigel Duncan)

HOBO'S FUNNIES

The end of the war in Germany heralded the end of the 79th Armoured Division. Created to fill a special rôle, it was continuously in the van of the assault from the landings in Normandy throughout the campaign to the crossing of the Elbe. The division invented its own technique, modified or invented equipment to meet the unexpected, and although hampered by weather and ground conditions never failed to carry out its allotted tasks despite enemy opposition.

At one period its five brigades, composed of 17 regiments, handled 1,566 tracked armoured fighting vehicles with a total strength of over 21,000 all ranks, compared to the normal armoured division's strength of 350 AFVs and 14,000 all ranks. The division operated all over 21 Army Group front and the problems of command and control demanded a very high standard of leadership which, however, could never have achieved results without the whole-hearted devotion to duty and the efficiency of all ranks.

The inverted triangle with its ferocious Bull's Head, the divisional sign of "Hobo's Funnies", was better known and more widely distributed in Second Army's area than any other. Inspired by its divisional commander, it pursued its way with gaiety tempered with the resolution to be defeated by no difficulty whether of Nature's or man's creation. With the whole-hearted support of its own services, continually kept in touch by its own signals, its regiments lacked nothing to back up their own determination to carry out successfully any task they were set.

Cleves during Operation "Veritable".

(Nigel Duncan)

OPERATIONS BY DD TANKS IN THE D-DAY ASSAULT ON NORMANDY

JUNE 6, 1944

Sector	Assault Formation	DD Units	Action
UTAH VII U.S. Corps	4th U.S. Infantry Division with one Regimental Combat Team up	70 Tank Battalion	30 tanks launched at 3,000 yards: one foundered
OMAHA V U.S. Corps	1st U.S. Infantry Division with two RCTs up	743 Tank Battalion	Not launched: all beached direct from LCTs
		741 Tank Battalion	29 tanks launched at 6,000 yards: 27 foundered, 2 swam in. 3 beached from LCTs
GOLD 30 British Corps	50th British Infantry Division with two Brigade Groups up (231 Brigade with 47 Commando and 69 Brigade)	Notts. Sherwood Rangers Yeomanry 4th/7th Royal Dragoon Guards (8 Armoured Brigade)	Not launched: all beached from LCTs on orders
JUNO 1 British Corps	3rd Canadian Infantry Division with two Brigade Groups up (7 Canadian Brigade and 8 Canadian Brigade)	6th Canadian Armoured Regiment (1st Hussars)	'A' Squadron launched 10 tanks at 1,500–2,000 yards: 7 touched down on beach. Another 6 beached from LCTs. 'B' Squadron launched 19 tanks at 4,000 yards of which 14 reached the shore.
		10th Canadian Armoured Regiment (Fort Garry Horse)	Not launched: all beached from LCTs
SWORD 1 British Corps	3rd British Infantry Division with one Brigade Group up (8 Infantry Brigade) and Commando Brigades on each flank	13th/18th Royal Hussars (27 Armoured Brigade)	40 embarked: 6 failed to launch. 34 launched at 5,000 yards: 3 sank during swim in, 31 reached shore

(With acknowledgments to Major-General Charles H. Miller *History of the 13th/18th Royal Hussars (Queen Mary's Own) 1922–1947*)

Scissors bridging Churchills moving up south of the Antwerp-Turnhout canal.

176

Sherman Beach Armoured Recovery Vehicle towing a truck ashore in Normandy, June 1944. (Photo: Imperial War Museum)

Armoured Recovery Vehicles
by Peter Chamberlain

BY 1942 it was recognized by the War Office that there was an urgent requirement for a tracked recovery vehicle, able to operate over the same terrain as the combat tanks and having the same tractive power to retrieve the dead tank by dragging or towing it to a point where the casualty could be loaded on to a wheeled transport and taken to a base workshop. The recovery vehicle should also be able to carry personnel, spare assemblies, repair equipment and a light jib crane, so as to be able to make repairs on the spot, and be capable of moving at the same speed as the armoured formation to which it was attached. It was realised that the basis for this type of specialised vehicle would be a tank and it was at first planned to convert various types of tanks then in service to this rôle so that they could operate with similar types of combat tanks.

Armoured recovery vehicles based on the Covenanter, Crusader, Grant and Churchill were built and tested by R.E.M.E. at Arborfield during February 1942. As a result it was decided to concentrate on the Churchill as a basic chassis for conversion to the ARV rôle because of its general characteristics and because it was becoming available in adequate numbers. Later, however, models of the Cavalier, Centaur and Cromwell ARV I were also produced. There were also Canadian Ram ARVs Mk. I and Mk. II.

CHURCHILL ARV I

This consisted of a Churchill IV with the turret and armament removed and a flat hinged lid substituted. A portable jib crane with the lifting capacity of five tons was fitted so that it could be easily erected, and gas cutting and welding equipment with tools and repair equipment was stowed in the hull. A crew of three was carried including the driver. The ARV Mk. I was primarily an armoured tug having a drawbar connector fitted at the rear. The jib booms were carried on the sides and when required they were mounted on the front of the vehicle and raised by a wire rope clamped to the track. The chain block carried at the head of the boom was capable of a three ton lift. Armament consisted of a 7·92-mm. Besa machine-gun in the hull, and a Pugh twin machine-gun mounting with two Bren or Sten guns. Weight was 33 tons.

SHERMAN ARV I

Because of the rearming of most of the British armoured divisions with the American M4 series of Medium tank (the Sherman) an ARV model based on this tank was very soon put into production. Based on the chassis of the M4A4 (Sherman V) model, the conversion equipment was very similar to that used on the Churchill ARV I.

The original turret, armament, turret fittings and stowage were removed and internal stowage revised and re-positioned. The hull roof plate opening, formerly occupied by the turret, was covered with a circular section of armour having two large hatches.

Churchill ARV Mk. I with front jib erected. Note the armament—7·92 mm. Besa machine-gun in the hull and twin Brens.
(Photo: Imperial War Museum)

Sherman ARV I with front jib erected and twin Brens. Note position of wireless aerials.
(Photo: Imperial War Museum)

Churchill ARV II with front jib stowed. Note fixed turret, fixed rear jib, and dummy 6-pdr. gun. (Photo: Imperial War Museum)

GRANT AND RAM ARV I AND II

The Grant ARV I was a British conversion equipped to the same standards as other British Mark I ARVs. The Grant ARV II was the British designation for the standard U.S. M31 TRV in British service. The Australians produced their own special ARV in 1944 by removing the guns from a standard Grant and installing a winch in the fighting compartment with a roller guide erected on the rear hull to give the winch purchase. Tool boxes were also added to the hull rear, as well as an earth spade.

The Canadians converted some of their Rams to the recovery rôle. The Ram ARV Mark I was a towing vehicle only with a winch on the hull front and tool boxes on the rear hull decking. The Mark II was more sophisticated and was equipped to the British Mark II ARV standard: dummy fixed turret and dummy gun, rear jib, earth spade, and electric winch.

CRUISER CHASSIS ARVs

The Covenanter and Crusader ARVs had a similar appearance. The turret was removed from a standard vehicle and it was fitted with a dismountable A-frame jib crane together with tools and equipment for front line repairs and recovery. Twin Bren A.A. machine-guns could be mounted in the former fighting compartment.

The Cavalier, Centaur, and Cromwell ARVs were also similar to each other in appearance. The turret was removed, though the forward hull machine-gun was retained, and twin Brens were mounted, as in the Crusader, for A.A. defence. The ARV had standard recovery vehicle equipment: dismountable jib crane, winch, drawbars, and detachable track grousers. The wireless set and aerials were re-positioned. The vehicle was fitted with a special type of track grouser when operating on soft ground. A 4½-in. vice was fitted to a curved slotted bracket welded to the front of the vehicle.

CHURCHILL ARV II

As the ARV I could only operate as a direct tractor and, when recovering heavy loads, had to work in conjunction with another AFV and a system of

holdfasts, service use in the field had shown that there was a need for a more powerful winch gear and some form of earth anchor. Development of a vehicle to this requirement was again undertaken by R.E.M.E. who made a pilot model, production vehicles being ready for issue by early 1944; conversions were produced on both Churchill and Sherman chassis.

The Churchill ARV Mk. II was based on the Churchill Mk. III and Mk. IV chassis, the standard turret being replaced by a fixed turret fabricated from 40-mm. armoured plate welded to the roof of the vehicle, with a turret roof of 14-mm. plate carrying two cupolas. A dummy 6-pdr. gun was mounted.

The special equipment carried consisted of a dismountable forward or front jib capable of supporting a 7½ ton load, a fixed rear jib for lifting or giving a combined lift and haul of 15 tons, and a two-speed winch driven from the engine capable of developing a direct pull of 25 tons through the winch rope which passed from a drum through a rectangular opening in the rear plate of the turret with suitable guide rollers. A spade-type earth anchor was hinged at the rear of the vehicle to prevent rearward movement of the vehicle, when the winch pull exceeded the tractive resistance of the AFV. Miscellaneous equipment and tools including 25 ton snatch blocks shackles, tow ropes, and gas welding equipment was carried for the crew of four. Weight of the vehicle was 40·1 tons. Armament consisted of one 7·92-mm. Besa in the hull and one Bren gun.

SHERMAN ARV II

Based on the Sherman V (Medium M4A4) chassis, the conversion was similar to that of the Churchill ARV II. The turret (a welded structure of armour plate) was welded in a fixed position on the hull roof plate and fitted with a dummy gun. On the turret roof was fitted two cupolas, each with a roof hatch covering nearly the whole area of the cupola roof. The special equipment carried consisted of a dismantled front jib capable of lifting a weight of 7½ tons at the height of approximately 17 ft. from the ground, a rear fixed jib for lifting or giving a combined lift and direct pull, and a two-speed winch driven from the engine capable of developing a direct pull of 25 tons. A spade type earth anchor was hinged at the rear. Miscellaneous equip-

Sherman ARV II with front jib erected. The conversion is similar to the Churchill ARV II—fixed turret, fixed rear jib, and dummy gun. The spade type earth anchor in raised position can be seen at rear. (Photo: Imperial War Museum)

Grant ARV Mark I.

Sherman Beach Armoured Recovery Vehicle waiting for a call on its services at the Rhine crossings in March 1945. (Photo: Major-General N. W. Duncan)

Knocked out flail tanks (Sherman Crabs) of 1st Lothians and Border Horse, 30 Armoured Brigade, 79th Armoured Division, being recovered by Sherman ARV Is after the attack on Le Havre, September 1944. (Photo: Major-General N. W. Duncan)

Three quarter left front view of Centaur ARV. Cavalier and Cromwell ARVs were similar in appearance.

Three quarter right rear view of the Australian Grant ARV Mark II, showing earth spade and roller guide.

ment and stores carried included 25 ton snatch block, shackles, tow ropes and gas welding equipment.

BEACH ARMOURED RECOVERY VEHICLES (BARV)

This was another form of recovery vehicle that was developed during 1943 to recover disabled vehicles from the beaches during the forthcoming landings in France.

Early experiments were carried out by R.E.M.E. who developed a trials vehicle based on the Churchill ARV I. Further tests were made with turretless waterproofed Churchill and Sherman tanks fitted with fixed fabricated box-type structures and wading equipment. Trials with these vehicles provided valuable experience which led to the choice of the Sherman tank with an all-welded hull.

The design of a BARV based on an M4A3 (Sherman IVA) was commenced in November 1943. Fitted with a welded armoured top superstructure and various modifications that included an internal structural design air intake to the crew and a bilge pump to eliminate any water intake, the vehicle proved capable of operating in water to a depth of nine feet with an 18 in. surge.

Because of the urgency of getting these vehicles into production by D-Day it was impossible to devote time to further development such as the installation of a winch and the fitting of earth anchors. The vehicle was therefore limited to straight pulls.

A requirement for 50 BARVs was placed, this being later raised to 66. By D-Day 52 vehicles were completed and delivered to Beach Recovery Section, production vehicles being based on the diesel-engined M4A2 (Sherman III).

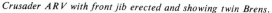

Crusader ARV with front jib erected and showing twin Brens.

Three-quarter rear view of Vickers Wolseley wheel-cum-track armoured car. Chain drive to rear wheels and casing for jacks to raise rear wheels can be seen. (Photo: Vickers Ltd.)

Wheels, Tracks and Transporters

by Major-General N. W. Duncan

TRACK wear raised its ugly head as a problem when Mother and Little Willie were completing their first trials and it has remained a major worry to the commanders of all armoured troops and to AFV designers ever since. Fifty miles was a considerable distance for the Mark I track and by then it had stretched to such an extent that continued use was no longer possible: the lengthened links no longer engaged properly with the driving sprocket whose teeth wore into hooked shape (see diagram) and ultimately broke off, or else the track plates rode over the sprocket teeth setting up such stresses that either the track plate or the track pin broke.

To get over this problem as far as possible tank movement was carried out by train. Special wagons were required to take the load and to keep within the loading gauge. Although a necessary evil rail moves were not popular with tank crews who in early days had to remove the sponsons and mount them on sponson trucks to reduce the overall width of the tank on the wagons. Matters improved with the Mark IV whose sponsons could be swung inboard but even then a lot of work was involved.

Entraining and detraining was taught as a drill and

every permanent camp of the Tank Corps had dummy tank wagons constructed of concrete on which practice could be carried out. Dummy ramps to ground level simulated conditions which would obtain when tanks could not be unloaded at a station's unloading dock.

The same problem occurred after Dunkirk in 1940 when the rapid movement of armour in the United Kingdom was imperative. Special wagons and portable ramps were built but their use was limited and they were ultimately replaced by the wheeled road tank transporter which had become a feasible proposition with the manufacture of heavy duty pneumatic tyres.

After World War I various attempts were made to produce a lubricated track which would keep at bay the abrasive mixture of dirt, sand and mud which played such havoc with the ordinary tracks. They failed because of the difficulty of devising satisfactory oil seals, the high cost of manufacture, and the amount of skilled labour involved in their production: track wear remained apparently insoluble and it was not until the Vickers Medium tanks had come into service that a new approach was made to the problem.

In 1926 Vickers modified a Wolseley car chassis to

The later version of the Vickers Wolseley wheel-cum-track car.
(Photo: R.A.C. Tank Museum)

Carden-Loyd carrier Mark V shown on wheels. Note small ground clearance below track, and chain to pivot wheel frame for steering. Clearance below mudguards shows how far wheels lift for tracked drive. *(Photo: R.A.C. Tank Museum)*

Vickers Wheel-cum-Track Tank, 1928. First prototype with track frames fixed rigidly to hull sides.
(Photo: R.A.C. Tank Museum)

Vickers Wheel-cum-Track Tank, 1928. Second prototype with track frames free to rise and fall in guides seen on hull sides.
(Photo: R.A.C. Tank Museum)

run on tracks or wheels at will. A track frame, based on that of the Medium tank but with better bogies, was attached to the chassis on either side, with the ordinary front wheels mounted on their axle sticking out in front of the track frame and the rear wheels protruding in similar fashion from the back of the vehicle. The drive was taken through the ordinary back axle to the rear driving sprocket and track tension could be adjusted by the movable front idler. The track sprocket carried a chain wheel by which the drive was transferred to the two rear wheels and a clutch to break this drive was also provided on the driving sprocket.

To change over to tracked drive the rear wheels were raised—the housing for the jacks to do this is clearly shown in the illustration, immediately above the left hand rear wheel. The geometry of the design allowed the wheel to be drawn upwards without disturbing the driving chain. The front wheels were also raised clear of the ground pivoting on the locating arms which kept them in position. When on tracks the vehicle was steered by independent brakes on either track, operating through the differential. The chassis carried a mock-up armoured body in mild steel and a rotating turret similar to those on the Indian pattern

Vickers Medium Mark I adapted for wheel or track movement shown on tracks with wheels raised.   (Photo: Imperial War Museum)

Vickers Medium Mark I experimental wheel and track tank with wheels on ground. Note original pattern suspension bogies and counter-balanced driver's hood here shown closed.
(Photo: R.A.C. Tank Museum)

Side view of the Schofield Wheel-and-Track Light Tank built in New Zealand in 1940. Unable to get tanks from Britain the New Zealand Government investigated the possibilities of building its own. This was the only true tank to reach prototype stage. Designed by E. J. Schofield of General Motors (Wellington) it was based on the chassis of the New Zealand-built GMC 6-cwt. commercial truck with track and suspension from a Universal Carrier. The wheels and mechanical units came from the 6-cwt. truck. The cylindrical open-topped turret mounted a 2-pdr. gun and a co-axial machine-gun. When running on wheels, as in this view, the tracks, which had little ground clearance, were looped up by chains. The Schofield had a crew of three.

A13 Mark IIA (Cruiser Tank Mk.IVA) on a Scammell 30-ton Semi-Trailer transporter in the Desert.

A10 (Cruiser Tank Mk.II) on a Mack 'EXBX' transporter in the United Kingdom.

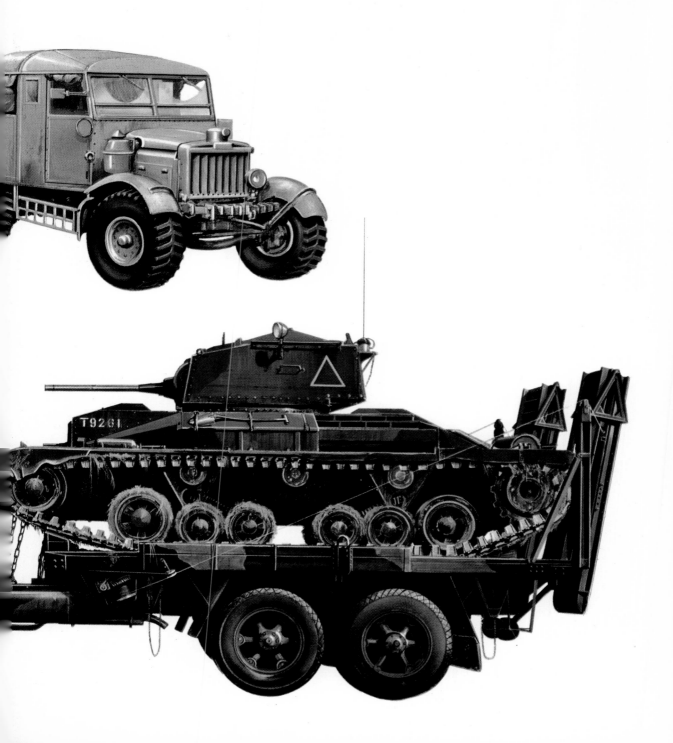

Three quarter right rear view of the New Zealand Schofield Wheel-and-Track Light Tank built in 1940. Whereas the wheels were outside the tracks at the rear they were inside them at the front. The wheels shared common stub axles with the sprockets and idlers. When the vehicle was running on tracks the wheels were removed and fitted to stub axles on the hull sides. The change from wheels to tracks was effected by pivoted arms which were operated from inside the tank. The Schofield weighed 5 tons, its armour thickness ranging from 6 mm. minimum to 10 mm. maximum. Its dimensions were: length 13 ft. 1 in., height 6 ft. 7½ in. on tracks, 6 ft. 10½ in. on wheels, width 8 ft. 6½ in. It had a maximum speed of 25 m.p.h. on tracks and 45 m.p.h. on wheels. Only this one prototype was built.

Very early type of track on a Ruston-Hornsby tractor, dating from before World War I now in the Royal Armoured Corps Tank Museum, Bovington. (Photo: Duncan Crow)

armoured car. The machine was only produced in prototype form.

A later version appeared as a touring car in more sophisticated form with a less obvious drive to the rear wheels. The method of transfer from wheels to tracks was the same as in the earlier armoured car version but the jacks were stowed more neatly. The illustration shows the modified form of bogie fitted to both types which is reminiscent of the box bogie introduced in 1931 for the Mark I Vickers Medium tank. The track frames were sprung but the ride was an uneven one and very liable to pitch badly. To overcome this shock absorbers were fitted to the front and back bogies and can be seen in the picture. The clearance when on wheels was small but it was sufficient for the vehicle to move with ease on good smooth going.

Carden-Loyd had investigated the possibilities of wheel and track drive and their Mark V machine-gun carrier had a wheel on either side of the body, mounted on a swinging arm. The wheels which had an optional chain drive from the front sprocket, could be lowered by hand-operated jacks: they were shod with pneumatic tyres and the drive to either wheel could be broken by using the track brakes which worked through the differential of the Ford back axle which was used for transverse drive. No means of disconnecting the track while wheel-borne was provided but the wheel drive could be broken by dog clutches on the driving sprockets. The change from track to wheels was completed by a third steerable wheel mounted on a sprung pivot in the centre of the back of the vehicle. Track clearance on wheels was a matter of inches: with the short wide wheelbase, the problems of reconciling the erratic operation of the track brakes with the vagaries of the steerable pivot wheel made a wheeled ride in one of these vehicles a succession of hair-raising incidents, each one presaging instant disaster!

By 1928 a certain amount of experience in the operation and design of wheel and track machines had been gained and on the strength of it Vickers built the first of several experimental tanks. It was a curious looking affair, constructed in mild steel with a circular turret perched on top of an odd looking box body, with another machine-gun turret behind the main one on the superstructure. Tracks were very narrow with pressed steel plates and the rear driving sprocket was on the ground. Eight independent coil sprung double wheels took the load and there were four return rollers which were so arranged that they gave an odd looking track profile. The rear wheels were inside the track frames while the front wheels were on the normal axle beam and were mounted in front of the track frames. Solid lorry pattern tyres took the load and the actual wheel loading must have been very high. No details exist about this tank but it is believed that the transfer from wheel to tracks was made by raising the wheels clear of the ground thus allowing the track to take the load.

This machine was followed by a second version the same year: in this model the track frames which were complete separate units were attached to the hull sides through slides at the front and back of the tank. The track was of better shape than in the first version and the rear idler had been raised so that it was clear of the ground. The change from wheeled to tracked drive was effected by power-operated jacks which forced down the track frames until the track bore the load. The body of the second model was little more than a cover for the necessary power trains to operate the jacks and to drive the vehicle. In one respect this tank was better than the first version; the drive to wheel or track was optional and geared to both. However this involved complicated engineering which with the power-operated jacks meant that there was very little room for the luggage in the shape of guns, ammunition and crew!

The second version with its running but not its operating gear is in the R.A.C. Tank Museum: it deserves study as an interesting and ingenious attempt to solve a very real problem. The wheel loading was very high and beyond anything but first-class roads. Wheel-borne the tank was tiring and difficult to drive, top-heavy and a sight to strike terror into all spectators, one of whom once summed up the matter succinctly. "As if," he said, "you had mounted a New York skyscraper on roller skates and driven it round an English barracks."

Vickers tried again in 1930 using a Vickers Medium Mark IA to which wheels were fitted in front and rear. These wheels were mounted in separate sub-assemblies with their own power jacks to raise and lower them. When down they were locked in position by struts, one of which can be seen in the picture together with the eye into which it fits on the steering wheel box. The contraption worked and was the best version produced, but the complications of the power operation for the jacks and the alternative drives to tracks or wheels took up a great deal of room and led to the abandonment of the project. The tank was stripped of the extra gear and sent to the 2nd Bn. R.T.C. as a normal gun tank in 1932.

By this time it was quite obvious that there was little chance of incorporating a separate wheel drive in a normal fighting tank. However in America Mr Christie had produced a series of machines which could run either on their large suspension wheels or else on their tracks. Despite the high speeds attained by these tanks the inevitable complications attendant on the problems of driving and steering the suspension wheels led to the abandonment of the dual drive both in America and also in Russia where it had been tried out on an extensive scale.

Track wear was still a problem, lessened it is true, by the inclusion of harder material in the tracks, but none the less present: to reduce it the question of wheeled transporters was examined again on the grounds that there were more roads than railways and that heavy duty tyres were becoming a possibility. In the 1930s light tanks had been delivered all over England on commercial low load multi-wheeled transporters. Attempts were made to develop these for military use without much success except for the Scammel 6 × 4 prime mover and its trailers which were principally used for recovery work where they performed admirably. The alternative semi-trailer versions were not so successful: they had a high centre of gravity when loaded and were apt to be on the unstable side in consequence. The problem was solved by the American Diamond T 6 × 4 prime mover and trailer, a big multi-wheeled affair capable of taking the largest tanks. This was a most satisfactory combination and the highly skilled crews who manned this and the

other transporters used in World War II saved an infinite amount of unnecessary track mileage. A set of tracks for a tank weighs anything between one and two tons. Replacement tracks for an armoured brigade of 150 tanks may therefore mean moving up to 300 tons of dead weight which can only be accomplished at the expense of something else, ammunition or petrol, each just as vital as the track. Anything that will lessen this burden is worth while and the only problem with the transporter is to make sure that the tank is never caught by the enemy while on its trailer.

Improvements in track design have increased the operational life of the track. Better materials, including the use of rubber, pioneered for tank work by the Americans who set new standards for track reliability, have contributed to this; and the latest British tracks with detachable rubber pads which reduce plate wear while still retaining the self-cleaning action of the grouser bars in heavy going would appear to have the best of both worlds.

Diagram to show type of wearon teeth of World War I tank driving sprockets.

Track driving sprocket with unworn teeth

sprocket centre

Track driving sprocket with teeth "hooked" after use

sprocket centre

AFV Series Editor: DUNCAN CROW

An early A.E.C. semi-trailer tank transporter.
(Photo: Imperial War Museum)

United States Marmon-Herrington Light Tank Type CTL-1 with rubber endless band tracks, 1935. The Americans pioneered the use of rubber for tank work and set new standards for track reliability. Different models of the Marmon-Herrington CTL Light Tank were built for commercial sale from 1935 to 1940. The CTL was inspired by the success of the Carden-Loyd Mark VI. (Photo: Colonel R. J. Icks)

Chieftain with detachable rubber pads which reduce plate wear in tracks. (Photo: Profile Publications)

Close-up of Chieftain track with rubber pads for reducing plate wear.
(Photo: Profile Publications)

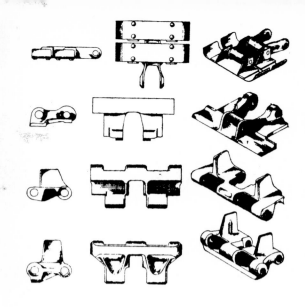

The evolution of the Carden-Loyd track from the modified original conveyor belt basis to the final malleable cast iron track, 1928. It founded a world-wide dynasty of AFV tracks.
(Photo: *Tracks for Fighting Vehicles* by E. W. E. Micklethwait, 1944)

Scammell tank transporter with Vickers Medium Mark II on board.

Federal tractor truck, 6 × 4 diesel.
(Photo: Imperial War Museum)

(Photo: Imperial War Museum)

Mack "EXBX" 18-ton Tank Transporter (W.D. No. L770073). Weight unladen 11 tons 1 cwt. gross, weight laden 29 tons 10 cwt. gross (18 ton tank).
(Photo: Imperial War Museum)

Crusader (Cruiser Tank Mark VI) on the ramps of a Scammell 30-ton Semi-Trailer Recovery Tank Transporter in the Western Desert.

Scammell 30-ton Semi-Trailer Recovery Tank Transporter with a Sherman on board in a desert supply column.

Side view of Mack "EXBX" 18-ton Tank Transporter. Length 29 ft. 5½ in., 30 ft. 10½ in. with folding ramps. Width 10 ft. 1 in. Height 8 ft. 3 in. (cab), 11 ft. 4 in. (folded ramps).
(Photo: Imperial War Museum)

Loading a Valentine on to a Mack "EXBX". The Mack was an American vehicle. (Photo: Imperial War Museum)

Scammell 30-ton Semi-Trailer Recovery Tank Transporter with Matilda on board. Length 49 ft. 8 in. (tractor and trailer with ramps raised). Width 8 ft. 7 in. (tractor), 9 ft. 5½ in. (semi-trailer). Height 10 ft. 11 in. (top of raised ramps), 9 ft. 5 in. (top of cab). Weight unladen 19 tons 18 cwt. gross, weight laden (with Matilda) 49 tons 16 cwt. gross. (Photo: Imperial War Museum)

Scammell 20-ton Semi-Trailer Tank Transporter (W.D. No. 4575956). This unit was designed to recover and transport tanks of up to 20 tons, such as the Crusader (Cruiser Mark VI). Length 49 ft. 3 in. (tractor and trailer with ramps raised). Width 8 ft. 7 in. (tractor), 9 ft. 2 in. (semi-trailer). Height 9 ft. 4 in. (top of raised ramps), 9 ft. 5 in. (top of cab). Weight unladen 15 tons 10 cwt. gross. (Photo: Imperial War Museum)

Scammell 30-ton Semi-Trailer Recovery Tank Transporter had the same tractor as the 20-ton version, but is easily recognisable because the floor of the semi-trailer is not parallel to the ground as in the 20-ton version. The Scammell 30-tonner earned a great reputation for reliability, especially in the Western Desert, where this picture was taken. (Photo: Imperial War Museum)

Diamond T 30-ton Semi-Trailer Recovery Tank Transporter being tested in difficult conditions with a Churchill on board. These vehicles, used by British and Canadian tank transporter and recovery units, were powered by a Hercules DFXE 6-cyl. diesel engine.
(Photo: Imperial War Museum)

The British Army's tank transporter of the 1970s is the Antar. Seen here is an Antar Mark 2: FV 12002, Tractor 30-ton 6 × 4 GS, Thornycroft Antar Mark 2 with FV 30011, Semi-Trailer 50-ton, Tank Transporter. The Antar Mk. 2 has a 285 b.h.p. Meteorite engine which gives it a maximum road speed of 28 m.p.h. (Photo: Society of Motor Manufacturers and Traders)

Three-quarter rear view of Diamond T 30-ton Semi-Trailer Recovery Tank Transporter. The vehicle was made by removing the ballast body from a standard Diamond T tractor and replacing it by a semi-trailer turn-table. Shelvoke and Drewry Ltd., who made the semi-trailers, gained an award for the spring-balanced ramp seen in this picture. Length 49 ft. 10 in. (tractor and trailer with ramps raised). Width 8 ft. 4 in. (tractor), 9 ft. 8 in. (semi-trailer). Height 8 ft. 3 in. (top of cab), 8 ft. 0 in. (front of semi-trailer). Weight unladen 22 tons 9 cwt. gross, weight laden 53 tons 8 cwt. gross (with Sherman). (Photo: Imperial War Museum)

Scammell 30-ton Semi-Trailer Recovery Tank Transporter bringing a damaged Sherman into a R.E.M.E. tank repair workshop in Normandy, July 1944. Powered by a 6-cyl. Gardner engine with 6F and 1R gears, the tractor had a cab large enough for seven men. The two ramps were lowered by small hand winches to give a ramp angle of 18 degrees. Two hydraulic jacks support the rear of the semi-trailer during loading and can be used in wheel-changing and in detaching the semi-trailer from the tractor. (Photo: Scammell Lorries Ltd.)

M19 Recovery Transporter unit with a captured German self-propelled weapon (Panzerjäger IV with 7·5 cm. Stu.K.42 L/70) near Goch during Operation "Veritable", February 1945.
(Photo: Major-General N. W. Duncan)

Shermans of the 9th Lancers, 2nd Armoured Brigade, 1st Armoured Division, loading on to M19 40-ton Recovery Transporter units near Halfway House on the Cairo-Alexandria Road, Egypt 1942. The M19 unit combined the Diamond T M20 tractor and the M9 trailer.

M19 40-ton Recovery Transporter unit, which combined the Diamond T 6×4 12-ton M20 tractor and the 24-wheel 40-ton M9 trailer, here seen loading an American M5 Light Tank (Stuart) "somewhere in England", 1944. Similar British trailers Mks. I and II were also used in the unit. Unlike the American version seen here which terminated the tank carrier runways in a sloping plate at the rear of the front wheels, the British-built trailer had runways continuing on to the front of the trailer and terminating in triangular stop blocks. Length 30 ft. 2 in. (American Rogers Brothers), 31 ft. 11 in. (British Mk. I). Width 9 ft. 6 in. (American), 10 ft. 0 in. (British). Height 4 ft. 9 in. (American), 5 ft. 10 in. (British). Weight unladen 10 tons 2 cwt. gross (American), 13 tons 12 cwt. gross (British). Weight laden (with Churchill) 50 tons 7 cwt. gross (American), 52 tons 14 cwt. gross (British). The tractor was 22 ft. 7 in. long, 8 ft. 4 in. wide, 8 ft. 3 in. high (to top of cab), and weighed 11 tons 18½ cwt. unladen without ballast, 18 tons 18½ cwt. laden with 6·65 tons of ballast. The M19 was the most widely used and longest in service during and since World War II in all parts of the world.

(Photo: Imperial War Museum)

Transporter in need of recovery! M19 Recovery Transporter unit with Buffalo of 11th Royal Tanks, 33 Armoured Brigade, 79th Armoured Division, well ditched near Arnhem, April 1945. (Photo: Major-General N. W. Duncan)

Left: *Morris Armoured Car, Reconnaissance (Model CS9/LAC). Produced in 1938 and the only recently built type of armoured car in service at the outbreak of war. The prototype is shown—this differed only in minor details from the production cars.* (B.M.C.)
Right: *Steyr-Daimler-Puch (Austro-Daimler) Model ADSK. This was the original type supplied to Britain for experiment.* (R. J. Icks)

Guy, Daimler, Humber, A.E.C.

by B. T. White

THE year 1938, during which it seemed increasingly apparent to the less sanguine students of European affairs that war with Germany was inevitable, found the British army with only one modern type of armoured car in service. This was a four-wheeled Morris type, based on the 15-cwt. truck chassis. This design allowed for the quick and relatively cheap production of 100 armoured cars to re-equip the two cavalry armoured car regiments of the Army but, reverting as it did in many ways to features that were no improvement on armoured cars designed in 1914, could be regarded as no more than a stop-gap.

Rolls-Royce armoured cars of a design only improved in details over that of the original 1914 Admiralty turreted pattern were still in service, although some were rearmed with an anti-tank rifle and in this form were actually used in action in Libya in 1940.

Armoured cars of the 1938 Morris type and the Rolls-Royce 1920/1924 pattern with their conventional suspension and transmission on the rear wheels only were not good in performance off roads, although the development of an efficient design of sand tyre helped improve their going in the desert. This is not to say that various vehicles that showed a much better cross-country performance had not been built in the inter-war years in Britain as well as—more widely—on the Continent. In Britain in the 1920's and 1930's, efforts were concentrated on the development of the rigid (as opposed to articulated) 6×4 chassis both as a military load carrier and later as an armoured car. This six-wheeled type, with drive to all four of the rear wheels, showed a considerable improvement over 4×2 vehicles, although it had the disadvantage of "bellying" —the chassis between the front wheels and the front pair of rear wheels grounding—in certain conditions. However, 43 Lanchester Armoured Cars of this type were built in 1927-1931, followed by 6 Crossleys and

these shared with some 76 Rolls-Royces armoured car duties with the British Army all over the world during the inter-war years and some were still in service even after the outbreak of World War II.

The Royal Air Force, which also used armoured cars—these were for internal security in Iraq and Palestine, in conjunction with aeroplane squadrons—mostly employed Rolls-Royces similar to those of the Army. Some 6×4 armoured cars of different pattern to the Army's were experimented with, however, as well as 4×4 types designed by Nicholas Straussler. Twelve of the latter were eventually ordered in 1937-1938. Perhaps the most advanced model of British 6×4 armoured car was the Armstrong-Siddeley, tested by the Air Ministry about 1938, which had a relatively short wheelbase, a well shaped hull and rear mounted engine, but the 6×4 layout was, as a whole, losing favour for A.F.V.s by this time.

On the Continent, several designs for armoured cars (besides those of Straussler, which originated in Hungary) were developed around the years 1933-1937 and which showed considerable advantages in cross-country going. Also, in Britain by 1937 there were several new designs of 4×4 chassis some of which were coming into use as gun tractors for the army.

ARMOURED CAR TRIALS

In 1938 the War Office decided to institute tests to determine the best form of chassis to develop as an armoured car both to replace all existing types and to be suitable for further production in the event of war. As a start, early in February, six different chassis from five manufacturers were got together for comparative tests. All were four-wheeled types, with four-wheel drive, but three had conventional suspension with rigid axles and three had independent suspension.

The three chassis with conventional suspension were a Guy Ant (supplied by Guy Motors Ltd.,

AFV 3L

Steyr-Daimler-Puch chassis with mock-up armoured car hull and turret. (British Official—Crown Copyright)

Morris Light Tank (Wheeled) in use by the Cairo City Police in 1941. The armament has been added locally.
(British Official)

Guy Light Tank (Wheeled)—the first prototype. (Tank Museum)

Left: *Morris Light Tank (Wheeled)—chassis. Note the rear-mounted Morris water-cooled engine with twin radiators; the tubular backbone with diagonally placed stub axles and volute springs.* (B.M.C.)

Wolverhampton), a Unipower, a forestry tractor type of vehicle, provided by Universal Power Drives Ltd. of Perivale, Middlesex, and an American G.M.C. chassis.

The three independently sprung chassis were a Morris Quad, supplied by Morris Commercial Cars Ltd., Birmingham, and two Steyr-Daimler-Puch vehicles imported from Austria. One of these Austrian vehicles (which were from the Austro-Daimler division of Steyr-Daimler-Puch A.G.) was a small turretless armoured car with a rear mounted air-cooled engine and the other was a front engined unarmoured troop carrying vehicle, also adaptable to towing light artillery.

The preliminary tests eliminated the Unipower and the G.M.C. chassis and further trials were then concentrated on the British-built Guy and Morris chassis (of which six of each were ordered for extended trials) and on the Austrian Steyr-Daimler-Puch vehicles. By the end of February 1938 the fact was established that the Steyr-Daimler-Puch models were of high performance, being fast and economical in fuel. However, the driving position was cramped (this applied more to the armoured car than the troop carrier), the air-cooled engine was noisy and the braking was poor.

The performance of the Guy was found to be about the same as that of the Austrian vehicles although

there were some problems with the suspension and the cooling of the water-cooled engine.

The Morris Quad proved to be the worst performer of the semi-finalists. The design of this vehicle was a completely new departure for the Morris Commercial firm. It consisted of a tubular chassis with a water-cooled engine mounted at the rear with the fan at the back and radiators at either side. The transmission was taken from a transfer box in front of the engine by means of diagonal shafts to bevel boxes at each wheel. Many faults arose in the tests carried out up to October 1938, including failure of the water pumps and stub axles. Also the Morris Quad was slower than the other types and the driver's position was uncomfortable. It was recommended, therefore, that further development should be limited to improvement of the steering position—modification of the steering column and of the driver's seat to make it adjustable—in order to make the six vehicles built suitable to be handed over to the Army for training purposes. To end their story at this point, the Morris Quads had armoured hulls and turrets similar to those of the Guy Armoured Cars. No armament appears to have been fitted during their trials although one car tested in Egypt was eventually handed over to the Cairo City Police for riot control purposes. Rejoicing in the name of "Ursula" it was equipped locally with a light machine-gun (possibly of Italian manufacture) plus crew weapons.

Tests continued through 1938 with the Guy armoured cars (three of which had been completed by September) and the Steyr-Daimler-Puch vehicles, five of which in all were obtained for experiment, four as armoured cars and the other as an armoured gun tractor.

The Steyr-Daimler-Puch armoured cars resolved themselves into three main types: the original model, turretless, with air-cooled engine; a modified version with a different hull with additional vision ports etc., in which the air-cooled engine was replaced by a Morris water-cooled type; and a chassis similar to that above with a Morris engine and fitted with a mock-up body with a rectangular turret (which was of identical pattern to the Guy and Morris turrets).

It had been felt desirable to try out the Steyr-Daimler-Puch design with a British-built engine since this would have obvious advantages if the Austrian vehicle were chosen for production. Also, the original air-cooled engine, although efficient, was noisy, which

was a liability in a reconnaissance vehicle. Therefore, Morris type CD water-cooled engines were fitted in some of the Steyr-Daimler-Puch armoured cars in order to compare their performance with that of the air-cooled engine. The water-cooled engine gave a markedly inferior performance in the Steyr-Daimler-Puch armoured car.

GUY ARMOURED CAR

In the meantime, trials of the Guy Armoured Car continued to show a good, if not spectacular, performance. Two out of the first three pilot vehicles were handed over in the autumn of 1938 to the Queen's Bays for troop trials. This was a newly-mechanized cavalry regiment which, it might be supposed, should be likely soon to reveal any mechanical weaknesses in the design. Such faults as showed up were not fundamental and were fairly easily rectified. They included some defects in the rear axle casing, the front anchorage of the rear springs, and the shock absorbers, while the cooling needed some improve-

Armoured Cars, Guy, Marks I and IA—a line-up of vehicles belonging to the Royal Canadian Dragoons, training in the United Kingdom in 1942. (Canadian Official)

A rear view of an Armoured Car, Guy Mark IA. This shows clearly the "solid" rear plate, with air intake underneath. This car is of the 2nd Derbyshire Yeomanry on an exercise in 1941.

Guy Light Tank (Wheeled)—sixth prototype vehicle. Apart from the riveted construction and minor details (including the positioning of the front shock absorbers), this car corresponds closely to the production vehicles which followed. (British Official)

Humber Armoured Car chassis. Rear mounted engine, rectangular frame, semi-elliptic leaf spring suspension. (Rootes Ltd.)

Armoured Car, Humber Mark III. This side view (of a car with full Desert equipment on patrol near the Qattara Depression) shows the new form of turret with increased head room.
(Imperial War Museum)

Left: A view from above of an Armoured Car, Humber Mark II, showing all the armament clearly, including the 15-mm. and 7·92-mm. Besa machine-guns, the twin smoke dischargers on the front plate of the turret and the 0·303-in. Bren machine-gun (with drum magazine) on a Lakeman A.A. mounting. The hull was basically the same as that of Humber Mark I but had a revised glacis plate incorporating the driver's vision hatch, and a different form of engine air intake at the rear.

(Rootes Ltd.)

Below: Humber Mark II Armoured Cars of the 12th Royal Lancers on patrol in the desert in the region of the Qattara Depression, 1942. Much extra equipment had to be carried on these long range patrols and the cars have fittings, including a sun compass on the turret side and a spare wheel, which were not on Home service.

(Imperial War Museum/Jaguar Cars Ltd.)

Armoured Car, Humber Mark IV. Apart from the 37-mm. gun, this model was similar in most respects, externally, to the Mark III. Note the un-ditching channel carried across the front glacis plate. (Rootes Ltd.)

Armoured Car, Humber Mark I. This particular vehicle was presented by the Maharajah of Bikaner in 1941 and was used by the 12th Royal Lancers.
(Imperial War Museum/Jaguar Cars Ltd.)

ments. Some of the necessary modifications appear to have been included in at least one, and perhaps all the last three of the six pilot vehicles built. The last of these, WD No. T4348, which was sent to Egypt for desert trials, shows in its layout all the external characteristics of the production vehicles, including larger tyres (10·50 × 20, replacing the original 10·50 × 16s), re-designed mudguards, allowing more clearance, and re-positioned shock absorbers.

The Guy Armoured Car had all the advantages of being based largely on well tried components, many of which were already in production for the Quad-Ant Field Artillery Tractor. The four-wheel drive ensured a good cross-country performance, although limited to some extent by the use of "solid" axles. The independent suspensions and other features of both the Morris and the Steyr-Daimler-Puch vehicles might, if sufficient time could have been devoted to further development, have resulted in the end in a better vehicle than the Guy, but by this time it was desired to get some modern fighting vehicles into production and a contract was given to Guy Motors Ltd. for 101 armoured cars in January 1939. By this time the new nomenclature of Tank, Light (Wheeled) was applied to this class of fighting vehicle intended for long range fighting reconnaissance for the armoured division or higher formation headquarters. This designation, followed by the maker's name was applied to both the six Guy and six Morris pilot vehicles described above, whilst the Guy production model was known, initially at any rate, as Tank, Light (Wheeled), Mark I.

When Guy Motors were given the contract for production of Light Tanks (Wheeled) the specification called for riveted construction of hulls and turrets in accordance with the designs which originated from Woolwich Arsenal. The company suggested, however, that welding of the armour plate would be much more satisfactory from a production point of view. Doubts were expressed by the War Office technical branches but a successful system for welding the hulls and turrets was developed by Guy's together with a rotary jig for handling the bodies during the welding process. After the war Guy Motors received an award from the Royal Commission for Awards to Inventors for this invention, which reduced both the cost and time of production of hulls and turrets for armoured cars.

The system was adopted for the 101 Guy armoured cars of the production order as well as for all subsequent British armoured cars.

CLASSIFICATION OF BRITISH ARMOURED CARS

It is appropriate at this point to explain the three main classes of armoured car employed by the British Army in World War II.

First was the Tank, Light (Wheeled), for which, by 1941, the simple designation of "Armoured Car" was again adopted.

Second was the "Car, Scout" a new class of armoured vehicle introduced in 1939. This type of vehicle was intended to be as small and inconspicuous as possible, but with a good on- and off-the-road performance, for employment with tank and armoured car regiments for liaison in the battle area and scouting only, although a light machine-gun was provided for protection. The evolution of this type of vehicle is dealt with below.

Finally there was the "Car, Light Reconnaissance" which was introduced as such in 1941 primarily for medium range reconnaissance duties with the Reconnaissance Regiments (the successors to divisional cavalry regiments) of infantry divisions. This class of vehicle was developed from the Light Armoured Cars built in the emergency of 1940, following the evacuation from Dunkirk of the British Expeditionary Force, which were at that time used in many instances as the principal and only equipment of many armoured units without tanks or proper armoured cars. The Morris 1938 armoured cars (the type based on 15 cwt truck chassis) were really in the Light Reconnaissance Car category, although before the introduction of more advanced vehicles they were used in the true Armoured Car rôle. The armament of this type of vehicle was most often a Bren light machine-gun and a Boys anti-tank rifle—both basically infantry weapons—and a smoke discharger. The Light Reconnaissance Car was developed both later and mainly on separate lines from the British Armoured Car and Scout Car of World War II although, mechanically, the specification came quite close to the latter by the end of the war and this was followed up after the war by the production of a

Armoured Car, Humber, A.A. Mark I.
(Imperial War Museum)

B.S.A. Scout Car with original hull without roof or rear protection. (Tank Museum)

Alvis Scout Car. This rear view shows the car in its original form, before it was decided to increase the protection on scout cars to include rear armour and a roof. Note the semi-elliptic transverse rear suspension. (Tank Museum)

Car, Scout, Mark IB. This view from directly overhead shows clearly the octagonal form of the crew compartment, the driver's seat and steering wheel set at an angle, and the close set inverted-V engine air louvres at the rear. (Tank Museum)

vehicle—the Daimler Ferret—which, with slight variations, was suited to carry out both scouting/liaison and reconnaissance functions.

SCOUT CARS

During the early part of 1938 the War Office requirement for a new class of vehicle, the armoured scout car, was evolved and three British firms—Morris Commercial Cars Ltd., Alvis Ltd., of Coventry, and B.S.A. Cycles Ltd., Birmingham were invited to submit prototypes. The idea of introducing into the army a small turretless armoured vehicle for scouting and liaison was almost certainly inspired by the performance and layout of the Steyr-Daimler-Puch vehicle submitted for the armoured car trials held in February. The Steyr-Daimler-Puch concern were not, however, asked to provide further chassis for trials as a scout car because the complete take-over of Austria by Germany in March 1938 made it obviously undesirable to rely further on that country for war materials.

The three firms which submitted chassis for the scout car trials were each, in different ways, qualified by experience to provide a suitable vehicle for cross-country employment.

The Morris firm had already done work on four-wheel drive chassis and independent suspensions for their armoured car prototypes as well as having

constructed the 100, more conventional, armoured cars based on the 15 cwt truck chassis.

The Alvis company already had behind it for nearly 20 years a reputation for building high quality good performance cars (some with front-wheel drive) but, in addition, since 1935 had been associated with Nicholas Straussler in the design and production of armoured cars, 12 of which were, at the beginning of 1938, being built for use by the Royal Air Force Armoured Car Companies. An interesting link with earlier armoured cars lay in George Lanchester who from 1936 to 1939 was on the design staff of Alvis, latterly in charge of the military vehicles department.

The third firm, B.S.A. Cycles Ltd., was basically a builder of motor cycles. Although the company had never built armoured vehicles before, it had a long association with the armaments industry through its parent organization, Birmingham Small Arms, but perhaps more relevant was the fact that it had successfully overcome the problems of designing a front-wheel drive car. This was in production from 1933 onwards, and as the "Scout" (the name is purely coincidental in that the firm later produced a military scout car) achieved a fair degree of popularity in the years before the outbreak of war. (It is fair to say that the transmission and suspension eventually adopted for the scout car was not, in fact, based on that used for the civilian vehicle, but, nevertheless, much of the design experience was almost certainly relevant.) A further point of interest is that the Lanchester Motor Company, which had constructed the six-wheeled armoured cars supplied to the army in 1927–1931, belonged to the B.S.A. group, having been absorbed in 1931.

The three different prototype Scout Cars were tested beginning in August 1938. All three weighed around two tons each and all had a similar layout of rear engine and four-wheel drive, with an armoured body, as first built, open at the rear.

The mechanical details of the three designs differed widely, however. The Morris Scout Car used a 15·9 h.p. 4-cylinder O.H.V. Morris-Commercial engine fitted at the off-side rear of a tubular chassis and linked to a four-speed gearbox. The suspension was an interesting adaptation from a Czechoslovakian design and consisted of four rear half-axles from a Tatra six-wheeled light car. The performance of this vehicle turned out to be inferior to that of the Alvis Scout Car with which it was compared at first, as the B.S.A. model was not ready until later than the other two. The road speed was poor and engine cooling inadequate and the car was returned to the manufacturers for modifications. When received back in March 1939, the Morris Scout Car was still found to be inferior to the Alvis as well as the B.S.A. vehicles and so it was recommended that no further trials of this model should take place.

The Alvis Scout Car was known as the "Dingo",— a name which was, not strictly correctly, applied to the Scout Cars not made by Alvis subsequently supplied to the army in World War II. The Dingo appears not to have been designed by Nicholas Strausler although it undoubtedly used features which were used by him in his series of armoured cars, which had culminated in the model A.C. III, produced by Alvis for the R.A.F. as well as for the Netherlands East Indies Government in a slightly different form. One notable characteristic was the transverse leaf spring suspension system which allowed a good degree of independent wheel movement. The Alvis Scout Car was quite a good vehicle, and fast—putting up an average speed of nearly 50 m.p.h. over a $\frac{1}{4}$-mile cross-country course. However, compared with the B.S.A. Scout Car it had a relatively high centre of gravity—increased when, by a later War Office decision, the Scout Cars were made fully armoured, including a roof.

The third model of scout car, and the one which was eventually chosen for a production order, was that designed by the B.S.A. firm. The drawings for this vehicle were commenced in June 1938 and the prototype was completed in September, only four months later. It did very well in the scout car trials carried out in Wales shortly afterwards. By December 1938 the B.S.A. prototype had covered 10,000 miles both on and off roads and very few major mechanical defects showed up. War Office policy now decreed, however, that scout cars should have complete armour protection in place of the side and frontal armour originally deemed adequate in this type of vehicle. Accordingly the hull was redesigned and an armoured roof added and this extra weight made it necessary for the engine power to be increased and the suspension to be strengthened.

A preliminary order for 172 "Cars, Scout, Mark I", as the vehicles were officially designated, was then placed by the War Office, in May 1939.

DAIMLER ARMOURED CAR

The highly satisfactory performance on trials of the B.S.A. Scout Car led to the suggestion that a larger version should be built as a Light Tank (Wheeled) and accordingly design work on this project was commenced in April 1939. This was again carried out quickly so that the first of the two pilot vehicles ordered was actually running before the end of the

Right: A Car, Scout, Mark IB, belonging to 5th Royal Tank Regiment (4 Armoured Brigade, of 7th Armoured Division) in the Western Desert, 1942. A large stowage bin has been created by adding a plate between the front and rear mudguards on the right side. The support bracket for the folding roof is an identification point. Mark I had a sliding roof and hence no support bracket. (Imperial War Museum)

Below: Car, Scout, Humber Mark I. One of the pilot vehicles, but carrying full standard equipment. The remote-controlled mounting carries one 0·303-in. Bren with a drum magazine. (Rootes Ltd.)

Below: Car, Scout, Ford Mark I, Lynx I. This rear view shows how much larger the engine was compared with the Daimler Scout Cars, and also the greater height of the Canadian vehicle. (Canadian Official)

Daimler Light Tank (Wheeled)—second prototype. This car has the turret and armament as used on the production vehicles, but there are several differences in the hull details.
(Imperial War Museum)

Armoured Car, Daimler Mark I. A general view in which some of the family likeness to the B.S.A.-Daimler Scout Cars is apparent. (Imperial War Museum)

Daimler Mark I Armoured Car. A good close-up of Winston Churchill and also a clear view of turret details of his car, including the twin smoke dischargers, the gun mounting and the P.L.M. mounting on top for two 0·303-in. Vickers "K" machine-guns.

Daimler Armoured Cars of the King's Dragoon Guards in Sicily, 1943. Note the inverted-V radiator armour and the turrets traversed to the rear. (Imperial War Museum)

year, when the Second World War had broken out. Although the design of the armoured car was based on that of the Scout Car, the increased weight (which was approximately double that of the smaller vehicle) and extra power resulted in transmission troubles which showed up in the early trials, together with other features needing revision.

The original vehicle had an armament consisting of two Besa machine-guns—15 mm. and 7·92 mm., the same as were fitted in the later Guy Light Tanks (Wheeled), but the second Daimler armoured car to be built had a turret mounting a 2-pdr. gun as well as a 7·92 mm. Besa machine-gun. This was the first time that a shell-firing weapon of this calibre (40 mm.) had been mounted in a British armoured car, giving it the hitting power of contemporary British infantry and cruiser tanks. The turret design was, in fact, that of a tank—the Tetrarch (Light Tank Mark VII) and the drawings for this turret were supplied by Vickers-Armstrong Ltd.

An interesting feature was carried over from the Scout Car to the armoured car—this was four-wheel steering which was, however, abandoned in the production vehicles as a complication of dubious value. A second steering wheel at the rear was retained in the final design, as were the Girling hydraulic disc

brakes—a new feature in armoured car design which also foreshadowed by several years the general introduction of disc brakes into civilian high performance cars.

The various problems to be overcome meant that the first production vehicles did not come off the assembly lines until April 1941. Known in the development stage as Tank, Light (Wheeled), Mark II, by 1941 the new designation of Armoured Car, Daimler Mark I had been adopted.

HUMBER ARMOURED CAR

The production facilities of Guy Motors were not great enough for them, once war had broken out, to manufacture the large number of Light Tanks (Wheeled) that were required in addition to gun tractors and trucks of various sorts. The Rootes Group of motor firms were asked, about October 1939, therefore, to undertake the design and production of an armoured car.

The design of this vehicle, which was closely modelled on that of the Guy Light Tank (Wheeled) was undertaken by Karrier Motors Ltd., of Luton, Bedfordshire. Taking as the basis the Karrier KT 4 field artillery tractor supplied for the Indian army just before the War, a very similar process to that used in the evolution of the Guy armoured car was carried out. In brief, the engine was moved to the rear, the suspension was suitably modified and an armoured hull and turret mounted. The hull and turret were supplied by Guy Motors (who continued to provide them for Rootes) and were almost identical to those of the Mark IA Guy vehicles.

Since this vehicle was, in effect, an assembly of existing component parts rather than an untried design, trials of the two prototypes in 1940 showed up relatively few snags so that a first production contract for 500 vehicles was awarded in June 1940 and the first of these were running in early 1941. This type of armoured car was known in the development stage as Tank, Light (Wheeled) Mark III but although the design was undertaken by Karrier Motors (who were also chiefly responsible, in the Rootes Group, for subsequent production) the name Armoured Car, Humber Mark I was later adopted in official nomenclature. The reason for this was to avoid confusion with vehicles of Carrier (Bren, Universal, etc.) type.

A.E.C. ARMOURED CAR

By 1941 British armoured car regiments had had considerable combat experience in the desert of North Africa, where, until about September when the first Humber Armoured Cars were received, their main equipment consisted of South African-built Marmon-Herringtons. These, like most contemporary British armoured cars, were armed only with light or heavy machine-guns and so the users adopted the expedient of mounting various captured Italian, and later German, guns of 20-mm. calibre upwards in order to have a weapon capable of knocking out enemy light armoured reconnaissance vehicles.

Although the Daimler Armoured Car with a 2-pdr. gun was under development in England during 1940–41 no official requirement existed at this time for an armoured car with armour as well as armament equivalent to that of a cruiser tank. This gap was filled by the Associated Equipment Company Ltd., of Southall (best known for building London omnibuses) who constructed a mock-up heavy armoured car with a 2-pdr. gun on a modified "Matador" medium gun tractor chassis. To draw attention to this project, the

vehicle was added, unofficially, to a demonstration of military vehicles held on Horse Guards Parade, London in early 1941. The A.E.C. armoured car aroused the interest of the Prime Minister and in due course a production contract—dated June 1941 for 120 vehicles—followed.

It is interesting to note, at this point, that another entirely different A.E.C. armoured mock-up was built also in 1941 but at No. 4 Base Ordnance Workshops of the British army in Egypt. This type (for which there was no real future, once details of the manu-facturers' own design became known in the Middle East) also used the "Matador" chassis but retained the original front-engined layout, although reduced in overall height.

DEVELOPMENT OF THE HUMBER AND DAIMLER SERIES

To supplement production of armoured cars in the British Commonwealth, the design of the Guy/Humber armoured cars was passed to the Canadian authorities so that a similar model could be manu-factured in Canada. The resulting vehicle, about 200 of which were built in 1942, was the Armoured Car, General Motors Mark I (Fox I). This design used a rear engined G.M. chassis fitted with an armoured hull of a pattern modelled very closely on that of the British original. The output of armoured cars by Britain, supplemented by American production, ultimately proved adequate and so, beyond the one relatively small order, no further cars of this particular type were built.

In the United Kingdom, the Humber Armoured Car was developed through four Marks (details of which are given in a later section) and there were two Marks of Daimler Armoured Car. The Daimler was the better design (although the Humber had advantages for command purposes) but was more complicated and required far greater production effort, while the resources of the B.S.A.-Daimler group were smaller than those of the Rootes Group. It was decided, therefore, to rationalize effort by designing a new armoured car which would combine some of the best features of both Humber and Daimler Armoured Cars and be produced by both manufacturing groups.

The Inns of Court Regiment passing through a town in Normandy. The nearest car is a "SOD" ("sawn-off Daimler") with the turret removed—a practice devised by this armoured car regiment. The two cars following have their 2-pdr. guns fitted with Littlejohn attachments. (Imperial War Museum)

Three-quarter rear view of Armoured Car, Humber Mark II. (Rootes Ltd.)

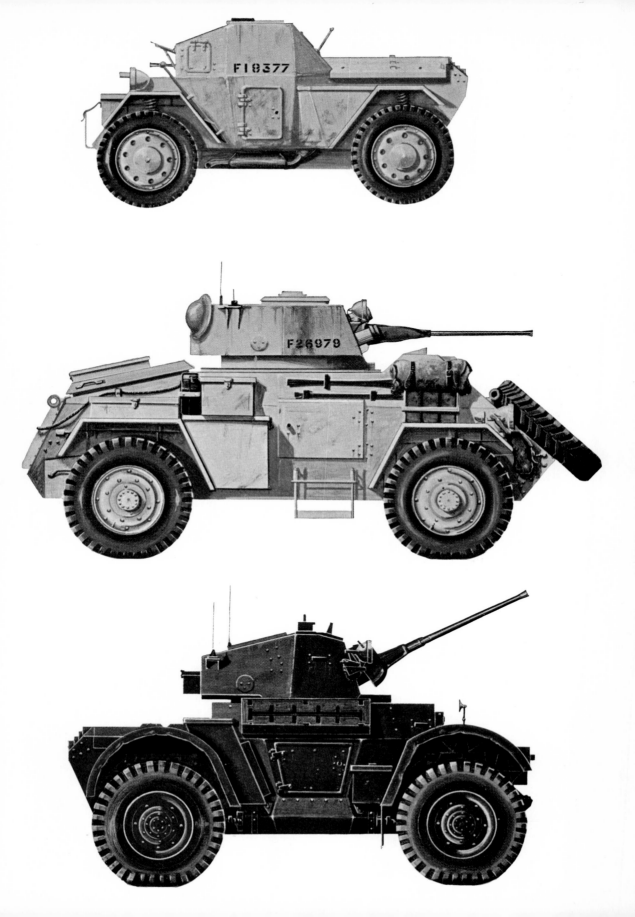

Top: A Car, Scout, Mark IB of 5th Royal Tank Regiment (4 Armoured Brigade, 7th Armoured Div.) as it appeared in the Western Desert 1942.

Middle: An Armoured Car, Humber Mark II of the 12th Royal Lancers (1st Armoured Division) in the Western Desert 1942.

Bottom: An Armoured Car, Daimler Mark I belonging to the 11th Hussars (7th Armoured Division) in Berlin 1945.

Drawn by Martin Lee
© *Profile Publications Ltd.*

A Daimler Armoured Car of the 2nd Household Cavalry Regiment waterproofed for deep wading trials in 1944.
(Imperial War Museum)

The Daimler Mark II Armoured Car on exhibition in the Royal Armoured Corps Tank Museum, Bovington, Dorset is fitted with the post-war pattern of smoke grenade dischargers, mounted in banks of six.
(B. T. White)

An Armoured Car, Daimler Mark I CS in which the 2-pdr. gun has been replaced by a 3-in. howitzer. (The Daimler Co.)

Car, Scout Humber Mark I. A view from above showing the fixed roof with two sliding hatches. (Tank Museum)

The design work for this project, known originally as A.F.V. W.19 and eventually as the Coventry Armoured Car, was undertaken by Humber Ltd., of Coventry, who coordinated the efforts of all concerned as well as doing the detailed work on the hull and turret, armament, stowage, and the installation of the American engine; Commer Cars Ltd., who designed the transmission, axles and gearbox; and the Daimler Company Ltd. (also of Coventry) who produced the drawings for the suspension and the steering gear. Two pilot vehicles each were built by the Rootes Group and the Daimler Company and the first of these were running in 1944. Big production orders of 1,150 for the Rootes Group and about 550 for Daimlers followed, but were cancelled when the war ended after only a few vehicles had been built. Some were sold to the French and used in Viet-Nam after World War II.

LATER SCOUT CARS

The B.S.A.-Daimler Scout Car was produced throughout the war and right from the start was highly successful, so that the demand for this type of vehicle continued to increase. In order that the resources of the Canadian motor industry could be brought in to help, the designs were sent to Canada where an equivalent vehicle was built on a Canadian Ford chassis. Because this had a more conventional form of transmission, however, the Ford Scout Cars (Cars, Scout, Mark III* in British nomenclature, later named Lynx I) were 11 inches higher. Together with an improved version, Lynx II, 3255 scout cars were built in Canada during World War II.

To help meet, from British production, the demand

for scout cars by many arms of service in the British and Commonwealth armies and allied forces, Humber Ltd. were asked in 1942 to design a new scout car to be produced by the Rootes Group. The opportunity was taken of using many features and actual components—including the 6-cylinder engine—of other four-wheel drive vehicles (notably the Light Reconnaissance Car) already in production by the Rootes Group and this helped to simplify development and production problems.

The first contract in late 1942 for Cars, Scout, Humber Mark I (followed later by Mark II with minor differences) was for 4,000 vehicles and this was followed by a second one for 300.

PRODUCTION

The manufacture of armoured cars was a relatively straightforward matter, compared with that of tanks, since the wheeled vehicles were both lighter and less complex in design, and they were built almost entirely on flow production lines in the factories of the big lorry and motor car manufacturers, together with the sub-contractors customary in the motor industry. There was in several cases co-operation between firms who were peacetime rivals, such as the supply of welded hulls and turrets by Guy Motors to Karrier Motors for building Humber Armoured Cars. All the turrets used on Armoured Cars, A.E.C. Mark I came from Valentine tank manufacturers because they were, in fact, ordinary tank turrets.

The numbers of vehicles of each type built during the War were as follows (excluding prototypes and purely experimental models):

Above: *Armoured Car, Daimler Mark I H.A. An experimental modification carried out in the Middle East to produce extra high elevation of the main armament. A special sight, with linkage to the mounting, was mounted on top of the turret.*
(Tank Museum)

Top right: *Armoured Car, Daimler Mark II. The more bulbous gun mantlet and the escape hatch incorporated in the roof of the driver's compartment show up well in this view.*
(Tank Museum)

Right: *Armoured Car, Daimler Mark II. This view shows the new type of armoured radiator grille.* (Tank Museum)

Armoured Cars

Morris (CS9/LAC)	99
Guy Mark I	50
Guy Mark IA	51
Daimler Mark I ⎱ Daimler Mark II ⎰	2,694
Humber Mark I (500) ⎱ Humber Mark II Humber Mark III Humber Mark IV ⎰	5,400 approx.
A.E.C. Mark I (120) ⎱ A.E.C. Mark II A.E.C. Mark III ⎰	629
Fox I	200 approx.
Coventry Marks I–II	a small number only

Scout Cars

B.S.A./Daimler Mark I ⎱ B.S.A./Daimler Marks IA, IB ⎰ B.S.A./Daimler Mark II B.S.A./Daimler Mark III	6,626
Lynx Marks I and II	3,255
Humber Marks I and II	4,300

TECHNICAL DESCRIPTIONS
Guy and Humber Armoured Cars

These two types had a similar line of development and had many features in common so they can conveniently be described together. They both had a rectangular chassis frame with a rear mounted engine with gearbox in front from which the drive was transmitted, via a transfer box approximately in the centre of the vehicle, to differentials on "solid" axles at front and rear. The suspension consisted of longitudinal leaf springs at front and rear, controlled by hydraulic shock absorbers. The welded armoured hull was flexibly mounted on the chassis at four points at the front, rear and sides and, to prevent excessive body movement in rough going, "snubbers" were provided at the corners of the hull. The crew consisted of three men: commander (who was also the wireless operator) and gunner—both in the turret—and driver, in the front part of the hull. (The Humber Mark III had four men, including a wireless operator.) The driver's vision was through a flap in the front of his cab (the cab was incorporated in the front glacis plate in Humber Mark II onwards) which for use when closed carried a bullet-proof Triplex glass block. These blocks could be replaced if damaged. There were also side lookout shutters. For driving in reverse, the engine cover at the back could be raised by a special hydraulic jack so that when a flap in the rear bulkhead of the fighting compartment was also opened the driver could obtain a somewhat limited view out of the rear of the vehicle. The turret, mounted on a ball race, was rotated by means of a hand traversing gear.

Daimler Scout Car and Daimler Armoured Car

The Daimler Armoured Car was developed out of the Scout Car and was in many of its mechanical features a scaled-up version of the smaller vehicle, so the basic points in common will be mentioned here first, followed by an outline of the main differences.

The Daimler armoured vehicles were powered by Daimler 6-cylinder engines mounted at the rear—a 55 b.h.p., 2,522 c.c. unit in the Scout Car and a larger

Experimental armoured car on modified front-engined A.E.C. Matador chassis. This work was carried out in Egypt in 1941.
(British Official)

Armoured Car, A.E.C., Mark I. What appears to be a window below the twin periscopes for the driver is a folded down windscreen, intended for use when the car is opened up and not in action.
(Imperial War Museum)

95 b.h.p., 4,095 c.c. version in the Armoured Car. The Scout Car had a shallow tray-shaped chassis, armoured underneath, but there was no chassis, as such, in the Armoured Car. The engine, suspension, transmission etc. were all built into the lower part of the armoured hull, which formed a shallow dish to which the upper parts of the hull comprising the fighting and driver's compartments and engine cover were attached. The most interesting point about the Daimler armoured vehicles was their form of transmission, which was of a type successfully introduced in Britain for the first time. The drive from the engine was led forward, through a "Fluid Flywheel" and pre selector gearbox, to a transfer box, situated almost exactly in the centre of the lower hull. This incorporated a single differential, from one half of which universally-jointed propellor shafts led forward to the front wheel on one side and back to the rear wheel on the same side. From the other half of the differential, similar shafts led to the wheels on that side. "Tracta" universal joints were employed at each wheel station. In the Armoured Car only, there were also reduction gears at each wheel hub. This transmission system, which avoided central drive shafts, enabled the crew and mechanical components to occupy a much lower position in the centre of the vehicle and helped to reduce overall height. This was of particular benefit in the Armoured Car; and the Scout Car, with a height of 4 ft. 11 in. was nearly a foot lower than the Canadian Lynx I, which had an almost identical hull but central transmission.

The suspension of the Daimlers was independent and consisted of vertical coil springs—one at each wheel station in the case of the Scout Car and a pair to each wheel for the Armoured Car. This system permitted, in the Armoured Car, a vertical upward movement of 16 in. of any one wheel independently of the others, which remained in contact with the ground. In the Scout Car the equivalent figure was about 8 in.

Four-wheel steering was provided in the earlier Marks of Scout Car built and this was also tried out in the Armoured Car. This system allowed a very close turning circle (23 ft., but 38 ft. with two-wheel steering) but was eventually abandoned in the Scout Car and not adopted for the Armoured Car, because inexperienced drivers, it was found, could get the car going

more or less indefinitely into a circle from which they could not get out!

The brakes on the Scout Car were Lockheed hydraulic drum type, but on the Armoured Car Girling disc brakes were used—new for employment in armoured cars and in wheeled vehicles generally.

The Daimler system of the Fluid Flywheel (taking the place of the normal engine clutch) linked with a pre-selector gearbox was introduced from pre-war motor cars built by the group to which the company belonged. In operation, the gear required was selected in advance and then brought in at the desired moment by depression of a pedal. This meant that, for example, reverse gear could be selected when the car was still travelling forwards—so ensuring a quick get-away from the awkward situations likely to be encountered by an armoured car unit on reconnaissance. It also had the advantage of instilling in the driver confidence that there was no likelihood of missing a gear in an emergency.

Amongst the differences between the Scout Car and the Armoured Car, apart from those of scale and the points already mentioned, was the incorporation in the Armoured Car of a duplicate steering wheel, plus hand throttle ignition cut-out switch and hand brake, for use by the commander when driving backwards in emergency. A special port was provided in the rear of the hull over the engine compartment for use in this contingency. However, this operation was avoided wherever possible since, as the historian of one armoured car regiment points out, the commander had to turn round in the confined space of the turret, then kneel and grab with one hand the second steering wheel whilst holding the intercom. microphone to direct the driver, who still controlled the gear-change. The consequent entanglement of wireless leads, the limited vision and the fact that the gunner was left without a loader meant that this system was used only in the "direst emergency". In the Daimler Scout Car, incidentally, although no separate steering wheel was provided the driver could, with practice, drive in reverse quite easily by looking over his left shoulder, since his seat in the octagonal-shaped crew compartment was set at an angle turned inwards slightly.

The turret of the Armoured Car (the Scout Car was, of course, without one) was mounted on ball bearings

210

on the roof of the fighting compartment and was fitted with hand operated traversing gear. The 2-pdr. gun, for which the car commander acted as loader, and 7·92-mm. Besa machine-gun were coaxially mounted.

A.E.C. Armoured Cars

These were the only British-built diesel-engined armoured cars in service in World War II and employed many components of the "Matador" Tractor, 4×4, Medium Artillery. Considerable rearrangement was necessary, however, and within a fairly conventional layout for a rear-engined four-wheel drive armoured car some ingenuity was shown in achieving a compact hull design. The engine, with the gearbox attached in front of it, was mounted inclined downwards—this not only helped reduce the angle of the shaft transmitting the drive through universal joints to a transfer box situated between the front and rear wheels, but also enabled the height of the rear hull deck over the engine to be reduced. The engine was also, in plan view, positioned at an angle which left sufficient room alongside it for the differential for the rear wheels, thus making for a lower mounting than would otherwise have been possible. The transfer box carried the drive forwards to an underslung differential mounted just right of centre on the front axle and rearwards to the rear differential. Drive for normal road conditions was on the front wheels only. The suspension of the armoured cars consisted of longitudinal semi-elliptic leaf springs.

The armoured hull of the A.E.C. Armoured Cars, mounted on a rectangular chassis, had vertical sides but was tapered from the centre, where it was at its widest, to the front and also, to a lesser extent, to the rear. It was chiefly remarkable in that no direct vision port was provided for the driver, reliance being placed on twin periscopes when closed down. At other times the driver's seat could be raised to allow him to look over the top of the glacis plate.

The turret, mounted on a ball race, was traversed by electrical power with optional traverse by hand. On the Mark I, a Valentine tank two-man turret was used but for the Marks II–III a special three-man turret was designed, making a four-man crew for the armoured car.

Coventry Armoured Car

Being developed from the Daimler and Humber Armoured Cars, the Coventry inherited many features of its predecessors but, basically, its layout was more closely akin to that of the Daimlers. The turret and hull were generally like the Daimler Armoured Car as also were some internal features like the rear steering wheel, for instance. The engine was unusual for a British armoured car in being of American manufacture—the Hercules model RXLD 6-cylinder petrol unit, which developed 175 b.h.p. at 2,600 r.p.m. More roomy than the Daimler, the Coventry had a four-man crew, although this had to be reduced to three in the Mark II version equipped with a 75-mm. gun in place of the 2-pdr. of Mark I.

The transmission of the Coventry was different from that of its predecessors in having the drive taken forwards and rearwards from a central transfer box to differentials on front and rear axles which were of the swinging type, sprung on dual vertical coil springs at each wheel station.

Armoured Car, A.E.C., Mark II. The Besa machine-gun is not fitted in this car and the driver's hatch is open and the windscreen erected.
(A.E.C. Ltd.)

Armoured Car, A.E.C., A.A. Hull like that of the Armoured Cars Mks. II-III with a turret as fitted on the Crusader A.A. II anti-aircraft tank. (A.E.C. Ltd.)

Armoured Car, General Motors Mark I, Fox I. Only the armament (two Browning machine-guns—0·5-in. and 0·3-in. calibre), the lighting equipment and the wheel hubs readily distinguish this Canadian-built armoured car from the Humber Mark III on which it was based. (Tank Museum)

Humber Scout Car

The Humber Scout Car had the same general layout as the Daimler Scout but was a larger vehicle capable of carrying three men. The rear-mounted engine (the same as that used on the Humber Armoured Cars and Light Reconnaissance Cars) transmitted power through a transfer box to differentials on the front and rear swing axles with "Tracta" universal joints. The front suspension was of the transverse leaf type (coil spring suspension was experimented with but not put into production) and the rear consisted of longitudinal semi-elliptic leaf springs.

Canadian Scout and Armoured Cars

The Ford Lynx and the General Motors Fox were counterparts of the Daimler Scout Car and the Humber Mark III Armoured Car respectively and used armoured hulls and turrets which closely resembled those of their United Kingdom cousins. The armament of the Fox followed North American practice, however, and was two Browning machine-guns of 0·5-in. and 0·300-in. calibre.

The transmission systems of both vehicles were based on components of Ford and General Motors four-wheel drive vehicles already in existence and used "solid" axles with a single differential on each, receiving the transmission from the engine via a transfer box.

ARMAMENT OF SCOUT AND ARMOURED CARS

The Daimler and Lynx Scout Cars were normally equipped with one 0·303-in. Bren light machine-gun, which was usually operated through a slot in the front plate of the hull. The 11th Hussars, however, modified their Scout Cars with a mounting for twin drum-fed Vickers "K" 0·303-in. machine-guns. This regiment, incidentally, experimentally fitted one of their Daimler Scout Cars with a captured 20-mm. Solothurn automatic gun.

In the Humber Scout Car, which had a fixed roof, provision was made for mounting single or twin 0·303-in. Bren machine-guns which could be operated by linkage from inside the vehicle.

The principal armament of the armoured cars is referred to in the main descriptions but special mention should be made here of the armament for anti-aircraft defence carried by all armoured cars. In 1940 this consisted of either a simple pintle mounting on the turret for a Bren gun or, later, the Lakeman mounting, a sprung counter-poised device from which the weapon was suspended. Armoured cars fitted with the latter included the Humber Marks I, II and III, A.E.C. Mark I and Daimler I. The Lakeman mounting was not very popular because, as one regimental historian put it, it was liable to turn inside out without warning and nearly throttle the car commander or cause him to fire the weapon in a totally unexpected direction!

Later in the war the P.L.M. mounting, used in the Coventry and the later Marks of Humber, Daimler and A.E.C. Armoured Cars (and also retrospectively) was introduced. This generally carried one or two Vickers "K" machine-guns and could be worked from the shelter of the turret.

During the North African campaign some regiments mounted captured German machine-guns (MG. 34) on their armoured car turrets.

For laying down a protective smoke screen, armoured cars carried twin 4-in. smoke dischargers—in the front plate of the turret in the Humbers, on the turret side in the Daimler and Coventry. The A.E.C. Armoured Cars had a 2-in. bomb thrower built into the turret.

MARKS, VARIANTS AND SPECIAL VERSIONS

Listed below are brief details of the different models and variants of the British Armoured Cars and Scout Cars dealt with in this Profile, together with some details of the versions (both experimental and production) that existed for special tasks.

Tank, Light (Wheeled) Mark I (Armoured Car, Guy Mark I).

Tank, Light (Wheeled) Mark IA (Armoured Car, Guy Mark IA)

15-mm. and 7·92-mm. Besa machine-guns instead of the Vickers 0·5-in. and 0·303-in. of Mark I.

Armoured Car, Daimler Mark I

Original production model. Some cars in Normandy had their turrets removed to make them less conspicuous.

Armoured Car, Daimler Mark ICS

Experimental close support version with 3-in. howitzer (able to fire effective high explosive and smoke ammunition) in place of 2-pdr. gun.

Armoured Car Daimler Mark II

Improved model with differences from Mark I including driver's escape hatch in driving compartment roof; new gun mounting (as on Harry Hopkins light tank); modified engine water pump with new type fan; and modified radiator and grille (the armoured louvres were now horizontal instead inverted V-shaped).

Armoured Car, Humber Mark I

Hull and armament as Guy Mark IA.

Armoured Car, Humber Mark II

Revised hull with driver's cab incorporated in front glacis plate; radiator armour grilles introduced at rear.

Armoured Car, Humber Mark III

Four-man crew and revised turret (front part of roof plate sloping forward, rear part sloping backwards). Humbers Marks I–III all had two Besa machine-guns—15-mm. and 7·92-mm.

Armoured Car, Humber Mark IV

New armament of one 37-mm. gun (U.S. model) and one Besa 7·92-mm. machine-gun. Crew three men.

Armoured Car, General Motors Mark I, Fox I

Canadian-built: similar to Humber Mark III. One experimental vehicle was fitted with a 6-pdr. gun in the front of the hull.

Armoured Car, A.E.C. Mark I

Valentine tank turret with 2-pdr. gun and Besa machine-gun. Some later re-armed in the Middle East with a 6-pdr. gun. Spiked rollers were attached to some A.E.C. Armoured Cars for use as minefield locaters in North Africa.

Armoured Car, A.E.C. Mark II

New three-man turret with 6-pdr. gun and Besa machine-gun, bigger engine, revised hull front, etc.

Armoured Car, A.E.C. Mark III

75-mm. gun instead of 6-pdr. and minor turret improvements, etc.

Basilisk

Experimental flame-thrower armoured car with small flame projector turret mounted on right-hand side of hull. The new hull nose design, used later in the A.E.C. Mark II and III armoured cars, was introduced in this model.

Armoured Car, Humber, A.A., Mark I

Anti-aircraft armoured car introduced in 1943 to give protection to armoured car regiments against air attack. One troop of four cars per regiment, but these troops were disbanded early in the Normandy Campaign in 1944 because they were no longer needed. The armament consisted of quadruple 7·92-mm. Besa machine-guns in a turret designed by Stothert & Pitt Ltd. There was also a version with twin 15-mm. Besa machine-guns.

Armoured Car, A.E.C., A.A.

Chassis of A.E.C. Mark II armoured car fitted with turret (like that of the Crusader A.A. II tank) equipped with two 20-mm. Oerlikon cannons. A prototype was built about the beginning of 1944, but production did not follow because the need for this type of vehicle ceased to exist soon afterwards.

Armoured Car, Coventry Mark I

Original version with 2-pdr. gun and Besa machine-gun.

Armoured Car, Coventry Mark II

Pilot models of type with 75-mm. gun and Besa.

Armoured Car, Daimler I (High Altitude)

An experimental modification carried out in the Middle East to permit very high elevation of the 2-pdr. gun.

Armoured Car, Humber Mark III R.L.

Armoured car modified as a Rear Link vehicle to act as a wireless link between Brigade and Divisional headquarters. Turret locked in forward position and guns replaced by dummies. No. 19 wireless converted to high power set by means of an amplifier.

Armoured Cars, Humber Mark II O.P., Humber Mark IV O.P., Fox O.P.

Conversions to artillery observation post officers' vehicles with radio equipment to maintain contact with field artillery batteries.

Carrier, Wheeled (Experimental), Guy

A pilot model of this type was built in 1940 to test its suitability for the function of tracked carriers but with greater speed and mobility in certain conditions. The layout was based on the Guy Light Tanks (Wheeled) but, despite modifications, the engine cooling remained unsatisfactory and as there were also other faults the type was abandoned. Over 4,000 Armoured Wheeled Carriers of the same general concept were, however, built later in India during the war.

Car, Scout, Mark I (Car, Scout, Daimler Mark I)

Original production model. Four-wheel steering and sliding roof.

Car, Scout, Mark IA (Car, Scout, Daimler Mark IA)

Folding roof, with supporting bracket on back of crew compartment.

Car, Scout, Mark IB (Car, Scout, Daimler Mark IB)

As Mark IA but engine fan draught reversed and revised (inverted-V) radiator armour grilles. Some converted to front-wheel steering only.

Car, Scout, Mark II (Car, Scout, Daimler Mark II)

As Mark IB but revised lighting equipment etc. and built without provision for steering of rear wheels.

Car, Scout, Daimler Mark III

No armoured roof fitted and waterproofed engine ignition included when built. After World War II Daimler Scout Cars were sometimes modified in various ways for use in such areas as Palestine and Malaya. These modifications included adaptations as rail vehicles or the addition of a fixed roof carrying a P.L.M. mounting for machine-guns.

Car, Scout, Mark III and Mark III* (Car, Scout, Ford Mark I, Lynx I)

Original Canadian-built Scout Car. Early vehicles had different radiator grilles and a heavier type of folding roof than later vehicles.

Car, Scout, Ford Mark II, Lynx II

Improved model of Lynx I—no armoured roof; sand channels mounted at rear instead of in front; extra stowage bins; revised air cooling grilles. One vehicle was experimentally fitted with a 2-pdr. gun in the front of the hull.

Car, Scout, Humber Mark I

First production model. Synchromesh on 3rd and top gears only.

Car, Scout, Humber Mark II

Identical externally to Mark I but synchromesh added to 2nd gear also.

Universal Scout Car

Prototype built in Canada, 1945, to broad specification supplied from U.K. as a vehicle intended to replace both Scout Cars and Light Reconnaissance Cars and foreshadowed the post-war Daimler Ferret series. (A Daimler Scout Car in England was fitted with a turret ring in early experiments on these lines.)

ARMOURED CARS AND SCOUT CARS IN SERVICE

"The good name of an armoured car regiment rested far more upon the accuracy of its information than upon the casualties which it succeeded in inflicting upon the enemy . . ." as the historian of The Royal Dragoons put it. This being so, the emphasis in the armoured equipment of British armoured car regiments throughout World War II was on speed and mobility rather than on armour and armament.

The organization for a British armoured car regiment in 1938–1940 consisted of a regimental headquarters and three fighting squadrons—each squadron had three troops, each with three armoured cars. The total number of armoured vehicles—which, at this stage of the war, were generally all of the same type—was 38, including those at regimental and squadron headquarters.

The earliest employment of British armoured cars in action in the war was in France in 1939–1940, where the 12th Lancers had Morris type CS.9/LAC vehicles. The only cars of really modern design were the six Guy Light Tanks (Wheeled) used by Phantom—as it was known throughout the war, but whose official title started as the "Hopkinson Mission", became No. 1 G.H.Q. Reconnaissance Unit from June 1940 until January 30, 1941 and then changed to G.H.Q. Liaison Regiment.

Scout cars were tried out in France in the form of two platoons (total 21 cars) incorporated in 4th Bn. Royal Northumberland Fusiliers—a motorcycle infantry reconnaissance battalion. Scout cars were also used in formation, regimental and squadron headquarters in 1st Armoured Division, sent to France in 1940. They continued to be used in this way for scouting and liaison ("armoured despatch riders") with tank units with great success throughout the war. By 1944, the establishment for a tank regiment was nine scout cars in a headquarters intercommunications troop with three more at the headquarters of the squadrons.

The fighting in the Western Desert proved the pre-war organization for an armoured car regiment to be too weak in numbers, because the maintenance of reconnaissance patrols often meant that armoured car regiments were more continuously in action than most other types of unit. Consequently the establishment was increased by mid-1941 to five troops (each of three armoured cars) per squadron; three armoured cars at each squadron headquarters and four armoured cars at regimental headquarters—total 58 armoured cars.

In 1939–41 the armoured car units in the Western Desert—the only active British war front after the evacuation from France—were equipped at first only with pre-war Rolls-Royce and Morris armoured cars, supplemented later by South African-built Marmon-Herringtons. These South African cars were produced in good numbers (5,746 by the end of the War) and were reliable and easy to handle, although not very modern in design. British-built Humber Armoured Cars were first issued to troops in the United Kingdom about June 1941, but did not begin to reach the Middle East Forces until September of the same year. The first Daimler Armoured Cars were not received in this theatre of war until about July 1942 and the first Humber Mark IIIs in October.

Both Humbers and Daimlers were welcomed in turn by the armoured car regiments as being progressive upward steps in the design of the fighting compartment, armour and armament, although there was a tendency to criticise both types as being underpowered. In desert conditions, to start with at any rate, the Humber's main disadvantage, according to the 11th Hussars, was a short engine life of only 3,000 miles. Another armoured car regiment's historian has reported the difficulty drivers had at first with the Daimler's fluid flywheel transmission, which did not seem able to stand up to the strain of the going in soft sand. However, both types soon proved themselves and generally speaking, were very effective in the open desert conditions. Steps were taken in 1941–1942 in the United States and South Africa to develop heavier vehicles, some with eight wheels to take advantage of these conditions, which placed no limits on size but where guns with longer range would be an asset. The U.S. Staghound was the only car out of these experiments to go into quantity production for Britain, but too late for the desert fighting. However, the first British A.E.C. heavy armoured cars were received by the Eighth Army in 1942.

A new organization for armoured car regiments was adopted in 1943 prior to the invasion of the continent of Europe, which opened with the landing in Sicily in which a squadron of The Royal Dragoons, equipped with Daimler Armoured Cars and Daimler Scout Cars, took part. The new organization introduced a fourth "Sabre" fighting squadron to the armoured car regiment which then had as typical equipment:—

Regimental headquarters

1 Daimler Scout Car
12 Humber Scout Cars (when these became available)
1 Daimler Armoured Car
3 Staghound Armoured Cars
4 Humber A.A. Armoured Cars
1 Armoured Command Vehicle

Four Squadrons each consisting of:—

Squadron Headquarters—with
1 Daimler Scout Car
1 Daimler Armoured Car
3 Staghound Armoured Cars
5 Reconnaissance Troops—each with
2 Daimler Scout Cars
2 Daimler Armoured Cars
1 Support Troop—with
1 Daimler Scout Car
3 White Armoured Personnel Carriers
1 Section—with
2 S.P. 75-mm. guns

Basilisk flamethrower armoured car. A small turret for a flame projector mounted on a hull adapted from that of the basic armoured cars. This vehicle was intended to accompany armoured car units in the field but did not get beyond the experimental stage because the requirement for this particular type of vehicle was cancelled. (A.E.C. Ltd.)

Armoured Car, Coventry Mark I. The Daimler influence in the parentage shows up clearly in this view. The weights bolted on to the nose plate are for trials purposes only.
(Imperial War Museum)

This organization gave a total of nearly 150 armoured vehicles for the regiment.

The Daimler Armoured Car had by 1944 become deservedly favoured as the basic vehicle in the armoured car regiment, although Humbers were still used and were generally preferred for command purposes because of their greater roominess. Staghounds, designed for open desert warfare were far less suited for reconnaissance in the narrow lanes and fields of Europe and were used at regimental and squadron headquarters. The place of the S.P. 75-mm. guns (built on U.S. armoured half tracked chassis) was in some regiments taken by a troop of two A.E.C. Mark III heavy armoured cars with 75-mm. guns.

Besides armoured car regiments, which performed reconnaissance duties for armoured divisions or higher formations, units of the Reconnaissance Regiment carried out roughly the same function for infantry divisions.* The organization of a battalion of the Reconnaissance Regiment included much more equipment for dismounted action, but in each of the three reconnaissance squadrons were three scout troops, each including one section composed of two armoured cars (by 1944 usually Humber Mark IVs but sometimes Daimlers) and two Light Reconnaissance Cars. The establishment for a Reconnaissance Regiment in 1945 included a total of 28 armoured cars and 24 Light Reconnaissance Cars. Scout cars remained a popular and essential item in the equipment of British tank regiments throughout the war for scouting and liaison duties. The usual establishment was 12 scout cars, distributed between regimental and squadron headquarters.

The large number of scout cars included in the armoured car regiment is an indication of the high value for reconnaissance purposes that had come to be placed on this type of vehicle. Common tactics in Normandy were to have a scout car leading the troop. When an enemy position was located the troop

commander and his second in command, both in Daimler Armoured Cars, would, if necessary try and out-flank the position and knock it out, so that the advance could be continued, led again by one of the two Scout Cars. The support troop was brought in where dismounted tactics were required and the 75-mm. gun vehicles where the heavier weapons could help to knock out stiffer opposition.

It was in Normandy that some armoured car regiments removed the turrets of their Daimler Armoured Cars to lessen their height and, in effect, turn them into large Scout Cars. The 2-pdr. guns of the Daimlers were, in any event, only effective against light armoured vehicles, although the penetration was considerably improved by the Littlejohn attachment (a "squeeze-gun" device which tapered the bore) used on a proportion of the Daimler Armoured Cars in the regiment. The disadvantage of the Littlejohn adaptor was that it precluded the use of the 2-pdr. with high explosive ammunition. Armoured cars were not expected to be able to knock out tanks but they were occasionally able to do so by "stalking" the tank and obtaining a hit on the track or other vulnerable spot. An unusual success was achieved by the 2nd Household Cavalry Regiment when two Daimler Armoured Cars shot up and sank an enemy tugboat towing a string of barges on the River Waal. It was the unfortunate fate of armoured car regiments to suffer heavy casualties in men and vehicles—one regiment lost 25 scout cars in the first month of the Normandy invasion, for example. Often the first to meet opposition, their armoured or scout cars could not offer the protection afforded by a tank. However, the relatively quiet approach of the armoured cars or scout cars combined with their speed and manoeuvrability often enabled them to get out of trouble.

CONCLUSION

The British army (and, of course, the armies of the Commonwealth countries, which were organized on similar lines to it) made far wider use of wheeled armoured vehicles than any of the other combatants on both sides in World War II.

The advantages for reconnaissance purposes of armoured cars and armoured scout cars over the fully-tracked or semi-tracked vehicles more generally used by other countries outweighed many of the dis-

*The Reconnaissance Corps was formed in January 1941 to carry out the reconnaissance for infantry divisions which in France in 1939-40 had been undertaken by the Mechanised Divisional Cavalry Regiments. On January 1st, 1944, the Corps was absorbed into the Royal Armoured Corps and was re-designated the Reconnaissance Regiment—Editor.

advantages where speed, range and silence were of high importance.

British designers tried, and generally succeeded, in developing these salient features which contributed more than a little to the success enjoyed by British and Commonwealth reconnaissance units during the War and also, incidentally, have led on to substantial world wide sales of British built wheeled armoured vehicles since 1945.

Armoured car units of Britain and the Commonwealth set a high standard of efficiency throughout the War and were in constant contact with the enemy, whether in advance or retreat. From Alamein to Tunis, in Italy and Burma, and Normandy to Berlin they provided a steady and invaluable stream of information to the commanders responsible for fighting the main battle. The quality of the armoured cars and scout cars used by these units—the 11th Hussars, 12th Royal Lancers, The Royal Dragoons, King's Dragoon Guards, 1st and 2nd Household Cavalry Regiments, Derbyshire Yeomanry, Inns of Court, Royal Canadian Dragoons, 11th Cavalry (Prince Albert Victor's Own), 16th Light Cavalry and 4th and 6th South African Armoured Car Regiments, to name some of them—contributed greatly to their success in carrying out their duties and helped materially to final victory in World War II.

All photographs are from the author's collection but the original copyright holders are named wherever possible. The author would like to record his thanks to his friends and to the various bodies who have made photographs available.

Series Editor DUNCAN CROW

BRITISH ARMOURED CARS & SCOUT CARS—LEADING DATA

Armoured Cars	Weight (tons)	Dimensions (overall) Length	Width	Height	Engine/brake h.p. at r.p.m.	Transmission (Gears)	Crew	Armament	Armour (max. mm.)	Speed (max. m.p.h.)	Range (miles)	Remarks
Morris (CS9/LAC)	4·2	15'7½"	6'8½"	7'3"	Morris 6 cyl. 96·2 b.h.p. at 2,900	4 forward 1 reverse	4	1—0·55 in. Boys anti-tank rifle 1—0·303 in. Bren m.g.	7	45	240	
Guy Marks I & IA	5·2	13'6"	6'9"	7'6"	Meadows 4 cyl. 53 b.h.p.	4 forward 1 reverse	3	1—0·5 in. Vickers m.g. 1—0·303 in. Vickers m.g.	15	40	210	Mark IA 1—15 mm. Besa m.g. 1—7·92 mm. Besa m.g.
Humber Mark I	6·85	15'0"	7'2"	7'10"	Rootes 6 cyl. 90 b.h.p. at 3,200	4 forward 1 reverse	3	1—15 mm. Besa m.g. 1—7·92 mm. Besa m.g.	15	45	250	
Humber Marks II & III	7·1	15'0"	7'2"	7'10"	Rootes 6 cyl. 90 b.h.p. at 3,200	4 forward 1 reverse	3 (Mk II) 4 (Mk III)	1—15 mm. Besa m.g. 1—7·92 mm. Besa m.g.	15	45	250	
Humber Mark IV	7·1	15'0"	7'2"	7'10"	Rootes 6 cyl. 90 b.h.p. at 3,200	4 forward 1 reverse	3	1—37 mm. gun 1—7·92 mm. Besa m.g.	15	45	250	
Daimler Marks I & II	7·5	13'0"	8'0"	7'4"	Daimler 6 cyl. 95 b.h.p. at 3,600	5 forward 5 reverse	3	1—2 pdr. gun 1—7·92 mm. Besa m.g.	16	50	205	
A.E.C. Mark I	11·0	17'0"	9'0"	8'4½"	A.E.C. Diesel 6 cyl. 105 b.h.p. at 2,000	4 forward 1 reverse	3	1—2 pdr. gun 1—7·92 mm. Besa m.g.	30	36	250	
A.E.C. Marks II & III	12·7	17'10"	8'10½"	8'10"	A.E.C. Diesel 6 cyl. 158 b.h.p. at 2,000	4 forward 1 reverse	4	1—6 pdr. gun (Mk. II) 1—75 mm. gun (Mk. III) 1—7·92 mm. Besa m.g.	30	41	250	Mk. III—18 5" long, overall
G.M. Mark I, Fox I	7·37	14'8½"	7'5½"	8'1"	General Motors 6 cyl. 104 b.h.p. at 3,000	4 forward 1 reverse	4	1—0·5 in. Browning m.g. 1—0·30 in. Browning m.g.	15	44	210	
Coventry Mark I	11·5	15'6½"	8'9"	7'9"	Hercules 6 cyl. 175 b.h.p. at 2,600	5 forward 1 reverse	4	1—2 pdr. gun 1—7·92 mm. Besa m.g.	14	41	250	Mk. II had 75 mm. gun and crew 3
Scout Cars												
Daimler Marks I-III	2·8	10'5"	5'7½"	4'11"	Daimler 6 cyl. 55 b.h.p. at 4,200	5 forward 5 reverse	2	1—0·303 in. Bren m.g.	30	55	200	Weight of Mk. II—3 tons; Mk. III—3·15 tons. Armour 30 mm. is front plate only—sides and rear 12 mm.
Humber Marks I & II	3·39	12'7"	6'2½"	6'11½"	Rootes 6 cyl. 87 b.h.p. at 3,300	4 forward 1 reverse	2—3	1 or 2—0·303 in. Bren m.g.	14	60	200	
Ford Mark I, Lynx I	4·01	12'1½"	6'1"	5'10"	Ford 8 cyl. 95 b.h.p. at 3,600	4 forward 1 reverse	2	1—0·303 in. Bren m.g.	30	57	200	Armour 30 mm. is front plate only—sides and rear 12 mm.
Ford Mark II, Lynx II	4·2	12'8"	6'4"	5'8½"	Ford 8 cyl. 95 b.h.p. at 3,600	4 forward 1 reverse	2	1—0·303 in. Bren m.g.	30	57	200	Armour 30 mm. is front plate only—sides and rear 12 mm.

Armoured car of C Squadron, King's Dragoon Guards, dug in at Tobruk, September 1941. This is an example of the early riveted-hull version of the South African Reconnaissance Car, Mark II.
(Photo: Imperial War Museum)

The South African built Marmon-Herringtons

by B. T. White

THE Government of the Union of South Africa gave orders in August 1938 for the construction of two experimental armoured cars. Work proceeded slowly, so when war broke out in September 1939 enquiries were made to see if either existing armoured car designs, adaptable to South African needs, could be provided by the War Office or if complete armoured cars could be supplied from the United Kingdom or the U.S.A. Since none of the requirements could be met, the order for two armoured cars was increased to seven of the same type and then another twenty-two were added so that an experimental armoured car company could be equipped. The orders for armoured cars to be manufactured in South Africa was further increased to a total of 266 in October 1939.

In the meantime, the original model of armoured car, based on a conventional Ford 3-ton lorry chassis with two-wheel drive, was joined by a new experimental model on the same basic type of chassis but with Marmon-Herrington conversion to four-wheel drive. This vehicle was delivered in Johannesburg on September 18, 1939, and subjected to an exhaustive series of tests over the next few months, both on roads and cross-country in the eastern Transvaal.

After modifications to the cooling and suspension systems and further tests in January 1940, this type was accepted for production.

The order for 266 armoured cars was increased to 1,000 following the *Blitzkrieg* in France in May 1940 and, in the following month, the spread of the war to the African continent. Delivery of 50 armoured cars per week was required and the resources of South African industry were marshalled to cope with what was an entirely new venture in the Union. No armoured vehicle had been built there before 1939, but although there was no local motor manufacturer there were subsidiaries of Ford and General Motors for the assembly of imported North American chassis (some bodies were built in South Africa), and heavy industry —chiefly associated with mining—was well represented.

Responsibility for the production of armour plate was taken by the nationalized South African Iron & Steel Industrial Corporation (Iscor); the chassis imported from Canada (together with four-wheel drive conversion kits from the Marmon-Herrington Co., Inc. of Indianapolis, U.S.A.) were assembled by the Ford Motor Company of South Africa (Pty.)

South African Reconnaissance Car, Mark I. This particular vehicle is now an exhibit in the South African National War Museum
(Photo: S.A. National War Museum)

Ltd., and the Dorman Long structural steel company, together with other contractors, undertook final assembly of the complete armoured cars. Many sub-contractors, including the South African Railways workshops, were involved. All the armament for the South African armoured cars was supplied from the United Kingdom, except Browning machine-guns for the Mark IV and later models.

Marmon-Herrington, Mark II, of C Squadron, King's Dragoon Guards, in the break-out from Tobruk at the end of November 1941.
(Photo: K.D.G. *History)*

MARKS I AND II

The first 1,000 armoured cars, of which the first few vehicles were delivered in May 1940, and in numbers from July onwards—the last in May 1941, were designated South African Reconnaissance Cars, Marks I and II. The former, of which 113 were built, was the original two-wheel drive version on a Ford 3-ton lorry chassis, shortened to a 134-inch wheel base and strengthened.

The hull was on fairly straightforward lines but, considering the lack of outside assistance, was a creditable design with no vertical surfaces. The interior was roomy and unobstructed, with adequate space for the crew of four men. The armament, as originally fitted, consisted of one Vickers 0·303-in. water-cooled machine-gun in a ball mounting in the circular turret and another in the left hand side of the hull. The last was an archaic idea of little use in practice, derived apparently from early British medium tanks.

The form of hull construction in early vehicles of both Marks I and II was either riveted on to a mild steel frame or welded. The welded type was much the better, however, and soon predominated, and welding alone was used for all subsequent Marks. Access to the armoured car was by means of a large double door at the rear and by two other doors each side of the driver's position. The design of these forward doors was changed during the production run to smaller square doors set further back and better suited to the welded type of hull. Some slight changes were made in the Mark II to accommodate the four-

"Breda" car. Marmon-Herrington Mark II of The Royal Dragoons modified to take a captured Italian 20-mm. Breda gun. Unless a patrol was accompanied by a Breda car it had very little striking power. "It was generally supposed that the Boys anti-tank rifle . . . was unable to pierce any armour other than that of the Marmon-Herrington armoured car itself," wrote The Royals' regimental historian.
(Photo: Major K. G. Balfour, M.C.)

wheel drive—chiefly in the design of the front mud-guards to allow greater clearance. Also, the unditching channels were re-positioned.

Mark I and Mark II armoured cars were first handed over to the South African Armoured Car Companies in May and November 1940, respectively, and were used in action against the Italians in East Africa. They were, on the whole, quite successful, but the going was very hard, particularly for the two-wheel drive cars and the engines used a lot of oil. The springs were found to be insufficiently strong and the U-bolts sometimes broke. Also, before bullet-proof tyres were introduced, punctures were often caused by thorns.

The successful initiative of the South African government in getting armoured cars into quantity

Marmon-Herrington, Mark II. Later version with welded hull and forward doors set further back. Ball mounts for machine-guns in turret and left hand side of hull can be seen.
(Photo: S.A. National War Museum)

production was followed with interest by the War Office in England, and the South Africans were asked to supply cars for use in the Middle East. As a first step 400 Mark II cars were provided out of the 887 built or building for the South African government. These were all four-wheel drive cars and mostly of the welded type. They were designated "Armoured Cars, Marmon-Herrington, Mark II" (although, incidentally, they were—and still are—frequently and incorrectly referred to in British circles as "Marmon-Harringtons") so that the Mark number, although not the rest of the designation, corresponded with South African usage. However, it seems that "Marmon-Herrington Mark I" may have been applied to the few four-wheel drive cars in the Middle East with riveted hulls, although this point does not appear to have been satisfactorily explained.

The cars supplied for service in the Middle East were equipped to a standard laid down by the War Office and a rectangular plate was added to the turret face to take a mounting for a 0·55-in. Boys anti-tank rifle (a few cars in East Africa had had this weapon) and a 0·303-in. Bren light machine-gun. There were also pintle mountings on the front and the rear of the turret for another Bren gun and a 0·303-in. Vickers machine-gun respectively, although it does not seem that the second Bren gun was usually carried in practice. The hull machine-gun position was plated over. A proportion of the cars were fitted with W.D. type wheels with split rims, although these may have been substituted for the standard rims after their arrival in Egypt. The first Marmon-Herrington Armoured Cars were received in the Middle East about March 1941.

Marmon-Herrington, Mark II, of the King's Dragoon Guards patrolling Benghazi, Christmas Day, 1941.   (Photo: K.D.G. *History*)

MARK III

Further large contracts for armoured cars were placed by the War Office and the South African government and before the Mark II went out of production in May 1941 a new model, Mark III, was designed to take its place in the production lines.

The South African Reconnaissance Car Mark III (or "Armoured Car, Marmon-Herrington, Mark III"

Marmon-Herrington, Mark II, had two large doors at the back and a roomy hull. This car of a South African armoured car unit HQ has a No. 9 wireless set.

(Photo: S.A. National War Museum)

to the War Office) again used the Marmon-Herrington Ford chassis, but this time further shortened to a wheelbase of 117 in. Mechanical improvements introduced by the designer, Captain D. R. Ryder, included a strengthened front axle, improved springs, a heavier pattern steering box and an additional radiator—all features suggested by experience with the Mark II. The all-welded hull was of the same general shape as that of the Mark II but was redesigned to improve the angles and increase the effectiveness of the protection. The turret also was redesigned—an eight-sided structure taking the place of the circular type. Access was by means of side doors only in the Mark III. The basic armament remained the same— an anti-tank rifle and two machine-guns, one of them for anti-aircraft use. No provision was made for a hull machine-gun in Mark III, however.

Total orders for Mark III cars for both the War Office and the U.D.F. (Union Defence Force) amounted ultimately to 2,630 and the last cars were delivered in August 1942. During the course of the production run various changes were introduced. The original vehicles had horizontal armoured radiator grilles and square headlamp covers. First, the grille front was replaced by "solid" front armour and subsequently the headlamp covers were omitted. The next and most important change was the introduction of a single rear door, necessitating moving the spare wheel from the back to the left hand side of the hull. Although these variants do not seem to have been distinguished in official nomenclature (all are referred to as "Mark III" in production figures) the final version with all the modifications including the rear door seems to have been known to the U.D.F., at any rate, as Mark IIIA. The rear door was included in response to user demand, because the original Mark III was found to be difficult for the crew to evacuate in emergency, compared with the Mark II with its two large doors at the back.

The South African armoured cars were arriving in good numbers in Egypt by early 1942 and they performed very useful service in the Desert campaigns with British and South African armoured car regiments—cars built to the order of the War Office and the Union Government (the latter bearing "U" registration numbers) soon became well mixed up and in a common pool. The main fault in the cars as supplied to the troops was the lack of a heavier weapon than the Boys anti-tank rifle, which was a single shot weapon of limited usefulness. Some Mark II cars in the Middle East were "officially" modified early in 1941 to take captured Italian Breda 20-mm. guns and these were the first of a host of modifications to improve the hitting power of the Marmon-Herrington Armoured Cars. Later changes were carried out by unit or formation workshops and because they were not formally sanctioned by G.H.Q. the captured weapons were usually removed when armoured cars were sent back to base for major repairs.

The weapons known to have been fitted included the Italian 47-mm., German 37-mm. and French 25-mm. anti-tank guns on both Mark II and Mark III series cars and the German 28-mm./20-mm. tapered bore gun on Mark IIIA.

The 4th South African Armoured Car Regiment claimed to be the first to fit into an armoured car a gun really effective against tanks and armoured vehicles—a 2-pdr. from a knocked out British tank was mounted in September 1941. This proved to be so valuable in use that by the following January each troop in this Regiment had at least one car fitted with a gun of between 37-mm. and 47-mm. calibre.

Top view of Marmon-Herrington, Mark II, The mounting of the guns in the turret was such that, according to The Royals' historian, "most car commanders preferred to forego the security of the armour and shoot always with the machine-gun mounted for anti-aircraft upon the top."

Side view of Marmon-Herrington, Mark II, showing full armament: Boys anti-tank rifle, two Bren guns, and a Vickers machine-gun. Dimensions are: Wheelbase 11 ft. 2 in., track 5 ft., length overall 16 ft., width overall 6 ft. 6 in., height to top of turret 7 ft. 3 in., tyres 9·75 in. × 18 in.

(Photo: R.A.C. Tank Museum)

Other modifications of S.A. Armoured Cars were as Light Aid Detachment vehicles and, with turrets removed, as O.P. cars for the artillery. A turretless Mark II car was fitted with a quadruple Bren anti-aircraft mounting, and twin 0·30-in. Brownings or a single Vickers were carried on others. A new design of Mark IIIA was produced in South Africa which had the normal late type of hull with rear door but the turret was omitted and an open ring mounting for single or twin Vickers machine-guns—usable against air or ground targets—provided in the turret ring. Like all the turretless versions, this car was better suited for close reconnaissance duties than the rather tall Marmon-Herrington Mark IIIs in their standard version.

South African armoured cars—chiefly Mark IIIs in their different versions—in addition to being supplied to the War Office were used by the Indian Army, and were exported to the British East and West African Colonies, Southern Rhodesia, Malaya and the Dutch East Indies. Many of those sent to the last two Far Eastern countries fell into the hands of the Japanese.

MARK IV

An entirely new design of armoured car built around a 2-pdr. gun, was drawn up in South Africa in 1941–42. This, the S.A. Armoured Reconnaissance Car, Mark IV, employed basically the same Marmon-Herrington Ford components and engine as the earlier models but, for the first time, no orthodox chassis was used, the armoured hull itself taking the place of a chassis. A rear-engine configuration was adopted, bringing the need for some special mechanical modifications and the provision of extra control linkages. In some of the early cars (designated Mark IV X) the engine at the rear was mounted facing forwards with the gearbox behind it, with the radiator at the back of the car, air being drawn through the rear of the hull. Only 96 cars of this type were built, all the others having the engine facing the rear, so that the gearbox was in front, and air was taken in from the fighting compartment through the radiator mounted on the dividing bulkhead.

The method of welding construction developed in earlier vehicles was used for the Mark IV, which had both hull and turret fabricated by the welding process.

South African Armoured Reconnaissance Car, Mark VI, second model. This has a 6-pdr. as its' main armament, and a co-axial 7·92-mm Besa, and a single 0·5-in Browning for anti-aircraft use. This car is in the South African National War Museum.
(Photo: S.A. National War Museum)

Experiments were conducted with a 2-pdr. gun tank mounting but it was decided that the turret of the Mark IV was too light for this type of mounting and so a 2-pdr. field mounting was adopted instead. No provision was at first made for a coaxial machine-gun in the turret, but later a water-cooled Vickers was mounted, to be replaced by a 0·30-in. Browning air-cooled machine-gun on a "coupled" mounting in most vehicles built. An anti-aircraft machine-gun was carried on the turret roof—a 0·50-in. Browning in some early vehicles, the 0·30-in. weapon being standardized later.

The delivery of Mark IV armoured cars was limited by the supply of automotive components from North America and guns from the United Kingdom. The armament difficulty was no doubt the reason why some cars supplied to the Union Defence Force for home use were equipped only with a 0·5-in. Browning in a turret ball-mount instead of the 2-pdr. Another large order for some 1,200 armoured cars for use in the Middle East was placed by the United Kingdom government in addition to the considerable quantity required by the South African Army and so to overcome the problem of uncertain deliveries of Marmon-Herrington-Ford components, arrange-

C Squadron of The Royals relieving A Squadron near Bir Tengeder, midway between Gazala and Msus. This photograph shows some of the variations in the Marmon-Herrington Mark III series. Car on the right has early horizontal armoured radiator grilles; the left one has "solid" front armour. Both have square headlamp covers.
(Photo: Major K. G. Balfour, M.C.)

South African Reconnaissance Car, Mark III, with its designer, Captain D. R. Ryder. Armament is a Boys anti-tank rifle, a Vickers machine-gun, and a Bren gun.
(Photo: S.A. National War Museum)

ments were made for Canadian Ford F60L four-wheel drive 3-ton lorry chassis to be diverted to South Africa from War Office orders for the Middle East Forces. A modified design, the S.A. Armoured Reconnaissance Car, Mark IVF (known, not strictly accurately, in War Office nomenclature as Armoured Car, Marmon-Herrington, Mark IVF) was produced which utilized the automotive components from these Canadian 4×4 lorry chassis in place of the Marmon-Herrington Ford parts. The changes needed were not great, because the Canadian-built 4×4 trucks used the Marmon-Herrington design of front axle and transfer box, etc. Almost the only external difference, in fact, between the Mark IV and the Mark IVF lay in the wheels, which in the latter were of the standard British W.D. split rim pattern and the front hubs lacked the embossed "MH" which appeared on the 4×4 converted vehicles.

A grand total of 2,116 Mark IV armoured cars (of which 1,180 were Mark IVFs) was built, although the anticipated production flow could not be achieved and none were received in the Middle East in time to be used in the North African battles. They performed useful service in the forces of colonial territories and Allied forces, including the Free Greeks and the Arab Legion. A few were employed after the war by the British Army in Palestine as rail cars, coupled together in pairs.

Marmon-Herrington, Mark III, stuck in soft sand. This is a late version (Mark IIIA) with "solid" front armour, absence of square headlamp covers, and spare wheel on left hand side of hull. The turret is fitted with a captured German 28/20-mm. tapered anti-tank gun. (Photo: K.D.G. History)

South African built Marmon-Herringtons found their way all over the Middle East—and further afield as well. This photograph was taken in Cyprus in February 1943, at the inspection of the 8th King's Royal Irish Hussars by the G.O.C.-in-C. Cyprus. The cars are Mark IIIs—without rear door. Whatever their faults, all users agreed on the reliability of the Ford V-8 engine.

South African Armoured Reconnaissance Car, Mark IV. This car is in the standard form for this Mark. The Mark IVFs sent to the Middle East forces were equipped in similar fashion, including the 0·30-in. Browning A.A. mounting. (Photo: R.A.C. Tank Museum)

MARKS VI, VII AND VIII

Besides the four basic Marks which were mass produced, several other designs were produced in South Africa in World War II which did not get beyond the prototype stage. The most interesting of these was the Marmon-Herrington Mark VI, an eight-wheeler armoured car inspired by the German heavy armoured cars and intended to take full advantage of conditions offered by the North African terrain. This car, with drive on all wheels, employed two sets of 4×4 Marmon-Herrington components and a power unit consisting of two Ford (Mercury) V-8 engines of 95 b.h.p. each mounted at the rear. Armour protection was increased to a maximum of 30-mm. (compared with the 12-mm. maximum of Marks I–IV) and the armament was carried in a multi-sided turret reminiscent of that of the British Crusader tank. The armament in the first car consisted of a 2-pdr. gun and coaxial 0·30-in. Browning machine-gun and, on top of the turret, a ring mounting for two 0·30-in. Browning anti-aircraft machine-guns. The second car of the only two Mark VIs to be built had a 6-pdr. gun instead of the 2-pdr. and a coaxial 7·92-mm. Besa machine-gun and the anti-aircraft weapon was a single 0·5-in. Browning on a pintle mounting. Seven hundred and fifty Mark VI armoured cars were on order in mid-1942—500 for the U.D.F. and 250 for the War Office—and production was

Consignment of South African Armoured Reconnaissance Cars, Mark IVF, leaving Dorman Long's factory in South Africa for the Middle East. (Photo: S.A. National War Museum)

South African Armoured Reconnaissance Car, Mark VI—Armoured Car, Marmon-Herrington, Mark VI. This car, the first model, with 2-pdr. as the main armament, is in the Royal Armoured Corps Tank Museum at Bovington, Dorset.

(Photo: S.A. National War Museum)

South African Reconnaissance Car, Mark VII.

(Photo: R.A.C. Tank Museum)

expected to commence early in 1943. However, supplies of automotive parts from North America held back production of all armoured cars in South Africa in 1942; by the beginning of 1943 the end of the war in Africa was in sight and, with operations in the greatly different terrain of Europe ahead, production orders for Mark VI were cancelled.

Other South African experimental armoured cars were the Mark VII, which was on very similar lines to the Mark IIIA version with a Vickers machine-gun on an open ring mounting, and the Mark VIII, a front engined car of broadly the same configuration as the earlier vehicles. It was, however, up-gunned and had a 2-pdr. gun and coaxial Besa machine-gun in an exceptionally long turret which followed the lines of the hull.

For a country which practically had to start from scratch in the development and manufacture of fighting vehicles, South Africa did well to produce armoured cars which were of such sound and practical design and which—particularly in the Middle East in 1941–42—played a very useful part in the war.

South African Armoured Reconnaissance Car, Mark VIII. The hull design of this car is derived from that of the Marks II and III, but the exceptionally long turret with a 2-pdr. gun is unique.

(Photo: R.A.C. Tank Museum)

FAUGH A BALLAGH

78th Division sign

The Car, 4 × 4, Light Reconnaissance, Humber Mark III of
the Commanding Officer of
56th Bn. Reconnaissance
Corps, 78th Infantry Division,
in Tunisia, 1943.

41

Unit sign

Armoured Car, Marmon-Herrington Mark II—one of a batch ordered by the War Office and fitted out with standard armament and equipment for the Middle East theatre.

Car, Light Reconnaissance, Canadian G.M. Mark I, or Otter I, as used by 4th Reconnaissance Regiment (4th Princess Louise Dragoon Guards), 1st Canadian Infantry Division in Italy. Air recognition sign is painted on bonnet.

The A.C.2 at a halt in the desert on its way to Baghdad in 1935. Behind it is a Rolls-Royce armoured car with R.A.F. markings.
(Photo: Alvis Ltd.)

Alvis-Straussler

by B. T. White

THE handful of Alvis-Straussler armoured cars that were used by the Royal Air Force in the Middle East during World War II were, of course, of no material importance at all as far as the war was concerned but these cars represented, for their time, a significant advance in the design of wheeled fighting vehicles. An interesting fact is that a much larger number of cars of a closely related basic design were in service with the German army.

A.C.1 AND A.C.2

The designer of the Straussler and Alvis-Straussler armoured cars was Nicholas Straussler, a Hungarian who later adopted British nationality. Straussler's first armoured car design, known as A.C.1, was constructed—as a prototype only—by the Budapest firm of H. Manfred Weiss R.T. This vehicle, built in 1933, was never fully completed as an armoured car, although the chassis was at a later stage of its trials fitted with a curved mock-up body. Several mechanical features were introduced, however, which anticipated their introduction in armoured cars and other cross-country vehicles built elsewhere. The engine was placed at the rear with the gearbox in front of it. The transmission was led to differentials on the front and rear axles. The suspension consisted of parallel transverse leaf springs under each axle which, in conjunction with the swing axle design, permitted considerable independent wheel movements. As well as

four-wheel drive, the A.C.1 had four-wheel steering.

This model led in 1935 to the development of a second type, A.C.2, in which several improvements were incorporated. The square radiator behind the engine with an ordinary fan in the A.C.1 was replaced in A.C.2 by a circular radiator with turbine fan cooling. A second steering-wheel was introduced at the rear so that better advantage could be taken of the ability to steer on all four wheels. The prototype of A.C.2 was fitted only with a mock-up body of curved sheet metal, with a turret ring. A fully armoured version was, however, built, and this had a curved armoured body which could easily be removed in one piece, leaving all the chassis accessible for servicing. The turret had a mounting for a single 0·303-in. Vickers water-cooled machine-gun, although the design provided for the alternative of two machine-guns or for an open mounting for two anti-aircraft machine-guns in lieu of the turret.

A car of the A.C.2 type was supplied in 1935 to the Air Ministry by Straussler Mechanisation Ltd. and trials were carried out by the R.A.F. in the Middle East, where, as a preliminary, it was driven from Port Said to Baghdad.

In 1937 Nicholas Straussler's firm linked up with Alvis Ltd., of Coventry, builders of high quality cars (a firm, incidentally, which had experience with features such as front wheel drive, swing axles and independent suspension) and Alvis-Straussler Ltd. was formed for the design and production of armoured fighting vehicles.

Straussler A.C.2. This photograph shows the high degree of wheel movement allowed by the transverse suspension.
(Photo: Alvis Ltd).

Three-quarter rear view of A.C.2 armoured car.
(Photo: Alvis Ltd.)

TYPE "LAC"

Before going on to the evolution of the Alvis-Straussler A.C.3, two others of Straussler's armoured car designs should be mentioned at this stage. The first was the type "LAC" which, together with a generally similar chassis designed as a Field Artillery Tractor, was tested by the War Office in 1938. This armoured car was unusual in having two Ford V-8 engines of 88·5 b.h.p. each complete with gearboxes and a novel form of four-wheel drive transmission. The engine on the nearside drove the wheels on that side and the other engine drove the offside wheels, but, as the gearboxes were interconnected, either engine could drive the vehicle in emergency. The trials of this vehicle showed a very good cross-country performance but the engine cooling was considered inadequate by War Office standards. Since the army was always liable to be involved in campaigns in hot countries the Straussler type LAC was accordingly rejected by the War Office.

ARTICULATED CHASSIS

The other experimental model of armoured car was a prototype chassis (with only a mock-up hull and turret) which was designed on a principle having features in common with the Italian Pavesi vehicles which first appeared in the late 1920s.

Straussler A.C.1 armoured car prototype with mock-up body.
(Photo: B. H. Vanderveen)

The curved armoured body of the A.C.2 could easily be removed in one piece. Note rear driving position. (Photo: Alvis Ltd.)

Straussler's "Hefty" tractor seen here on test in Belgium. The position of the tractor shows how the front and rear halves were able to pivot independently. (Photo: Alvis Ltd.)

Front driving position of the A.C.2. (Photo: Alvis Ltd.)

Alvis-Straussler Type A.C.3D. This is one of the twelve armoured cars built for the Netherlands East Indies Army.
(Photo: Alvis Ltd.)

Rear view of the Alvis-Straussler Type A.C.3D showing the hexagonal radiator grille. The vehicle is on test in Britain. It is at Carter Bar on the border between England and Scotland.
(Photo: Alvis Ltd.)

In this vehicle, the front and rear halves of the chassis were able to pivot independently about the horizontal axis, although in Straussler's design normal steering was retained, unlike the Pavesi vehicles in which steering was achieved by articulation of the two parts of the chassis. Straussler supplied some tractors to the Air Ministry built on this system, but for an armoured car particular problems with the design of the fighting compartment are involved and by 1938 less unconventional systems of suspension were able to give comparable cross-country performances. Straussler's articulated chassis armoured car does not seem to have got very far, but it is relevant to note that interest in this type of vehicle has been revived in recent years.

A.C.3

The next step in the development of what could be called the main-stream of Straussler's armoured car design was the A.C.3 of 1937, which inherited many features of the A.C.2, including the general layout of body, engine and transmission. The power unit was now the Alvis 4·3 litre engine and the armour was this time made up of faceted plates instead of the previous curvilinear design. The original A.C.1 chassis appears to have been used for mounting the mock-up body for the A.C.3. The six-cylinder in-line engine developed 120 b.h.p. and the Alvis four-speed gearbox was coupled to a two-speed transfer box giving eight speeds both forward and in reverse. Cooling was by means of a radiator each side of the engine. The four-wheel steer-

ing feature of earlier models was retained and there was a full set of driving controls at the rear as well as in the front.

The change to drive on the rear wheels only and steering on the front wheels for normal road work could be effected by a single lever. There was also a choice of two steering ratios for roads or heavy cross-country going.

The armament consisted of one water-cooled machine-gun in the turret with the option of a second machine-gun in a mounting added to the left of the driver's visor.

Twelve armoured cars of this model—Alvis-Straussler Type A.C.3D—were ordered for the Dutch East Indies Army (Koninklijk Nederlands-Indische Leger) and were delivered in 1938–39. A change affecting engine cooling appears to have been made in the course of production, because the hexagonal engine grille at the rear was reduced in height in some cars.

Three cars of very similar specification were also supplied to the Portuguese Army.

Earlier, the trials of the A.C.2 by the Royal Air Force had given quite satisfactory results and it was decided to order twelve cars of the later type and a contract was given to Alvis-Straussler Ltd. by the Air Ministry in 1937. These cars were basically the same as those ordered by the Dutch but some changes were specified to meet Royal Air Force requirements. The lower half of the sides of the hull was vertical instead of inward-sloping, giving more interior space, and the hull machine-gun position was absent in the R.A.F. version, which had twin vision hatches for driver and

Front view of "Hefty" tractor (second from left) in Belgium.
(Photo: Alvis Ltd.)

A.C.3Ds after being off-loaded at Batavia Docks, Netherlands East Indies, New Year's Day 1938. (Photo: Alvis Ltd.)

The A.C.3Ds on arrival at Bandoeng, Netherlands East Indies, 1938. (Photo: Alvis Ltd.)

Front driving position in the A.C.3D. These cars had a crew of four, a top speed of 68 m.p.h., and could climb a 1 in 2 gradient.
(Photo: Alvis Ltd.)

A.C.3D rear driving position. (Photo: Alvis Ltd.)

Type A Alvis-Straussler in Jerusalem, 1939. (Photo: Alvis Ltd.)

Type A Alvis-Straussler with the R.A.F. armoured car detachment at Aden, 1938–39. (Photo: Alvis Ltd.)

co-driver. Also, the wheel and tyre sizes were changed from 9·00–22 to 10·50–20, presumably in order to coincide with standard sizes already in use. There were also various internal changes of equipment to meet the needs of the R.A.F., by whom the cars were designated "Cars, Armoured, Alvis-Straussler, Type A".

One of the cars built for the R.A.F. was tested for the Army by the Mechanization Experimental Establishment in the summer of 1938 and although it put up a generally satisfactory performance was deemed to be not really fast enough for use by armoured car regiments.

Most of the R.A.F. cars were sent to the Middle East, where the R.A.F. Armoured Car Companies were based, and some, at least, joined the armoured car detachment at Aden.

The earlier Straussler armoured cars were built, as mentioned above, in Hungary where, later, the Manfred-Weiss firm built a quantity of armoured cars which were broadly similar to the A.C.3D. Fifty-three vehicles were exported and 171 built for the Hungarian Army by whom they were known as the 39M Csaba. Some, at least, of these served on the Eastern Front with the German Wehrmacht.

The Hungarian cars mounted a long-barrelled heavy machine-gun together with a light machine-gun in the turret and the front of the hull sloped down to end in a seven-sided nose plate.

Nicholas Straussler's connection with Alvis ended in 1938 (when Alvis Mechanisation Ltd. was formed to take the place and commitments of Alvis-Straussler Ltd.) but he continued to be very active in the field of military equipment. His most famous invention was the DD tank, but he did not neglect wheeled armoured vehicles, one of his later projects being a six-wheeled armoured car on the lines of the Alvis Saladin.

Alvis-Straussler armoured car built for the Royal Air Force—"Car, Armoured, Alvis-Straussler Type A". The two main external differences from the cars built for the Dutch were the vertical hull sides and the absence of a hull machine-gun. (Photo: Alvis Ltd.)

Cars, 4 × 2, Light Reconnaissance, Standard Mark II, Beaverette II. These vehicles are on parade with the Sheffield Home Guard in September 1940, but the numbers on the front of the nearest car shows that it was originally ordered by the War Office (and was allocated a "T" prefix applicable to tanks) and then handed over to the R.A.F., presumably for airfield defence.

(Photo: Imperial War Museum)

Light Reconnaissance Cars
by B. T. White

WHEN the Reconnaissance Corps was formed in January 1941 to provide specialized reconnaissance units for infantry divisions in place of the former mechanized divisional cavalry regiments, large numbers of light armoured vehicles were needed to equip it. A proportion of these were found in tracked Carriers similar to those used in infantry battalions, but the majority of the wheeled armoured vehicles needed for operations requiring greater speed and range were Standard and Humber "Light Armoured Cars"

The "Light Armoured Car" class had been evolved of necessity in June 1940 in order to provide as rapidly as possible armoured vehicles to re-equip the British Army after the Dunkirk evacuation and to defend aircraft factories and other key industrial points.

The two principal manufacturers of chassis for the Light Armoured Cars were the Standard Motor Company Ltd. and Humber Ltd.—both Coventry firms. The Standard vehicle was initially, at any rate, produced primarily for aircraft factory defence and was known as "Beaverette" after Lord Beaverbrook, the Minister of Aircraft Production. As supplies of armour plate at that time were at a premium, the protection, limited in the Mark I version to the front

and sides of the crew compartment, was built up of $\frac{3}{8}$-in. or $\frac{7}{16}$-in. mild steel plates, backed by 3-in. oak planks at the front. There was no overhead protection or armour at the rear and the armament usually consisted of a Bren light machine-gun. The chassis used was the ordinary 14-h.p. (RAC) type with little modification.

The Humber Light Armoured Car, known as "Humberette", was ordered by the War Office and consisted of an open-top armoured body on a Humber Super Snipe car chassis with a six-cylinder 75/80 b.h.p. engine. Few vehicles appear to have been produced in this form, because an improved version "Ironside I", broadly the same but carried on W.D. pattern wheels with Run Flat tyres, followed soon afterwards and work on the 1,200 of these ordered was being carried out by the Rootes Group in July 1940. The Ironside was named, not descriptively, but after the recently retired Home Forces commander, Field Marshal Lord Ironside.

A slightly improved Beaverette, Mark II, with rear protection added and some slight adjustments in design, was also built, and several mechanized cavalry regiments received Beaverettes as their sole equipment in the summer and autumn of 1940. Pictures of them appeared in the press with highly

233

Light Armoured Car, Humberette.   (Photo: War Office)

Car, 4 × 4, Light Reconnaissance, Humber Mark III, with radiator doors closed (operated from driver's seat), Boys anti-tank rifle in hull front, Bren gun in turret, and smoke discharger. Driver's visor closed.

coloured accounts of their capabilities—("very fast . . . can negotiate the roughest country"). They were also used in numbers by the Home Guard and the R.A.F. for the defence of aircraft factories, airfields and other vulnerable points.

Humberettes and Ironsides were likewise issued to tankless cavalry regiments and, in addition, to some tank regiments in lieu of scout cars. However, as more tanks, scout cars and proper armoured cars came off the production lines to make up for the losses incurred by the Royal Armoured Corps at Dunkirk, Beaverettes and Ironsides became available in January 1941 to equip the first battalions of the newly raised Reconnaissance Corps, and the new nomenclature of "Cars, 4 × 2, Light Reconnaissance" was adopted for them.

In order to increase production of Light Reconnaissance Cars in 1941, a third major motor concern, the Nuffield Group, was brought in and built the "Car, 4 × 2, Light Reconnaissance, Morris Mark I". This was a rear-engined vehicle with the crew at the front—the driver in the centre, a gunner in a small turret (normally mounting a Bren gun) at the right and the third man at the left, where a 0·55-in. Boys anti-tank rifle could be operated through hatches in the roof. The smooth enclosed design of the under-belly of this car helped to give it a quite good cross-country performance for a 4 × 2 vehicle. About 1,150 Morris Mark I Light Reconnaissance Cars were completed when production ceased in 1942. To jump ahead in the story, a Morris Mark II was produced to follow the Mark I. This was externally much the same as its predecessor but four-wheel drive was introduced and the front suspension was changed from independent coil springs to semi-elliptic leaf springs. Both models had semi-elliptics at the rear. Approximately 1,100 cars of the new version were built.

Turreted versions of the Standard and Humber vehicles also first appeared in 1941—the Mark III and Mark II, respectively. Both were fully enclosed and in the Beaverette III the wheel base was shortened considerably from 9 ft. 0 in. to 6 ft. 2 in. and large cross-section tyres 9·00–13 were fitted. This car was

Humber Light Reconnaissance Cars, Mark III, 4 × 4, in Tunisia, late May 1943. They belong to Battalion Headquarters, 56th Bn. Reconnaissance Corps of 78th Infantry Division.
(Photo: Imperial War Museum)

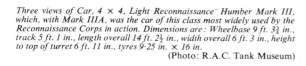

Three views of Car, 4 × 4, Light Reconnaissance Humber Mark III, which, with Mark IIIA, was the car of this class most widely used by the Reconnaissance Corps in action. Dimensions are: Wheelbase 9 ft. 3¾ in., track 5 ft. 1 in., length overall 14 ft. 2½ in., width overall 6 ft. 3 in., height to top of turret 6 ft. 11 in., tyres 9·25 in. × 16 in.
(Photo: R.A.C. Tank Museum)

Armoured Car, Dodge—later known as Car, 4 × 2, Light Reconnaissance, Dodge, and also, unofficially, as the "Malcolm Campbell Armoured Car." (Photo: B. H. Vanderveen)

Car, 4 × 2, Light Reconnaissance, Morris Mark I.

(Photo: British Motor Corp.)

Car, 4 × 4, Light Reconnaissance, Canadian G.M. Mark I, Otter I, of 4th Canadian Reconnaissance Regiment in Italy.

(Photo: Canadian Official)

Mark I, or Otter I as it was usually known, followed the broad general layout and carried the same armament as the Humber III LRC. Standard Canadian General Motors mechanical components were mainly used and the vehicle was slightly longer and 10 in. higher than the Humber. It was also well over a ton heavier than the British vehicle and despite the use of a 104-b.h.p. engine the general performance was poorer, although the Otter was generally quite satisfactory and the 1,761 vehicles built gave useful service with Canadian and British units (they were used by the Army and the R.A.F. Regiment) in the Mediterranean theatre and North West Europe. The standard armament of the Otter consisted of a Bren light machine-gun in the turret and a Boys anti-tank rifle in the front hull (replaced by a wireless set in some cars) although in some R.A.F. Regiment cars aircraft armament was substituted—a 20-mm. cannon in the front hull and twin Browning machine-guns in the turret.

Besides these main types of British and Canadian Light Reconnaissance cars of World War II, there were also a number of armoured cars of various types which were built only as prototypes or in a small production run and which subsequently were classified as Light Reconnaissance Cars mainly, it seems, for administrative tidiness and because they were of inadequate performance for the scout car or true armoured car rôle.

These miscellaneous vehicles included the Car, 4-wheeled, Light Reconnaissance, Dodge, and the Hillman Gnat and Morris Salamander. The two latter types, of 1941–42, were small turreted rear-engined two-seater vehicles designed to use components of existing light cars. Only prototypes were produced. The Armoured Car, Dodge, as it was first known, was conceived by Sir Malcolm Campbell and the first prototype (using a Fordson lorry chassis) was built by Mr. Leo Villa, Campbell's chief racing mechanic. Seventy vehicles on Dodge chassis were produced in 1940 by Briggs Motor Bodies Ltd. They became known among the troops as "Malcolm Campbells".

known also as "Beaverbug I". A further improved model, Beaverette IV, had a redesigned driver's front plate which gave both more room and increased protection.

The Car, 4 × 2, Light Reconnaissance, Humber, Mark II, was a version of the Ironside I roofed-in and with a turret added. At the end of 1941 a four-wheel drive version, Humber Mark III, appeared, looking much the same as Mark II, except for the front wheel hubs and detail changes, but the cross-country capability was greatly improved. The final version was Mark IIIA, in which some improvements were made in the hull design, including extra observation ports at the front corners of the fighting compartment. In all, 3,600 Humber Light Reconnaissance Cars were built (including the 400 Ironside Is) and the Marks III and IIIA were the cars of this class most widely used by the Reconnaissance Corps in action, although many were also employed overseas by the Royal Air Force Regiment for airfield defence. The Beaverettes (2,800 of which in all were built) were, in all Marks, used mainly for home defence by the Army and the R.A.F.—the Marks III and IV perhaps more widely by the latter. The Morris Light Reconnaissance Cars were also widely used by the Royal Air Force.

Morris, Humber III or Beaverette IV cars were sometimes allotted as reconnaissance vehicles to the commanders of other types of army unit such as Royal Engineers companies. In this form the turrets were often removed. Humber III and IIIAs were also used as armoured staff cars, with varying degrees of modification, by formation commanders, recalling (although in a somewhat more utilitarian form) the special enclosed versions of the Ironside, five or more of which were built in 1940 for the transport of Royalty, Cabinet Ministers or other V.I.P.s.

The Canadian Government agreed to produce a Light Reconnaissance Car based on the British Humber Mark III in order to help meet the considerable demand by both British and Commonwealth forces for vehicles of this class in 1942.

The Car, Light Reconnaissance, Canadian G.M.

A.F.V. Series Editor: DUNCAN CROW

Addenda to Guy, Daimler, Humber, A.E.C. Profile by B. T. White.

Under section headed "Scout Cars," add to end of seventh paragraph:

> Some information suggests that the Morris design was probably based on one drawn up by Percy Riley in 1937. This vehicle had a tubular backbone and was to have been powered by a shortened version of the 9 h.p. Riley car's 4-cylinder engine, but no more than a full-scale mock-up had been built when the Riley Engine Co. Ltd. was acquired by Lord Nuffield in September 1938.

and add to end of ninth paragraph in same section:

> Weight was always a problem with this small class of vehicle. The original specification called for a 25-mm. front plate as the *only* armour protection in a vehicle first intended primarily to lead and protect mobile columns against light anti-tank weapons. This was then increased to 30-mm. and the side plates were introduced as a practical feature to support the front plate. The later requirement for full protection brought problems also with the four-wheel steering and helped the decision to eliminate this feature in later models of the Daimler Scout Car. Subsequently, the call for improved floor protection led to the elimination of the roof in Mk. III to avoid further increase in weight.

Valentines of A Squadron, 17th/21st Lancers, 26th Armoured Brigade, 6th Armoured Division, lined up at Lakenheath, Suffolk, September 1941. The occasion was H.M. King George VI's inspection of the whole division which contributed to the halving of the tank strength of an armoured division in 1942.
(Imperial War Museum)

British Armoured Units and Armoured Formations (1940-1946)

by Duncan Crow

IN September 1941 the 6th Armoured Division was inspected by H.M. King George VI at Lakenheath in Suffolk. For this inspection the whole division less details was on parade. As the establishment of an armoured division at that time was 14,736 officers and men (including 1,067 first reinforcements) and 4,581 vehicles (including 561 fighting vehicles of which 340 were tanks and 58 were armoured cars) it was an impressive sight.

It was also an alarming one. This was the first time that an armoured division had been drawn up complete at the same time and in the same place. While the problems of movement control and supply had seemed formidable enough on paper they became unnerving in practice—and this was without interference from the enemy! According to the divisional commander, Major-General (later General Sir John) Crocker, it was the practical presentation of what two armoured brigades in a single armoured division meant in terms of mechanical transport for supply that caused the amount of armour in an armoured division to be halved the following year.

The organization of an armoured division from the autumn of 1940 until the spring of 1942 was two armoured brigades, each of three armoured regiments and an infantry motor battalion, a support group of three artillery regiments and an infantry battalion, and divisional troops including an armoured car regiment and three squadrons of engineers.

By 1942, in the words of the Commander of the Royal Armoured Corps, Lieutenant-General Sir G. Le Q. Martel, "quite clearly the 'all-armoured' idea was dead." Not only was there the Lakenheath inspection to make this point, but British experience in the Western Desert and German experience in Russia had shown the need for a change in organization to match the change in tactical thinking. Instead of having lateral organization with two armoured brigades side by side under one command and two infantry brigade groups of the supporting infantry division side by side behind the armour under another, experience had shown that there must be the closest co-operation between the armoured and the infantry brigades and that therefore there must be organization in depth with the leading armoured brigade and the supporting infantry brigade group under the same divisional command. Instead of having two divisions advancing one behind the other they would advance side by side, each of them in depth.

To give effect to this the organization of the

Scout car and tanks of 3rd Armoured Brigade, 1st Armoured Division, in France, June 1940. The absence of support brackets for a folding roof identifies the scout car as a Mark I which had a sliding roof.
(Imperial War Museum)

Original Desert Rats. Sergeant M. H. Brown, B Squadron, 7th Queen's Own Hussars, 4th Armoured Brigade, 7th Armoured Division, keeping a look-out on his Mark VIA Light tank while his crew are busy with personal maintenance near Fort Capuzzo, June 1940. The 7th Hussars were part of the force that captured Capuzzo on June 14th, three days after war began against Italy.
(The Seventh and Three Enemies)

armoured division was changed in 1942. One armoured brigade was removed and replaced by an infantry brigade, while the support group lost its name as well as its infantry battalion and received instead a second 25-pdr. regiment, making four artillery regiments in all. Thus the organization was: one armoured brigade of three armoured regiments and an infantry motor battalion; one motorized infantry brigade; and two field, one anti-tank, and one anti-aircraft artillery regiments. The armoured car regiment remained, as well as the other divisional troops—engineers, signals, supply, transport, and medical.

In April 1943 it was announced that a new type of unit would be introduced. The armoured car regiment was not considered to be able to carry out adequately the functions of both medium and close reconnaissance for the armoured division. The need for a unit which could fight for its information and which could, if necessary, be used to protect the advance or withdrawal of the division without having to be stiffened

Desert Rats in Burma. Sergeant M. H. Brown, B Squadron, 7th Hussars, now of 7th Armoured Brigade, and his crew on their Stuart M3 Light tank in Burma, March 1942. Sergeant Brown is still wearing his distinctive headgear of cap comforter. The 7th Armoured Brigade was newly equipped with Stuarts before it left the Middle East in January 1942. The Stuart had a crew of four – the fifth man in the picture is a R.E.M.E. fitter.
(The Seventh and Three Enemies)

by other arms, particularly tanks, was considered essential. To meet this need each armoured division was to have an armoured reconnaissance regiment. The armoured car regiment was removed and was to carry out medium reconnaissance as corps troops— one armoured car regiment per corps.

The first establishment for an armoured recce regiment was: RHQ (4 cruiser tanks, 8 AA tanks, 1 Universal carrier), HQ squadron (SHQ, recce troop of 12 scout cars, inter-communication troop of 7 scout cars, and administration troop with one personnel carrier), and three squadrons each of SHQ (3 cruisers, 1 close support cruiser, 1 recovery tank, and 1 slave battery carrier), three tank troops (each of 2 cruisers and 1 close support cruiser), and three carrier troops (each of 4 Universal carriers, one with 3-in. mortar). The strength was 698 (39 officers and 659 other ranks).

Later this changed and the armoured recce regiment had roughly the same establishment as an armoured regiment though it was usually equipped with a different tank. The AFV establishment of the 15th/19th The King's Royal Hussars, for example, when they took over as the armoured recce regiment of the 11th Armoured Division in August 1944 was: three sabre squadrons each with 19 tanks divided into four troops of three Cromwells and one Challenger, and SHQ of three Cromwells of which two carried a 95-mm. howitzer in place of the normal 75-mm. gun. RHQ consisted of four Cromwells, and the Recce Squadron had three patrols equipped with Humber and Daimler scout cars, and two HQ cars. Squadron leaders and various other officers also had scout cars. The armoured regiments of 11th Armoured Division at this period, like the armoured regiments of all Allied armoured divisions except the 7th British (The Desert Rats) which had Cromwells, were equipped with Shermans. But despite the differences of equipment the armoured recce regiment on the battlefield came to be used as a fourth armoured regiment.

The other major alteration in the armoured division

B Squadron, The Royal Dragoons, in their Marmon-Herrington Mark II armoured cars, taking part in the victory parade at Aleppo after the Syrian campaign in which they fought, July 1941. The Royals were the armoured car regiment of the 10th Armoured Division when it was formed in the Middle East in 1941 mainly from regiments of the 1st Cavalry Division. (Major K. G. Balfour, M.C.)

after 1942 was that one of the two field artillery regiments and half the anti-tank regiment were re-equipped with self-propelled guns.

Thus by 1944 the organization was:

Div. HQ

Armoured recce regiment (666 officers and men, 61 medium tanks, 11 light tanks)

Armoured brigade (10 medium tanks at Brigade HQ)

consisting of three armoured regiments (each 666 officers and men, 61 medium tanks, 11 light tanks)

and an infantry motor battalion (819 officers and men)

Lorried infantry brigade (2,944 officers and men)

consisting of machine-gun company (12 Vickers MGs) and three lorried infantry battalions.

Divisional artillery

consisting of

a field regiment (24 towed 25-pdr. guns)

a motorised regiment (24 SP 25-pdrs.)

an anti-tank regiment (48 17-pdr. a/t guns)

an anti-aircraft regiment (54 Bofors 40-mm. AA guns)

Divisional engineers (1,000 officers and men)

Signals regiment (728 officers and men)

Supply, Transport, and Medical troops

The total divisional strength was 14,964 officers and men. Its fighting vehicles were 306 tanks (262 mediums, 44 lights) plus scout cars, carriers, and armoured OPs.

At the time of the King's inspection in September 1941, the 6th Armoured Division was one of ten armoured divisions in the British Army: the 1st, 2nd, 6th, 7th, 8th, 9th, 10th, 11th, Guards, and 42nd. Of these, three (1st, 2nd, 7th) had been in action, and one (the 2nd) had virtually ceased to exist. Three of the others (10th, Guards, and 42nd) had only just been formed. One more armoured division (the 79th) was formed in September 1942.

As well as these there were other armoured formations—the Army tank brigades, which were independent formations under direct Army command but

were allocated to corps and divisional commanders for training and operations as required. At the maximum in 1942 there were 11 Army tank brigades: 1st, 10th, 11th, 21st, 25th, 31st, 32nd, 33rd, 34th, 35th, and 36th. As part of a policy which the RAC Commander, Lieutenant-General Martel, described as "the absorption of the armoured forces into the rest of the army," five of these Army tank brigades in mid-1942 each replaced the third infantry brigade of an infantry division so that in these new model "mixed" divisions the infantry would have their own integrated tank support. To bring their title into line with their purpose the word "Army" was dropped and henceforward all the brigades were called simply tank brigades, as opposed to armoured brigades in the armoured divisions:

21st Tank Brigade joined 4th Division

25th Tank Brigade joined 43rd Division

31st Tank Brigade joined 53rd Division

33rd Tank Brigade joined 3rd Division

34th Tank Brigade joined 1st Division.

In practice the idea of the "mixed" division, made by replacing one infantry brigade by one tank brigade, did not turn out to be very successful; there was an insufficient reserve of infantry in the division. In 1943

Near miss for a Marmon-Herrington armoured car of C Squadron, The King's Dragoon Guards, during the break-out from Tobruk, November, 1941. The K.D.G.s were the 2nd Armoured Division's armoured car regiment and were part of the force in Tobruk during the eight months' siege.

(History of The King's Dragoon Guards)

Sidi Rezegh, November 1941.

the "mixed" division was therefore abolished, though the rôle of the tank brigade remained as close support of infantry. Their tank, with a few exceptions, was the Churchill.

But although the scaling down of the infantry component in the infantry division to create new model divisions was not a success and led to their abandonment, the exigencies of the campaign in Italy in the latter part of 1944 brought about their revival in fact if not in name. The nature of the fighting in the close, mountainous terrain revealed a shortage of infantry in the armoured divisions. Each of these was therefore given a second infantry brigade, created from the armoured brigade's motor battalion and from divisional troops. Thus these new "mixed" divisions, though they continued to be described as armoured divisions, had arrived at the old formula in the reverse direction: by the scaling up of the infantry component in the armoured division. This did not happen in the armoured divisions in the North-West Europe campaign.

Only one division continued as a "mixed" division

after the end of 1943 and that was the 2nd New Zealand which had converted one of its infantry brigades to armour. It retained its "mixed" character throughout its part in the Italian campaign. When the other armoured divisions (the 5th Canadian, the 6th British, and the 6th South African) increased their infantry strength by creating a second infantry brigade, the 2nd New Zealand increased its infantry to three brigades while still retaining its armoured brigade.

The total number of armoured brigades and tank brigades in the British Army at the maximum, in 1942–43, was 29.

THE ARMOURED DIVISIONS

1st Armoured Division

After fighting in France in May-June 1940 the 1st was re-formed with the 2nd and 22nd Armoured Brigades and the 12th Lancers as its armoured car regiment. In 1941 it went to Egypt, 22 Armd Bde (2nd Royal Gloucestershire Hussars, 3rd and 4th County of London Yeomanry) arriving first and coming under

Crusader of RHQ, 9th Queen's Royal Lancers, 2nd Armoured Brigade, 1st Armoured Division, in the Desert. The 1st was one of five British armoured divisions that fought in the Desert. The 2nd Armoured Brigade's armoured regiments (The Queen's Bays, the 9th Lancers, and the 10th Hussars) remained unchanged from 1938 until after the war had ended in 1945.
(Imperial War Museum)

Universal carrier with Bren gun in action south of El Alamein, August 1942, after Rommel had been brought to a halt only sixty miles from Alexandria.   (Imperial War Museum)

A column of British tanks moving up at night to the Second Battle of Alamein, October 1942. (Imperial War Museum)

command of 7th Armoured Division when it reached the Desert in October. By the time of Gazala and Knightsbridge (May–June 1942) the 1st Armoured Division had both its armoured brigades under command again, but the 22nd went to 10th Armoured Division for Alam Halfa (August 31–September 7, 1942) and to the 7th Armoured Division for second Alamein (October 1942) remaining with that division for the remainder of the war. The 1st Armoured Division, with 2 Armd Bde, fought through the rest of the North African campaign and, in May 1944, still with 2 Armd Bde and with the 4th Hussars as its armoured recce regiment, crossed to Italy, where it was broken up in September, the armoured brigade (still with the same three armoured regiments—the Bays, the 9th Lancers, the 10th Hussars—it had had since it was formed in 1938) becoming the 2nd Independent Armoured Brigade and fighting throughout the rest of the Italian campaign. The brigade's motor battalion was the 1st Rifle Brigade until October 1942 when it was replaced by the Yorkshire Dragoons. The division's infantry in Italy was the 18th Infantry Brigade.

2nd Armoured Division

In January 1940, the 1st Light Armoured Brigade came under the division's command, and in September the 3rd Armoured Brigade which had fought with the 1st Armoured Division in France. The armoured regiments of 1 Armd Bde were the King's Dragoon Guards, the 3rd Hussars, and the 4th Hussars. In August 1940 the 3rd Hussars (which in April had been warned for the expedition to Narvik, although in the event only a detachment went) sailed for the Middle East where it joined 7 Armd Bde of 7th Armoured Division, its place in 1 Armd Bde being taken by 3rd Royal Tank Regiment from 3 Armd Bde. As 2nd RTR from 3 Armd Bde (and 7th RTR from the 1st Army Tank Brigade) had gone with the 3rd Hussars, this left 3 Armd Bde very weak.

In November 1940 the 2nd Armoured Division, with its two armoured brigades, sailed for Egypt. On arrival at the end of the year the KDGs left 1 Armd Bde to be converted to an armoured car regiment, which they remained for the rest of the war, serving in North Africa, Italy and Greece.

In March the rest of 1 Armd Bde was part of the British force sent to Greece, where it suffered heavily.

The 2nd Armoured Division, without part of its support group which had gone to Greece and with only 3 Armd Bde which was a scratch formation (only 5th RTR remained of its original units), was overwhelmed in Rommel's first advance in March–April 1941 and ceased to exist as a formation. What was left of it was besieged in Tobruk. The 3rd Armd Bde had been given the 3rd Hussars and the 6th Royal Tanks, the latter equipped with Italian M.13 tanks captured at Beda Fomm. In Tobruk it also had the KDGs, the division's armoured car regiment, under command. In October the 3rd Hussars were withdrawn and the brigade was re-named the 32nd Army

Valentines of 23rd Armoured Brigade (40th RTR and 50th RTR) at the Gabes Gap in southern Tunisia after it had been forced, April 1943.

241

Universal carrier with Vickers medium machine-gun in action in Tunisia, March 1943. (Imperial War Museum)

Churchills prepare for action near the Sbiba-Sbeitla road, Tunisia, February 21, 1943. These are tanks of 142nd (Suffolk) Regiment, R.A.C., 25th Tank Brigade, and were the first Churchills in action since the Canadian raid on Dieppe, apart from a trio used as command tanks in the Western Desert about the time of Alamein. (Imperial War Museum)

Tank Brigade, consisting of 1st RTR, 4th RTR, and D Squadron of 7th RTR. (See also 1st Armoured Brigade below.)

6th Armoured Division

Formed with the 20th and 26th Armoured Brigades and the 1st Derbyshire Yeomanry as its armoured car regiment. When one armoured brigade was removed the 26th remained with the division while the 20th was subsequently broken up and its units went to other armoured formations. The 6th Armoured Division fought in Tunisia and then in Italy, joining the campaign at Cassino and fighting through to Austria. The armoured regiments of 26 Armd Bde were the 16/5th Lancers, the 17/21st Lancers, and the 2nd Lothians and Border Horse. Its motor battalion was the 10th Rifle Brigade. (See also 20th Armoured Brigade below.)

The 1st Derbyshire Yeomanry remained with the division as its armoured recce regiment.

The division's infantry brigade initially was the 38th Irish. After Bou Arada in the Tunisian campaign the 1st Guards Brigade (3rd Grenadiers, 2nd Coldstreams, 3rd Welsh) replaced the 38th. In Italy in May 1944 the second infantry brigade was the 61st—a Green Jackets brigade of 2nd, 7th, and 10th Rifle Brigade.

After the end of the war the division was re-numbered the 1st Armoured Division and adopted the former 1st Armoured Division's formation sign of the White Rhino.

7th Armoured Division

Formed in 1938 as the Mobile Division, Egypt, it was re-named 7th Armoured Division in April 1940, with the 4th and 7th Armoured Brigades, and the 11th Hussars as its armoured car regiment. The division fought through the North African campaign from the first shot on June 11, 1940 to the last on May 12, 1943. It landed at Salerno, Italy, in September 1943, and three months later returned to England. It landed in Normandy on D+1, June 7, 1944, and fought right through to the Baltic. By this time both its original armoured brigades had long ceased to be under its command, though the 11th Hussars remained with it to the end.

The 4th Armoured Brigade, after fighting in North Africa mostly under command of 7th Armoured Division, became an independent armoured brigade in 13 Corps for the conquest of Sicily, then landed at Taranto and fought on the Adriatic flank from October to December 1943 when it returned to England in preparation for the invasion of North-West Europe. It landed in Normandy on June 9 and fought throughout the campaign. Its armoured regiments in Europe were, initially, the Royal Scots Greys, the 3rd (after July 1944, the 3rd/4th) County of

Churchill III of C Squadron, 51st RTR, 25th Tank Brigade, with First Army in Tunisia. On the left is a carrier of 6th Armoured Division. The third armoured formation in First Army was 21st Tank Brigade, part of 4th Division. (Imperial War Museum)

London Yeomanry, and the 44th RTR. Its motor battalion was the 2nd KRRC. In March 1945 the Staffordshire Yeomanry joined the brigade for the Rhine crossing. (See also 4th Armoured Brigade below.)

The 7th Armoured Brigade was withdrawn from the Desert after it had been almost wiped out at Sidi Rezegh (November 1941). In January 1942, consisting of the 7th Hussars, 2nd RTR, 414 Battery (Essex Yeomanry) RHA, and A Battery 95th Anti-Tank Regt., RA, it sailed for Malaya, was diverted to Burma after the fall of Singapore, took part in the retreat through Burma, was moved to Iraq, Syria, and Palestine, was trained for Italian conditions in the mountains of Lebanon under command of 10th Armoured Division. The brigade went to Italy in May 1944, fought through to the end of the campaign, and then joined the Army of Occupation in Austria. (See also 7th Armoured Brigade below.)

The 7th Armoured Division's armoured brigade from second Alamein onwards was the 22nd, originally in 1st Armoured Division. The 22nd's armoured regiments from September 1942 to July 1944 were the 4th County of London Yeomanry, the 1st RTR, and the 5th RTR. Its motor battalion was the 1st Rifle Brigade which had been the motor battalion of the 2nd Armoured Brigade. In July 1944 casualties in Normandy were such that the 4th CLY was withdrawn from the brigade to amalgamate with the 3rd CLY in 4 Armd Bde and its place was taken by the 5th Royal Inniskilling Dragoon Guards which had been part of 28 Armd Bde now broken up (see 9th Armoured Division).

In December 1943 when it returned home from Italy the 7th Armoured Division was joined by one of its original regiments, the 8th Hussars, which returned from the Middle East to become its armoured recce regiment.

The division's infantry component in 1942 until September was the 7th Motor Brigade (4th RHA, 9th KRRC, 2nd and 9th Rifle Brigade). Thereafter, until November 1944, it was the 131st (Queen's) Brigade (1st/5th, 1st/6th, and 1st/7th Queens Royal Regiment). In November, because of the reinforcement situation 131st Brigade became 1st/5th Queens, 2nd Devons, 9th Durham Light Infantry.

Shermans of the Royal Scots Greys, at that time in 23rd Armoured Brigade, in action near Vesuvius, Italy, at the end of September 1943. The Greys returned to the U.K. and took part in the North-West Europe campaign in 4th Armoured Brigade.
(Imperial War Museum)

8th Armoured Division

Formed with the 23rd and 24th Armoured Brigades and the 2nd Derbyshire Yeomanry as its armoured car regiment, it went to Egypt in 1942, but despite its divisional sign—a green traffic light with GO—it never went into action as a formation. The 23rd Armoured Brigade was thrown straight into battle at first Alamein (July 1942) under command of 1st Armoured Division, and at Alam Halfa it came under command of 10th Armoured Division while the 24th was still kept in reserve. Before second Alamein the division was broken up, the 23rd being used in an infantry support rôle and the 24th being placed under command of 10th Armoured Division. After the battle the 24th, which suffered heavy losses, was itself broken up to provide reinforcements for other units. (See also 24th Armoured Brigade and Dummy Tank Formations below.)

The 11th Hussars, armoured car regiment of the 7th Armoured Division, on its way from Eighth Army to join First Army when the division, together with the 4th Indian Division, the 201st Guards Brigade, and some medium artillery, was transferred from one Army to the other for the last days of the North African campaign.
(The Eleventh at War)

Humber armoured cars of C Squadron HQ, The Royal Dragoons, at Cerignola, Italy, 1943. The Royals returned to the U.K. to become the armoured car regiment of 12 Corps in February 1944.
(Major K. G. Balfour, M.C.)

Churchill IV of 25th Tank Brigade at Cassino, Italy, May 1944. The brigade supported the 1st Canadian Infantry Division in 1 Canadian Corps' piercing of the Hitler Line. In honour of this co-operation the brigade was invited by the Canadians to incorporate a maple leaf in its formation sign. 21st Tank Brigade also fought in Italy, though no longer as a brigade of 4th Division.
(Imperal War Museum)

B Squadron, 17th/21st Lancers, 6th Armoured Division, waiting to attack at Cassino, May 1944. The Squadron Leader, Major Buxton, in the nearest Sherman, is giving out orders over the air.
(Imperial War Museum)

The 23rd Armoured Brigade advanced from Alamein to Tunisia, took part in the Sicilian campaign as an independent armoured brigade in 30 Corps, landed at Salerno under command of 7th Armoured Division, and after fighting in Italy until mid-May 1944 was relieved by 7 Armd Bde and went first to Egypt, then to Palestine, then to Egypt again, and then to Greece in October 1944. (See also 23rd Armoured Brigade below.)

9th Armoured Division
Formed with the 27th and 28th Armoured Brigades and the Inns of Court Regiment as its armoured car regiment. It never went into action as a division, indeed it never left England as a division, and for long had a draft-finding rôle. Its armoured recce regiment was the 1st Royal Gloucestershire Hussars (originally in 20 Armd Bde).

In June 1942 the 7th Infantry Brigade (2nd South

The Anzio beach-head, January 1944. Carriers of 1st Division and, in the background, Shermans of 46th RTR, the armoured support of the division. The assault was carried out on January 22 by 6th U.S. Corps of Fifth U.S. Army, the force consisting of 1st British Division (with 46th RTR), 3rd U.S. Division, 45th U.S. Division, and elements of 1st U.S. Armoured Division.
(Imperial War Museum)

At Orford, Suffolk, where part of the 79th Armoured Division's training for the Normandy assault was carried out, exact reproductions of the German coastal defences were built. Brigadier (later Major-General) N. W. Duncan, commander of 30th Armoured Brigade, points out to General Sir Bernard (later Field-Marshall Viscount) Montgomery, C-in-C 21 Army Group, features of the assault plan on a model during the C-in-C's visit to Orford.   (Major-General N. W. Duncan)

The use of DD tanks meant that, for the first time, infantry in the assault could count on immediate armour support when they landed in Normandy on June 6, 1944. But many DD tanks did not survive to support the infantry inland: like this disabled DD Sherman of the 13th/18th Royal Hussars, 27th Armoured Brigade.   (Imperial War Museum)

Wales Borderers, 2nd/6th Surreys, and 6th Royal Sussex) came into the division and in September 27 Armd Bde left to become part of the new 79th Armoured Division.

The 9th Armoured Division was disbanded in May 1944 and 28 Armd Bde, after being for a short time under command of 21 Army Group and then in 79th Armoured Division until the end of July, was broken up, its armoured regiments going as follows: the 15th/19th Hussars to the 11th Armoured Division as its armoured recce regiment in place of the 2nd Northants Yeomanry (originally in 20 Armd Bde) which was withdrawn because of casualties; the 5th Dragoon Guards to 22 Armd Bde (see 7th Armoured Division); the 1st Fife and Forfar Yeomanry to be equipped with Crocodiles and to join 31 Armd Bde (see 31 Tank Bde below) in 79th Armoured Division. Its motor battalion was the 8th KRRC.

The armoured regiments of 27 Armd Bde were the 4th/7th Dragoon Guards, the 13th/18th Hussars, and the East Riding Yeomanry, until January 1944 when the 4th/7th went to 8 Armd Bde (see 10th Armoured Division) and were replaced by the Staffordshire Yeomanry from that brigade. This was in accordance with General Montgomery's policy of leavening "novices" with battle-experienced troops; the Staffordshire Yeomanry had seen much fighting in the Middle East. Its motor battalion was the 2nd Queen Victoria's Rifles.

The 27th Armoured Brigade equipped with DD tanks was part of the assault wave on D-Day in Normandy. At the end of July it was broken up because of casualties, the 13th/18th going to 8 Armd Bde, the East Riding Yeomany to 33 Armd Bde (see 33 Tank Bde below), and the Staffordshire Yeomanry returning to England for further specialized training in DD tanks before taking part in the operations to clear the Scheldt estuary and then joining 4 Armd Bde for the Rhine crossing.

10th Armoured Division

Converted from the 1st Cavalry Division in Palestine in August 1941, two of its three cavalry brigades being re-designated the 8th and 9th Armoured Brigades, with the Royals as its armoured car regiment. The 10th Armoured Division came into the Desert after the first battle of Alamein in July 1942 and fought at Alam Halfa and second Alamein. But in neither battle did it have both its original armoured brigades under command. In order to make good battle losses after the Gazala operations both 8 and 9 Armd Bdes had to hand over their tanks to other armoured brigades and by the time of Alam Halfa only 8 Armd Bde had been re-equipped. For second Alamein the 10th had 8 and 24 Armd Bdes, while 9 Armd Bde (3rd Hussars, Royal Wiltshire Yeomanry, and Warwickshire Yeomanry) was under command of 2nd New Zealand Division and had the unenviable task of getting through the enemy anti-tank gun screen in the dark.

A shoot by the 75-mm Battery of The King's Dragoon Guards in Italy. Each armoured car regiment had a section of two self-propelled 75s per squadron – they were frequently grouped together into a battery.

(History of The King's Dragoon Guards)

Cromwell of the 8th King's Royal Irish Hussars, the armoured recce regiment of the 7th Armoured Division. The division's armoured units landed on D + 1 (June 7) at Arromanches.
(Imperial War Museum)

The brigade was caught in front of the guns as dawn broke and was virtually wiped out. But it forced the all-important gap.

After Alamein the 10th Armoured Division went to the Levant where 9 Armd Bde was re-formed and subsequently took part in the Italian campaign as an independent armoured brigade. 8 Armd Bde stayed in the Desert and took part in the next four months' fighting to Enfidaville, Tunisia, its armoured regiments being the 3rd RTR, the Nottinghamshire Sherwood Rangers Yeomanry, and the Staffordshire Yeomany. It then returned to England where 3rd RTR went to 29 Armd Bde of 11th Armoured Division and were replaced by the 24th Lancers from that brigade, while the Staffordshire Yeomanry went to 27 Armd Bde and the 4th/7th Dragoon Guards joined 8 Armd Bde in their place. 8 Armd Bde equipped with DD tanks landed in Normandy on D-Day in support of the 50th Division. At the end of July, because of the impossibility of bringing all the armoured regiments in the British Liberation Army up to strength after the casualties they had suffered, the 24th Lancers to their dismay and chagrin were disbanded and the 13th/18th Hussars came into the brigade in their place. The order for disbandment almost caused a mutiny in reverse, the survivors of the regiment threatening, with gunner support, to launch their own attack against the enemy rather than obey it. The 12th KRRC was the brigade's motor battalion. (See also 9th Armoured Brigade below.)

The Royals, too, stayed in the Desert and fought through to Tunisia; then, after serving in Sicily and Italy, they returned to the U.K. to become the armoured car regiment of 12 Corps in the North-West Europe campaign.

The 10th Armoured Division was disbanded in 1944.

11th Armoured Division

Formed in March 1941 with the 29th and 30th Armoured Brigades and the 27th Lancers as its armoured car regiment. When the armoured divisions were re-grouped in 1942 the 11th retained the 29th Armoured Brigade, while 30 Armd Bde went to the 42nd Armoured Division replacing its 10th and 11th Armoured Brigades (converted from infantry) which became (Army) tank brigades. The 27th Lancers, having left the division, subsequently served in Italy, and the 2nd Northamptonshire Yeomanry (from the broken-up 20 Armd Bde) was the 11th's armoured recce regiment until it was withdrawn because of casualties in Normandy in August 1944 and replaced by the 15th/19th Hussars from 28 Armd Bde (see 9th Armoured Division).

The 11th Armoured Division fought in the North-West Europe campaign, landing in Normandy on June 17, 1944, and reaching Lubeck and the Baltic Sea (the first British troops in history to do so) on May 2, 1945. The armoured regiments of 29 Armd Bde were, from formation until early 1944, the 23rd Hussars, the 24th Lancers, and the 2nd Fife and Forfar Yeomanry, with the 8th Rifle Brigade as its motor battalion. Early in 1944 the 24th Lancers changed brigades with the 3rd RTR (see 10th Armoured Division), which remained in 29 Armd Bde until the end of the war.

The infantry brigade of the 11th Armoured Division was the 159th (3rd Monmouthshires, 4th King's Shropshire Light Infantry, and 1st Herefords).

The armoured regiments of 30 Armd Bde were the 22nd Dragoons, the 1st Lothians and Border Horse, and the Westminster Dragoons. Its motor battalion was the 12th KRRC which later went to 8 Armd Bde. After the disbandment of 42nd Armoured Division in 1943, 30 Armd Bde joined 79th Armoured Division and was equipped with Sherman Crabs for minesweeping.

Guards Armoured Division

Formed in June 1941 with the 5th and 6th Guards Armoured Brigades and the 2nd Household Cavalry Regiment as its armoured car regiment. The 5th Guards Armoured Brigade had the 2nd (Armoured) Battalion Grenadier Guards, 1st (Armoured) Battalion Coldstream Guards, and the 2nd (Armoured) Battalion Irish Guards, with the 1st (Motor) Battalion Grenadier Guards as its motor battalion. The 6th Guards Armoured (later Tank) Brigade had the 4th (Armoured) Battalion Grenadier Guards, 3rd

(Armoured) Battalion Scots Guards, and the 2nd (Armoured) Battalion Welsh Guards, with the 4th (Motor) Battalion Coldstream Guards as its motor battalion.

When armoured divisions were reduced to one armoured brigade the 6th left the division in October 1942 to become a tank brigade. When armoured recce regiments were added the 2nd (Armoured) Battalion Welsh Guards left 6th Guards Tank Brigade to fulfil this rôle for the division and the 4th (Motor) Battalion Coldstream Guards was converted to the third tank battalion in 6 Gds Tk Bde. The reason why the 4th Coldstreams did not become the armoured recce regiment was that they were not already trained in wireless whereas the 2nd Welsh Guards were.

The Guards Armoured Division fought in North-West Europe arriving in Normandy at the end of June 1944. Its infantry brigade was the 32nd Guards Brigade (5th Coldstreams, 3rd Irish, 1st Welsh). Among its many exploits was the famous liberation of Brussels on September 3, the fifth anniversary of the war.

The 6th Guards Tank Brigade arrived in Normandy at the end of July 1944 and first went into action south of Caumont during the fighting for the break-out.

The Guards Armoured Division was broken up at the end of the war.

42nd Armoured Division

Converted from the 42nd Infantry Division in August 1941. The 42nd was a north country Territorial division which had distinguished itself at Dunkirk. On conversion its armoured brigades were numbered 10th and 11th. These subsequently left the division when re-grouping took place in 1942 and the 30th Armoured Brigade joined in their stead (see 11th Armoured Division). The displaced brigades now became the 10th and 11th (Army) Tank Brigades. Their regiments, all converted from infantry battalions were:

10 Tank Bde—
  108th Regiment Royal Armoured Corps (formerly 1/5th Lancashire Fusiliers)

Personal maintenance in Normandy. Shermans of the 13th/18th Royal Hussars and their crews.

  109th Regiment RAC (formerly 1/6th Lancashire Fusiliers)
  143rd Regiment RAC (formerly 9th Lancashire Fusiliers)
11 Tank Bde—
  107th RAC (5th The King's Own Royal Regt)
  110th RAC (5th The Border Regt)
  111th RAC (5th Manchester Regt)
Both brigades were disbanded in December 1943.

The armoured car regiment of the 42nd was also converted from infantry—from the 9th Battalion The Sherwood Foresters—and became 112th RAC. In March 1943 the 112th left to become the armoured car regiment of 12 Corps but was replaced by the Royal Dragoons in February 1944. The armoured recce regiment of the 42nd was the 161st Recce Regiment (formerly the 12th Battalion Green Howards).

The 42nd Armoured Division was disbanded at the end of 1943, its 30 Armd Bde going to the 79th Armoured Division.

79th Armoured Division

Formed in September 1942 with the 27th Armoured Brigade (see 9th Armoured Division) and the 185th Infantry Brigade as a normal armoured division. In spring 1943 its rôle was changed. It was to become an all-armoured formation responsible for the evolution,

Shermans in action near Cheux during the Odon offensive, June 24-29, 1944. The armoured formation was the 11th Armoured Division which had 4th Armoured Brigade under its command as well as its own 29th Armoured Brigade. The right-hand Sherman is a Firefly. The 31st Tank Brigade was also engaged in the Odon offensive with the 8th Armoured Brigade on its right. (Imperial War Museum)

Cromwells of 2nd Battalion Welsh Guards, the armoured recce regiment of the Guards Armoured Division, in Normandy. The division arrived in Normandy at the end of June.

(Major L. F. Ellis)

Cromwells of 7th Armoured Division forming up for Operation "Goodwood" July 18-20, 1944. For "Goodwood" 8 Corps became an entirely armoured corps, with the 7th, 11th, and Guards Armoured Divisions attacking south-east from Caen.
(Imperial War Museum)

development, training and operational control of the specialized armour needed for the assault across the Channel.

The infantry brigade left the division; the 27th Armoured Brigade remained as the nucleus of the formation in its new rôle, and was trained to operate the Sherman DD tanks when these became available. 1st Assault Brigade Royal Engineers (5th, 6th, and 42nd Assault Regiments) joined the division to operate the Churchill AVREs (Armoured Vehicles Royal Engineers) which were to destroy the beach defences and fortifications. In November, 30 Armd Bde came from the disbanded 42nd Armoured Division and became the minesweeping brigade, equipped with Crabs (Shermans with flails). Also in the division was the 35th Tank Brigade equipped with CDL (Canal Defence Light) tanks carrying armoured searchlights. In April 1944, after it had been with the 79th for a year, it was replaced by the 1st Tank Brigade, also CDL-equipped. Matildas were originally used for CDL conversions, then Grants; 1st Tank Brigade had Grant CDLs. 43rd RTR was the division's experimental unit which carried out trials on which the divisional equipment was based.

The 27th Armoured Brigade left the division early in 1944 to join the infantry formation (3rd British Infantry Division) which it was to support in the D-Day landings in Normandy. Other armoured units —British, Canadian, and American—were also trained in DD work by the 79th Armoured Division.

During the course of the campaign in North-West Europe other brigades and units came into the division. First came the 141st Regiment RAC (converted from the 7th Battalion The Buffs) which was the first regiment to be equipped with Crocodiles (flame-throwing Churchills). Although part of the 31st Tank Brigade it came under command of 30 Armd Bde in Normandy. In September 31 Tank Bde came into 79th Armoured Division and was re-designated 31st Armoured Brigade. Later in the year the brigade took over two armoured personnel carrier regiments (see 31st Tank Brigade below).

In January 1945 the 33rd Armoured Brigade joined the division and was converted to Buffaloes in preparation for the Rhine crossing (see 33rd Tank

Churchill of 31st Tank Brigade in Maltot, west of Caen. The brigade (7th RTR and 9th RTR), in support of 43rd Division, suffered heavy casualties on two occasions (July 10 and 22) in this village which was dominated by the Tiger-infested Hill 112. The Churchill, like other Allied tanks, was no match for the Tiger. (Imperial War Museum)

The end in Normandy: C Squadron of the Royals, the armoured car regiment of 12 Corps, passing through the ruins of Falaise.
(Major K. G. Balfour, M.C.)

Brigade below). Buffaloes were initially manned in the division by the 5th Armoured Regiment RE in clearing the west bank of the Scheldt in September 1944, and then by 11th RTR, from 1st Tank Brigade, for the attack on Walcheren on November 1st.

For the Rhine crossing 4th Armoured Brigade, with DD tanks and including the Staffordshire Yeomanry (see 7th Armoured Division), was under the division's command.

The 79th Armoured Division was broken up at the end of the war.

THE ARMOURED BRIGADES AND TANK BRIGADES

Brief histories of many of the armoured brigades are included in the foregoing account of the armoured divisions, but in order to complete the picture some additional details are given in this section as well as short accounts of all those other brigades not previously listed.

1st (Army) Tank Brigade

Two battalions of the brigade (4th and 7th RTR) fought in France in 1940. The third battalion (8th RTR) stayed in England. 4th and 7th RTR went to Egypt unbrigaded, the 7th arriving (with 2nd RTR and the 3rd Hussars—see 2nd Armoured Division) in September 1940, the 4th in February 1941.

In April 1941 the brigade, now consisting of 8th, 42nd, and 44th RTR, left the U.K. and arrived in Egypt on June 13. It took part in the Desert battles over the next year. By second Alamein, while the 8th RTR remained a gun tank regiment, 42nd and 44th RTR had Scorpion (mine-clearing) detachments, the first use of specialized armour in the war. Subsequently the brigade, consisting of 11th and 42nd RTR, was equipped with CDL tanks and returned from the Middle East in April 1944 to join 79th Armoured Division in that rôle, replacing 34th Tank Brigade which was similarly equipped. 49th RTR was transferred from 35th Tank Brigade to complete the brigade.

The 1st Tank Brigade was never used in the CDL rôle. 42nd RTR was disbanded and the rest of the brigade converted to other rôles. But early in 1945 a change of mind resulted in a call for CDL units to help in the Rhine crossing. One strong squadron of 24 CDL tanks of 49th RTR was used—and again in the crossing of the Elbe. 43rd RTR, the 79th Armoured Division's experimental unit, was converted to the CDL rôle in May 1945 to take part in the landing in Malaya planned for September. The operation never took place because of the Japanese surrender in August.

1st Armoured Brigade

See under 2nd Armoured Division. After Greece the brigade was re-formed with 1st and 6th RTR and was about to be sent to join 7th Armoured Division in the Desert when Rommel struck at Gazala in May 1942. In consequence the brigade was broken up on arrival at the front to reinforce battle-shrunk brigades and never fought again as a formation.

2nd Armoured Brigade

See under 1st Armoured Division.

Cromwell of 22nd Armoured Brigade greeted by the newly-liberated inhabitants of Gournay-en-Bray on the way to Amiens, August 31, 1944. (Imperial War Museum)

3rd Armoured Brigade

See under 2nd Armoured Division.

4th Armoured Brigade

See under 7th Armoured Division. During its North African service it was sometimes a Light Armoured Brigade. Its regiments there were: in November 1940 —7th Hussars, 2nd RTR (less one squadron), 6th RTR, one battery 3rd RHA, one squadron 3rd Hussars; in November 1941—8th Hussars, 3rd RTR, 5th RTR, 2nd Scots Guards, 2nd RHA; in April 1942 —8th Hussars, 3rd RTR, 5th RTR, 1st KRRC, 1st RHA; October-November 1942—Royal Scots Greys, 4th Hussars with one squadron of 8th Hussars, 2nd Derbyshire Yeomanry, 1st KRRC, 3rd RHA.

The liberation of Brussels by the Guards Armoured Division, September 3-4, 1944. (Imperial War Museum)

Sherman Crabs and Churchill AVREs of 79th Armoured Division advancing to the attack. The AVRE on the left is carrying a fascine.
(Imperial War Museum)

5th Guards Armoured Brigade
See under Guards Armoured Division.

6th Guards Armoured (later Tank) Brigade
See under Guards Armoured Division.

7th Armoured Brigade
See under 7th Armoured Division. When it went to Italy in May 1944 the brigade consisted of 2nd and 6th RTR, and the 7th Hussars, as it had done in the Desert campaign in 1941. In June the 7th Hussars were removed from the brigade and put under command of the 2nd Polish Corps, their place being taken by 8th RTR. In September they rejoined the brigade as a fourth regiment for a few weeks.

8th Armoured Brigade
See under 10th Armoured Division.

9th Armoured Brigade
See under 10th Armoured Division. The brigade went to Italy with its three "Alamein" regiments—3rd Hussars, Royal Wiltshire Yeomanry, and Warwick-

shire Yeomanry. The two yeomanry regiments returned to the U.K. in October and November 1944, and the 7th Hussars joined the brigade from 7 Armd Bde. Two squadrons of the 3rd Hussars and two squadrons of the 7th were equipped with DD tanks. In November the 4th Hussars came under command as a Kangaroo regiment. The brigade was also responsible for the command and training of three armoured car regiments when they were not allotted to other formations for operations; and it controlled the two Fantail (LVT) units, the 755th Tank Battalion (United States) and the RASC Fantail Regiment.

10th Armoured (later Tank) Brigade
See under 42nd Armoured Division.

11th Armoured (later Tank) Brigade
See under 42nd Armoured Division.

20th Armoured Brigade
See under 6th Armoured Division. Its regiments were 1st Royal Gloucestershire Hussars, and 1st and 2nd Northamptonshire Yeomanry. After the brigade was

Sherman Crab Mark I of 1st Lothians and Border Horse coming ashore from a Landing Craft Tank during the assault landing on the west coast of Walcheren, November 1, 1944. Churchill AVRE with SBG (Small Box Girder) bridge can be seen still on board. The landing was made by three Royal Marine Commandos and a detachment of the 79th Armoured Division. (Imperial War Museum)

broken up the 1st RGH became the armoured recce regiment of the 9th Armoured Division until the division was disbanded in May 1944, when it became a training regiment: the 1st Northants Yeomanry went to the 33rd Tank (later Armoured) Brigade, and the 2nd went to the 11th Armoured Division as its armoured recce regiment until it was withdrawn and amalgamated with its first line in August 1944.

21st Tank Brigade

Formed in 1939 as part of the Territorial Army, it fought in Tunisia and then in Italy. Its units were the 12th and 48th RTR, and the 145th RAC (converted from the 8th Battalion The Duke of Wellington's Regiment). In the "mixed" division re-organization it became part of 4th Infantry Division with which it went to Tunisia, landing there between March 23 and 27, 1943. The other brigades in the division were the 10th and 12th Infantry Brigades.

In January 1945 the 145th RAC was disbanded and the North Irish Horse came into the brigade from 25th Tank Brigade.

It is incorrectly stated in a caption on p. 79 of *Armoured Fighting Vehicles of the World* Volume 2, that the 21st Tank Brigade was the first to take Churchills into action. The first unit to do this was in fact the Calgary Regiment of 1st Canadian Army Tank Brigade at Dieppe on August 19, 1942. Apart from three Churchill IIIs used in the Western Desert in 7th (Motor) Brigade HQ at about that same time, the next Churchills in action were tanks of the 25th Tank Brigade in Tunisia in February 1943. The error about the 21st Tank Brigade also occurs on p. 254 of *The Tanks* Volume Two (The History of the RTR), where the 51st RTR is included in the brigade's order of battle instead of the 145th RAC. The 51st RTR was in 25th Tank Brigade.

22nd Armoured Brigade

See under 1st and 7th Armoured Divisions.

23rd Armoured Brigade

See under 8th Armoured Division. Originally formed as the 23rd Army Tank Brigade it was re-designated in November 1940. Its units were 40th, 46th, and 50th RTR, and 11th KRRC.

24th Armoured Brigade

See under 8th Armoured Division. Originally formed as the 24th Army Tank Brigade it was re-designated in November 1940. Its units were the 41st, 45th, and 47th RTR. Although the brigade was broken up after second Alamein to provide reinforcements it did not disappear altogether—at any rate in essence! From 1940 onwards a number of dummy armoured formations and tank units were invented in orders of battle to deceive the enemy. 24th Armoured Brigade had a dummy existence in Cyrenaica in 1944, its dummy units at different times being 39th RTR, 62nd RTR, 101st RTR, 3rd Royal Gloucestershire Hussars, and 4th Northants Yeomanry.

Some other dummy formations are given in a later section.

25th Tank (later Armoured Engineer) Brigade

One of the first three Tank Brigades to be formed,

Cromwell of B Squadron, 15th/19th The King's Royal Hussars, 11th Armoured Division, in the ruins of Udem, during Operation "Veritable", February 28, 1945. (Imperial War Museum)

apart from the 1st, the other two being the 21st and the 31st. The brigade fought in Tunisia, arriving there in February 1943, and then in Italy. Its units were the 51st RTR, the North Irish Horse, and the 142nd RAC (converted from the 7th Battalion The Suffolk Regiment).

In January 1945 the 142nd RAC was disbanded and the North Irish Horse went to 21st Tank Brigade. The 51st RTR, with two squadrons converted to Crocodiles and one converted to Crabs, remained in the brigade, where it was joined by 1st Armoured Engineer Regt., RE. The brigade, re-designated 25th Armoured Engineer Brigade, was now equipped and trained on the pattern of the 79th Armoured Division for the assault across the Senio in April 1945.

In the "mixed" division re-organization 25th Tank Brigade was allotted to 43rd Division, but the division did not go to Tunisia and the brigade fought there variously in support of 1st (with which it had also trained in England), 4th Indian, 46th, and 78th Divisions, and 19th French Corps.

26th Armoured Brigade

See under 6th Armoured Division.

27th Armoured Brigade

See under 9th and 79th Armoured Divisions.

28th Armoured Brigade

See under 9th Armoured Division.

29th Armoured Brigade

See under 11th Armoured Division.

30th Armoured Brigade

See under 11th and 79th Armoured Divisions.

31st Tank (later Armoured) Brigade

The 7th and 9th RTR of this brigade landed in Normandy on June 21, 1944. Its third unit, the 141st RAC (converted from the 7th Battalion The Buffs (Royal East Kent Regiment)), was the first in the army to be equipped with Crocodile flame-throwing tanks and was already in Normandy under command of the 30th Armoured Brigade. It remained under command while 31st Tank Brigade (7th and 9th RTR) took part in the Odon crossing and the fighting for the break-out towards Falaise. After the crossing of the Seine 7th and 9th RTR were transferred to 34th Tank Brigade and took part in the assault on Le Havre on September 10.

11th RTR loading its Buffaloes near Nijmegen at the start of Operation "Veritable" (February 1945), during which it waged a semi-naval war in the flooded area on the left flank between the Rhine and the Nijmegen-Cleve road.

(Major-General N. W. Duncan)

Immediately after this 31st Tank Brigade, to which 141st RAC now reverted, came into 79th Armoured Division and was re-designated 31st Armoured Brigade. Early in October a second flame-throwing unit, the 1st Fife and Forfar Yeomanry (from the broken-up 28th Armoured Brigade) joined it. The 49th Armoured Personnel Carrier Regiment (formerly 49th RTR in 35th and then 1st Tank Brigades) and the 1st Canadian Armoured Carrier Regiment came into the brigade with their Kangaroo troop carriers at the end of 1944. In February 1945 the 7th RTR were converted to Crocodiles and returned to the brigade.

Originally the 31st Tank Brigade included the 9th and 10th RTR, but not the 7th. After the 7th was lost with 32nd Army Tank Brigade in Tobruk in June 1942 the 10th was re-numbered to take its place and became the "new" 7th in 1943. The 31st Tank Brigade was allotted to 43rd Division in the 1942 "mixed" division re-organization.

32nd Army Tank Brigade

See under 2nd Armoured Division. Re-designated from the 3rd Armoured Brigade in October 1941, the brigade at the outset of the Gazala battle in May 1942 consisted of the 4th and 7th RTR, with 42nd RTR (from 1st Army Tank Brigade) under command. Most of 8th RTR came under command later in the battle,

while 4th RTR from its arrival at the front came under command of 4th Armoured Brigade and then, later, of 22nd Armoured Brigade. After the battle the 8th and 42nd RTR handed over what was left of their tanks, with some crews, and went back to the frontier to re-organize and re-equip, while 4th RTR, which had rejoined the brigade, and 7th RTR withdrew into Tobruk, where they were lost after fierce fighting when it surrendered on June 21, 1942.

33rd Tank (later Armoured) Brigade

Formed in 1941 as an army tank brigade and allotted to 3rd Division in 1942, the 33rd was re-designated as an independent armoured brigade in 1943 and landed in Normandy on June 14, 1944. Its units were 144th RAC (converted from 8th Battalion The East Lancashire Regiment), the 148th RAC (converted from 9th Battalion The Loyal Regiment (North Lancashire)), and the 1st Northamptonshire Yeomanry (see under 20th Armoured Brigade). After the break-out in August, the 148th RAC was disbanded because of shortage of reinforcements and was absorbed into 144th RAC, which later became the re-born 4th RTR (see under 32nd Army Tank Brigade). As the third unit, the East Riding Yeomanry came into the brigade from the 27th Armoured Brigade which had just been broken up. The 33rd Armoured Brigade took part in the assault on Le Havre.

In January 1945 the brigade came into the 79th Armoured Division for conversion to the Buffalo rôle for the Rhine crossing. The 11th RTR, formerly of 1st Tank Brigade, which had been converted to Buffaloes in October 1944 for the attack on Walcheren, was incorporated in the brigade. The Buffaloes of 33rd Armoured Brigade led the Rhine attack, carrying the assault infantry across the river on the night of March 23/24, 1945.

34th Tank Brigade

Formed in 1941 and allotted to 1st Division in the "mixed" division reorganization of 1942, it did not accompany that division to Tunisia. From July 1944 the brigade fought in Normandy where its units were the 107th, the 147th, and the 153rd RAC, until in August, because of casualties, the 153rd RAC was disbanded and formed C Squadron of the 107th RAC.

In January 1945 the 25th Tank Brigade in Italy was converted to the specialised armour role and re-designated 25th Armoured Engineer Brigade. The 51st RTR had one squadron of Sherman Crabs and two of Churchill Crocodiles. A Crocodile of 51st RTR in Italy.

(Imperial War Museum)

The end of the war in Italy. DD Sherman of B Squadron, the 7th Hussars, 9th Armoured Brigade, in the Piazzale Roma, Venice, May 1945.

(The Seventh and Three Enemies)

7th and 9th RTR then joined the brigade from 31st Tank Brigade. The brigade's subsequent actions included the assault on Le Havre and the clearing of the Reichswald. The 107th RAC was converted from 5th Battalion The King's Own Royal Regiment, the 147th from 10th Battalion The Hampshire Regiment, and the 153rd from 8th Battalion The Essex Regiment.

35th Tank Brigade
This brigade, which was experimenting with tank-borne armoured searchlights called, for secrecy, CDLs (Canal Defence Lights), was taken over by 79th Armoured Division in April 1943. Its units were the 49th RTR, the 152nd RAC (converted from the 11th Battalion The King's Regiment (Liverpool)), and the 155th RAC (converted from the 15th Battalion Durham Light Infantry). In April 1944 the brigade was replaced by the 1st Tank Brigade, also CDL-equipped, which had just returned from the Middle East. The 49th RTR was transferred to the 1st Tank Brigade to bring it up to strength; the rest of the brigade was disbanded.

36th Tank Brigade
Formed in January 1942, its units being the 154th RAC (converted from the 9th Battalion The North Staffordshire Regiment), the 156th RAC (converted from the 11th Battalion The Highland Light Infantry), and the 157th RAC (converted from the 9th Battalion The Hampshire Regiment). Disbanded on July 30, 1943.

137th Armoured Brigade
Formed in July 1942 by the conversion of 137 Infantry Brigade in 46th Division, its units were 113th RAC (2/5th Battalion The West Yorkshire Regiment), 114th RAC (2/6th Battalion The Duke of Wellington's Regiment), and the 115th RAC (2/7th Battalion The Duke of Wellington's Regiment). By this conversion 46th Division theoretically became a "mixed" division, its two infantry brigades being the 138th and 139th. But before 137 Brigade was trained in its armoured rôle 46th Division went overseas to fight in Tunisia and then in Italy where it consisted of three infantry brigades (128 (Hampshire), 138, and 139). The 113th RAC was re-converted to infantry as the 14th Battalion West Yorkshire Regiment, and the 114th RAC and 115th RAC were turned into Tank Delivery Squadrons in September 1943.

THE ARMOURED REPLACEMENT GROUPS
Tank delivery squadrons belonged to armoured delivery regiments. These played a vital part in armoured operations. Their job was to hold reserves of vehicles and trained personnel in the forward areas and to replace tank and crew losses as rapidly as possible. Together with armoured refitting regiments, which took over recovered knocked out vehicles and made them into "runners" again, the armoured delivery regiments formed armoured replacement groups.

In the desert fighting the delivery formation was called the Desert Tank Delivery Organization. This was developed in the Italian campaign into the 1st Armoured Replacement Group consisting of the 1st

Lee M3 Medium tank of 3rd Carabiniers (Prince of Wales's Dragoon Guards) supporting Indian infantry in jungle fighting in Central Burma, 1945. Twelve units of the Royal Armoured Corps, apart from the 7th Hussars and 2nd RTR of 7th Armoured Brigade in 1942, served in armoured formations of the Indian Army in India, Burma, and the Middle East. They were: 3rd Carabiniers, 14th/20th King's Hussars, 25th Dragoons, 26th Hussars, 116th (Gordon Highlanders) Regt. RAC, 146th (Duke of Wellington's) Regt. RAC, 149th (KOYLI) Regt. RAC, 150th (York and Lancaster) Regt. RAC, 158th (South Wales Borderers) Regt. RAC, 159th (Gloucestershire) Regt. RAC, 160th (Royal Sussex) Regt. RAC, and 163rd (Sherwood Foresters) Regt. RAC.

Armoured Delivery Regiment, the 200th Armoured Delivery Regiment, and the 1st Armoured Refitting Regiment.

For the operations in North-West Europe 21 Army Group had the 2nd Armoured Replacement Group consisting of the 2nd Armoured Delivery Regiment and the 2nd Armoured Refitting Unit.

DUMMY TANK FORMATIONS
As well as the large number of armoured formations whose brief histories are given above there were other formations which played their own specialized part in operations. These were the dummy, or camouflage, brigades whose task was to confuse enemy intelligence. For example when 4th Armoured Brigade of 2nd New Zealand Division left Castelfrentano on the Sangro front to take part in the opening Cassino battle in January 1944 the exact positions it had vacated were occupied by 101 Royal Tank Regiment to conceal the fact that it had moved. 101st RTR was in fact a camouflage unit, its tanks made of lathes and canvas. Camouflage units were also widely used in the Desert, especially during the build-up for second Alamein.

Among the dummy units and formations were the 74th Armoured Brigade which c.1941 consisted of 54th RTR (formed from infantry), 101st RTR (formed originally from RE drafts), and 102nd RTR. In 1942 74 Armd Bde was shown in the Middle East order of battle as consisting of 39th RTR and 101st RTR. 101st RTR in February 1942 was formed by a detachment of six officers and 115 other ranks from the 1st Household Cavalry Regiment. The detachment called itself "Smithforce". 39th RTR appeared as "Army Tank Battalion (Special)".

Early in the war, in October and November 1940, when many armoured units almost qualified as dummy because of the scarcity of their equipment there were two actual dummy units at West Lavington and

To celebrate VE-Day the 79th Armoured Division demonstrated one of its Churchill Great Eastern Ramps in Deventer, Holland. The Great Eastern was evolved for wall and ditch crossing in assault and its ramp was fired into position by rockets fitted to the ramp itself. It was never used in action.
(Major-General N. W. Duncan)

1. *Approaching*
2. *The obstacle*
3. *Rockets gone*
4. *Up and over the ramp*

Devizes: 99th RTR and 100th RTR. In June 1943 British Troops Egypt Area had 118th RTR and 124th RTR, and in March 1944 the 24th Armoured Brigade which had been disbanded after second Alamein re-appeared in Cyrenaica as a dummy formation.

There was also 87 Armd Bde, a dummy formation with four dummy units (3rd Royal Gloucestershire Hussars, 4th Northants Yeomanry, 60th and 62nd RTR) in Ninth Army, in July 1944. All these except 60th RTR also appeared under dummy command of 24th Armoured Brigade at other times.

No doubt there were other dummy armoured units and dummy formations.

RECONNAISSANCE CORPS

In 1940, after Dunkirk, the Mechanised Divisional Cavalry regiments that had carried out reconnaissance for infantry divisions in France were absorbed into the new armoured divisions which were being formed. Six of the seven, indeed, became the armoured regiments of 9th Armoured Division, while the seventh

(1st Lothians and Border Horse) went into 30th Armoured Brigade of 11th Armoured Division.

To carry out reconnaissance for infantry divisions a new Reconnaissance Corps was formed in January 1941. Each infantry division had a battalion (later re-designated a regiment) of the Recce Corps. These units were organised for dismounted action, but in each of their three recce squadrons there were a proportion of AFVs—armoured cars and light reconnaissance cars. Initially there was little resemblance between the organisation and equipment of Recce Corps units and the organisation and equipment of Royal Armoured Corps units. But later the work of the Recce Corps and the equipment which that work demanded brought it closer to the R.A.C., especially as experience showed that the "all-arms" concept was the only effective one—except on rare occasions—in the later stages of World War II. Eventually it was decided that the Reconnaissance Corps should become a part of the Royal Armoured Corps; the absorption formally took place on January 1, 1944.

Italian M13/40 medium tanks, captured at Bardia earlier in the month, manned by crews of the 6th Australian Divisional Cavalry Regiment during the Tobruk operations, January 1941. The kangaroo was the divisional sign. (Australian War Memorial)

Commonwealth Armoured Units and Armoured Formations (to 1946)

by Duncan Crow

AUSTRALIA

THE original Australian mechanised unit was the 1st Australian Light Car Patrol consisting of six Ford cars, each armed with a machine-gun, which took part in operations in the Western Desert in 1917 and then in Palestine where it worked with Australian Light Horse units until the end of the war.

Although the probable need for a Tank Corps as part of Australia's armed forces was appreciated in 1920 its formation was deferred until 1928 when approval was given for the purchase of the first tanks—five Vickers Mediums. A cadre of tank-trained officers and men was raised and in 1929 a militia unit, the 1st Australian Tank Section, was formed at Randwick, New South Wales; this was the first unit in Australia to be equipped with tanks. On April 29, 1933, the Australian Tank Corps was allied to the Royal Tank Corps.

In 1935 eleven Vickers Light Tanks Mark VIA were ordered. When these were taken into service in

1937 five went to the 1st Australian Tank Section at Randwick and five to the 2nd Australian Tank Section which was raised in Victoria. A further 24 tanks were then ordered.

Meanwhile an armoured car unit had been formed. In 1933 the 17/19th Light Horse Regiment was unlinked and the 19th Light Horse was raised as an armoured car regiment to form part of the 2nd Cavalry Division (Victoria). Late in 1938 the 2nd Armoured Car Regiment was formed in N.S.W. as part of the 1st Cavalry Division. In 1939 the 19th Light Horse was re-designated the 1st Armoured Car Regiment. Both armoured car regiments were equipped with Australian-designed and built Ford armoured cars. These two units and other Australian Light Horse Regiments contributed many trained personnel to the Divisional Cavalry regiments of the 6th, 7th and 9th Divisions and to other armoured and motor units of the Australian Armoured Corps as these were raised after the outbreak of war in September 1939.

Each of the first three A.I.F. divisions raised for service overseas (6th, 7th, and 9th) included a Divi-

Australian divisional cavalry regiments fought in the Middle East in a variety of vehicles. Here Crusader tanks of 9th Australian Divisional Cavalry Regiment have stopped at the water point at Amiriya on their way to the El Alamein front, July 1942.
(Australian War Memorial)

Grant tanks of 1st Australian Armoured Division in Australia, 1942. The Grant was the most numerous type of tank in Australian service. (Australian War Memorial)

sional Reconnaissance Regiment, later re-designated Divisional Cavalry Regiments. These regiments fought in the Middle East with a variety of vehicles, ranging from, initially, carriers and Vickers light tanks to French R35s, Italian M13/40s, British Crusaders, and American Stuart/Honeys. When the divisions of 1st Australian Corps returned to Australia (the last of them after Second Alamein at the end of 1942) to face the threat of Japanese invasion, the Divisional Cavalry Regiments were re-organised as Divisional Cavalry (Commando) Regiments and saw action in the South-West Pacific as dismounted troops. The 6th, 7th, and 9th Divisions all fought in New Guinea, together with the 3rd, 5th, and 11th Divisions of 2nd Australian Corps. The 5th Division also fought in New Britain, and the 9th Division in Borneo. The 1st, 2nd, 4th, and 12th Divisions of 3rd Australian Corps served in 'Australia, and the 8th Division went to Malaya in February 1941. During the subsequent campaign it went into action against the Japanese on January 14, 1942 and fought a stubborn rear-guard battle across the Johore Strait back to Singapore where it was lost with the rest of the British and Commonwealth forces at the fall of Malaya.

The build-up of armoured forces in Australia started at the end of 1940. In December the AFV

School was opened at Balcombe, moving to Puckapunyal, Victoria, in February 1941. Armoured Training Regiments were also formed and in July 1941 the raising of the 1st Australian Armoured Division was begun. The intention was that this division would embark for the Middle East in February/March 1942, but this deployment did not take place. Nor did the deployment of two light tank squadrons which were raised in December 1941 for service in Malaya with the 8th Division. Both cancellations were the result of Japan's entry into the war and the flood of Japanese successes across South-East Asia which presented a direct threat to Australia and New Zealand.

In 1942 cavalry formations were re-grouped to provide motor regiments plus an armoured brigade and a tank brigade. The tank brigade was equipped with Matildas and the armoured brigade with Stuarts and Grants. By September approval had been given for a total armoured force of three light armoured divisions and the independent tank brigade (3rd Australian Army Tank Brigade).

The three armoured divisions were the 1st, the 2nd (formed from the 2nd Cavalry Division which for a short time had been designated the 2nd Motor Division), and the 3rd (formed in November 1942 from the 1st Motor Division which until March had been the 1st Cavalry Division). In 1943 the 1st Australian Armoured Division was re-designated the 1st Australian Armoured Brigade Group and saw active service in New Guinea.

As the threat of invasion receded armoured formations and armoured units, which had been dispersed throughout Australia in an anti-invasion rôle, were disbanded, until by the end of the war only the 4th Australian Armoured Brigade remained in being. This brigade, formed in New South Wales in 1943, served in Queensland until later that year when it went to New Guinea. It was the parent formation of the armoured units which fought in New Guinea from the latter part of 1943 onwards, and on Bougainville Island and, in 1945, in Borneo. Because of the close jungle conditions there were never opportunities for armoured manoeuvre; consequently the 4th Armoured Brigade's units were organised as self-supporting groups with their own services, and actually fought as self-supporting squadron groups, isolated from each other at the end of intermittent supply lines that were

Bren Carriers of the 8th Australian Division in Malaya, 1941, before the Japanese invasion

frequently cut by the enemy and by the hazards of the jungle.

The first Australian tank actions in the Pacific theatre were on the Buna track in Papua, New Guinea in December 1942. The unit was the 2/6th Armoured Regiment equipped with Stuarts (M3 Lights). Tanks were not popular with Australian infantry—a mistrust which had arisen in World War I at Bullecourt in 1917, had been removed at Hamel and Amiens in 1918, but had then sprung into new life in the Middle East in 1941–42. For this reason it was not until November 17, 1943 that Matildas of C Squadron, 1st Australian Tank Battalion (The Royal New South Wales Lancers), 4th Armoured Brigade, were given a chance to prove their worth in support of 9th Division in the assault on the Sattelberg Road on the Huon Peninsula in north-east New Guinea.

Operations for the 1st Australian Tank Battalion ended in February 1944 and the unit returned to the Australian mainland in May, having been in New Guinea since August 1943. Another unit of 4th Armoured Brigade, the 2/4th Armoured Regiment, took its place in August 1944. This unit had three squadrons of Matildas which took part in the operations along the north coast of New Guinea from Aitape to Wewak and on Bougainville Island from January 1945 until the end of the war.

The 2/9th Armoured Regiment took part in the assault landings at Tarakan, at Brunei, and at Labuan in the Borneo campaign in June and July 1945, while the 1st Tank Battalion, now re-named the 1st Armoured Regiment, returned to action in the same campaign in the fierce fighting at Balikpapan. Another armoured unit in the Borneo campaign was the 2/1st Armoured Brigade Reconnaissance Squadron. Detachments of this squadron went into action with the armoured regiments in the assault landings with Matilda "circus equipment". This consisted of two troops of Frogs—Matildas with flamethrowers in place of their main armament. One troop landed with 2/9th Armoured Regiment at Labuan on June 10, another landed with 1st Armoured Regiment at Balikpapan on July 1. The Frogs were specifically developed for burning out bunkers and tunnels in the Pacific campaigns. This development was the work of 4th

M3 Light Tank (Stuart/Honey) of 2/6th Australian Armoured Regiment in the fighting on the Buna track in Papua, December 1942, when the tanks showed their value in bunker-busting.
(Australian War Memorial)

Armoured Brigade. Other items of Australian "circus equipment" were Matilda Hedgehogs for launching bombs at bunkers and Matilda Dozers. A troop of Dozers landed at Balikpapan, but the troop of six Matilda Hedgehogs of 4th Armoured Brigade that went to Bougainville in 1945 were too late to see action.

In January 1946 the 1st Australian Armoured Car Squadron was formed for service in the Occupation Forces in Japan. The squadron sailed from Sydney in April, equipped with Staghounds and Canadian Scout Cars ("Doodlebugs"), and returned to Puckapunyal three years later, in January 1949. On July 7, 1949 it was re-named the 1st Armoured Regiment and issued with Churchills. It was the only regular Royal Australian Armoured Corps unit to remain on the active list following a major reorganisation of the army in 1948. This reorganisation included the raising of two Citizen Military Force armoured brigades and a number of independent CMF armoured regiments, which were linked through the war-time armoured and motor units to the original regiments of the Australian Light Horse. These CMF units were variously equipped with Matildas, Grants, Staghounds, and White scout cars/APCs.

Matilda tanks of 2/4th Australian Armoured Regiment proved very effective in repelling Japanese attacks on the forward positions of 25th Australian Infantry Battalion in close jungle conditions at Slater's Knoll, Bougainville Island, April 1945.
(Australian War Memorial)

CANADA

Armoured cars of 1st Canadian Motor Machine-Gun Brigade, C.E.F., on the Western Front, 1917. The cars were built in the United States by the Autocar Company and were simply armoured open top boxes on wheels. (Canadian Official)

The Canadians included a small armoured unit in the first contingent of their expeditionary force which arrived in England in October 1914. Designated the Automobile Machine-Gun Brigade No. 1 C.E.F. on September 15, 1914 this motor machine-gun unit had a strength of 230 men and 20 armoured cars. It was commanded by Major Raymond Brutinel, a retired French officer living in Canada, who had persuaded a group of Canadian business-men led by Sir Clifford Sifton to raise and equip it. The armoured cars were simply armoured open top boxes on wheels, armed with two machine-guns; they were built in the United States on commercial chassis by the Autocar Company of Ardmore, Pa., and armoured with 10 mm. Bethlehem Steel Corporation plate. The second Canadian contingent which arrived in England a few months after the first also included a few armoured cars—this time Packards built in Detroit on car chassis with a cylindrical turret containing a machine-gun. On May 16, 1915 the Automobile Machine-Gun Brigade was re-designated 1st Canadian Motor Machine-Gun Brigade, C.E.F.

Current military thinking had no enthusiasm for these armoured cars, but King George V when he reviewed the Brigade at Aldershot told them that he thought they would be "very useful". So it proved. The armoured cars were highly effective in France from their arrival in June 1915 and played a particularly significant part during the March 1918 retreat by plugging gaps in the crumbling line with their mobile fire-power. In 1919 the Brigade became the 1st Motor Machine-Gun Brigade, Canadian Machine-Gun Corps. On October 1, 1935 it was converted and re-designated 1st Armoured Car Regiment, and on December 15, 1935—a date on which the Canadian Army was considerably reorganized—it was amalgamated with the 6th Duke of Connaught's Royal Canadian Hussars.

As well as the 1st Motor Machine-Gun Brigade the Canadians had a small Tank Corps formed in 1918 and equipped with British Mark V and French Renault F.T. tanks. This did not survive the war and it was not until after 1930 that armoured tracked vehicles were again in service with the Canadian Army. These vehicles were a dozen Carden-Loyds bought from the U.K. to equip the machine-gun platoons of the small Permanent Force.

The deteriorating international situation brought about the revival of a Canadian armoured element in the shape of a cadre of 24 all ranks including its commander, Captain (Brevet Major) F. F. Worthington. A Fighting Vehicles School was set up at London, Ontario, and later moved to Camp Borden, Ontario. On December 15, 1936 six militia regiments were designated as tank regiments. These included The Ontario Regiment, Le Régiment de Trois-Rivières (The Three Rivers Regiment), The Calgary Regiment, and The Essex Regiment. The Essex militiamen became the first students at the Camp Borden School. Training was carried out on the carriers and on a couple of Mark IV light tanks. In the summer of 1939 the vehicle strength was increased by

At the end of the war in August 1945 the Australian Army had 373 Stuarts, 752 Grants/Lees, 409 Matildas, 279 Staghounds, 507 Canadian scout cars, 30 LVTs(A) Mk. 4, 65 Australian Cruisers Mk. 1 (Sentinel), 25 uncompleted Australian Cruisers Mk. 3, and 51 Churchills. Both the Churchill and the Sherman underwent trials in New Guinea in 1944, the Churchill clearly demonstrating its suitability for jungle operations. But the war ended before it could be used in action in this theatre, and the 51 received (part of an order for 510 of which the balance was cancelled) were stored for post-war use. The M24 Chaffee was also tested in New Guinea, in 1945, but its light armour and lack of ability for low speed jungle "slogging" made it unsuitable for this type of operation despite its excellent armament (75-mm. gun) and mechanical characteristics. The Centurion arrived in Australia in 1951 and was issued to the 1st Armoured Regiment the following year.

(With acknowledgments to the R.A.A.C. Centre.)

Ross Munro, the war correspondent, who accompanied the Dieppe raiders, wrote: "The Calgary tanks, under Lieur-Col. Johnny Andrews, had a bad time from the start. The tank-landing craft were large targets and German shell-fire blasted them as they beached. More than a squadron was landed and immediately the tanks struck the heavy shale. Some sank into it and were stopped right on the beach. Others wallowed through it, worked round by the Casino, got over the sea-wall, which is only a foot or two high there, sloping from about ten feet on the Essex beach. They fought on the Esplanade and at least a few of them broke into the streets of the town. But German guns in the hotels and houses and entrances to the streets fired point-blank at them. The other squadrons were not landed but lay most of the morning off the main beach in their landing craft". The beach at Dieppe after the raid, with the Esplanade in the background.

Dieppe, August 19, 1942. The Calgary Regiment of 1st Canadian Army Tank Brigade, equipped with Churchills, were part of the raiding force which consisted mainly of 2nd Canadian Infantry Division.

The Canadians built their own cruiser tank, the Ram, in two marks. Seen here is a Ram Mark I with 2-pdr. gun, side-doors in hull, and an auxiliary machine-gun turret in front.

(Canadian Official)

the arrival of 14 Mark VI light tanks from the U.K.

On September 1, 1939 two of the six tank regiments were mobilised—The Ontario Regiment and The Three Rivers Regiment—as well as a number of cavalry regiments which were later to form part of the Canadian Armoured Corps, including the Royal Canadian Dragoons, Lord Strathcona's Horse (Royal Canadians), the Fort Garry Horse, and the 1st Hussars, which was mobilised as the 1st Canadian Cavalry Regiment.

The period of the "phoney war" delayed the development of Canada's armoured force. In March 1940 the 1st Hussars were mechanized and became 1st Canadian Cavalry Regiment (Mechanized), but apart from this armoured expansion was at a standstill. The Defence Department had decided that there seemed little requirement for Canadian tank formations. The blitzkrieg in May and June 1940 harshly demonstrated the fallacy that armoured forces would not be needed. As a start five motor-cycle regiments were formed

from cavalry regiments in May-July. These were:

1st Canadian Motor-Cycle Regiment (Royal Canadian Dragoons/Lord Strathcona's Horse (Royal Canadians)).

2nd Canadian Motor-Cycle Regiment (The Governor General's Horse Guards).

3rd Canadian Motor-Cycle Regiment (17th Duke of York's Royal Canadian Hussars).

4th Canadian Motor-Cycle Regiment (8th Princess Louise's (New Brunswick) Hussars).

5th Canadian Motor-Cycle Regiment (The British Columbia Dragoons).

The next stage was the formation of the Canadian Armoured Corps, which was formally embodied on August 13, 1940, with Worthington, now a Colonel, as its Commandant. Its initial establishment was to be an army tank brigade and an armoured division. In order to obtain tanks for training Worthington went to the United States and bought all the obsolete vehicles that had been retired from U.S. Army service.

The Ram Mark II had a 6-pdr. with gyro-stabiliser as its main armament. Rams equipped the Canadian armoured divisions for training in England, but were replaced by Shermans before the divisions went into action. These Ram IIs still have the auxiliary machine-gun turret which was eliminated in the last 692 (out of 1,899) built.

(Canadian Official)

These amounted to 219, mostly M1917 six-tonners (the American-built version of the Renault F.T.), but including some Mark VIIIs. To equip the tank brigade with the tanks it would need for active service the Defence Department ordered 488 Valentines (Infantry Tank Mark III) from the Canadian Pacific Railway Co., who were already building Valentines for the British Ministry of Supply. By the time the first Valentines were delivered, however, the 1st Canadian Army Tank Brigade was in Britain.

The 1st Canadian Army Tank Brigade and the 1st Canadian Armoured Division were formed with the following armoured units which were designated on February 11, 1941:

1st Cdn Army Tank Bde—
    11th Army Tank Bn. (The Ontario Regt.).
    12th Army Tank Bn. (The Three Rivers Regt.).
    14th Army Tank Bn. (The Calgary Regt.).
1st Cdn Armoured Division—
    1st and 2nd Cdn Armoured Brigades with 1st Armoured Car Regt. (Royal Canadian Dragoons) as the division's armoured car regiment.
1st Cdn Armoured Bde—
    2nd Armoured Regt. (Lord Strathcona's Horse (Royal Canadians)).
    8th Princess Louise's (New Brunswick) Hussars—designated as 5th Armoured Regt. (8th Princess Louise's (New Brunswick) Hussars) on October 14, 1943.
    9th Armoured Regt. (The British Columbia Dragoons).
    The Westminster Regt. (Motor battalion).
2nd Cdn Armoured Bde—
    3rd Armoured Regt. (The Governor General's Horse Guards).
    6th Armoured Regt. (1st Hussars).
    10th Armoured Regt. (Fort Garry Horse).
    The Perth Regt. (Motor battalion).

The 1st Canadian Army Tank Brigade embarked for the U.K. in June 1941. It was commanded by Brigadier Worthington. On arrival it was equipped with Matildas (Infantry Tank Mark II); later the Matildas were replaced by Churchills (Infantry Tank Mark IV).

This was the third Canadian formation to arrive in Britain. The first was the 1st Canadian Infantry Division which arrived on December 17, 1939, under the command of Major-General (later General) A. G. L. McNaughton. One of its brigades was warned for the Trondheim operation which was cancelled, another went to Brest in the Second B.E.F. in June 1940. The division then formed part of 7 Corps, the lone corps which was Britain's bulwark against invasion in the summer of 1940.

In late August 1940 the 2nd Canadian Infantry Division arrived to join the 1st—apart from three of its units which went to Iceland and arrived in the U.K. in December. On Christmas Day the Canadian Corps was formed to command the two divisions.

The fourth formation to arrive was the 3rd Canadian Infantry Division which left for the U.K. in July 1941. It was followed in November by the armoured division which had been re-numbered as the 5th Canadian Armoured Division.

On January 26, 1942 a second armoured division and a second army tank brigade were formed by converting the 4th Canadian Infantry Division. The designations of the units after conversion were:

    20th Recce Bn.—The Battleford Light Infantry (16th/22nd Saskatchewan Horse). On May 22, 1942 this unit was re-designated the
    20th Army Tank Bn. (16th/22nd Saskatchewan Horse).
    21st Armoured Regt. (The Governor General's Foot Guards).
    22nd Armoured Regt. (The Canadian Grenadier Guards).
    23rd Army Tank Bn. (The Halifax Rifles).
    24th Army Tank Bn. (Les Voltigeurs de Québec). On May 22, 1942 this unit was re-designated 24th Recce Bn., an exchange of rôles with 20th Recce Bn.
    25th Armoured Regt. (The Elgin Regt.).
    26th Army Tank Bn. (The Grey and Simcoe Foresters).
    27th Armoured Regt. (The Sherbrooke Fusiliers Regt.).
    28th Armoured Regt. (The British Columbia Regt.).
    29th Armoured Regt. (South Alberta Regt.).

The armoured division, designated the 4th Canadian Armoured Division, consisted of the 3rd and 4th Cdn Armoured Brigades. The 3rd had the 25th, 27th, and 29th Armoured Regiments with the Princess Louise Fusiliers as its motor battalion, the 4th had the 21st, 22nd, and 28th Armoured Regiments with the Lake Superior Regiment as its motor battalion. The division's armoured car regiment was the 12th Manitoba Dragoons which was mobilised as the 18th (Manitoba) Recce Bn. in May 1941, re-designated the 18th (Manitoba) Armoured Car Regt. on January 26, 1942, and further re-designated the 18th Armoured Car Regiment (12th Manitoba Dragoons) on December 16, 1942.

The army tank brigade, after the exchange of rôles between the Battleford Light Infantry and Les Voltigeurs de Québec, consisted of the 20th, 23rd, and 26th Army Tank Bns. The brigade was posted to the U.K. in June 1943 and disbanded there in November 1943. By this time the organisation of the armoured formations had been changed to conform with the new establishment for an armoured division.

When the new organisation for an armoured division (one armoured brigade and one infantry brigade) was introduced in the spring of 1942 the Canadians did not adopt it immediately. The 1st Cdn Army Tank Brigade and the 5th Canadian Armoured Division remained as they were until after the 4th Canadian Armoured Division arrived in the U.K. later in the year. Worthington was promoted Major-General and given command of the 4th Armoured Division. With the 4th's arrival the 2nd Canadian Corps was formed, both it and the 1st Corps being under command of First Canadian Army which had been raised on April 6, 1942.

The Canadian Armoured Corps adopted the new armoured division organisation in 1943. The result was that First Canadian Army had two armoured divisions and two independent armoured brigades.

1st Canadian Armoured Brigade (which retained its previous designation of 1st Canadian Army Tank Brigade until August 1943 when it was in Sicily) consisted of its three original units—11th, 12th, and

Canadian Shermans attacking towards Falaise, Normandy, August 1944. The nearest tanks are Fireflies (Shermans with 17-pdrs.), all with barrels heavily camouflaged since German tanks and gunners had orders to knock out the Fireflies first. (Canadian Official)

Sherman Vs (M4A4) of 1st Canadian Armoured Brigade in leaguer before the attack on Florence, Italy, August 1944.

(Canadian Official)

Sherman V (M4A4) of the 12th Canadian Armoured Regiment (The Three Rivers Regiment/Le Regiment de Trois-Rivieres), 1st Canadian Armoured Brigade, in action in the fierce fighting in Ortona, Italy, December 1943. (Canadian Official)

Canadians in Falaise, August 1944. Sherman of 27th Canadian Armoured Regiment (The Sherbrooke Fusiliers Regiment), 2nd Canadian Armoured Brigade, supporting infantry of 2nd Canadian Infantry Division in their capture of the town. (Canadian Official)

Canadian Shermans forming up for Operation "Totalize" south of Caen, Normandy, August 1944. In the foreground is a Sherman Crab flail tank of the 79th Armoured Division. There were two Canadian armoured formations in Normandy: 2nd Canadian Armoured Brigade and 4th Canadian Armoured Division.

(Canadian Official)

14th which were re-designated army tank regiments in May 1942 and then armoured regiments in August 1943.

2nd Canadian Armoured Brigade left 5th Cdn Armoured Division and became an independent armoured brigade. Of its original armoured units (3rd, 6th, and 10th Armoured Regiments) the 3rd stayed with the division as its armoured reconnaissance regiment and its place was taken in the brigade by the 27th Armoured Regiment from 3rd Cdn Armoured Brigade. The motor battalion of 2nd Cdn Armoured Brigade while it was in 5th Cdn Armoured Division was the Perth Regiment. The Perths remained with the division as one of the three infantry units in its infantry brigade.

4th Canadian Armoured Division shed 3rd Cdn Armoured Brigade, which was broken up, and now consisted of 4th Cdn Armoured Brigade with its original units (21st, 22nd, and 28th Armoured Regi-

ments, and the Lake Superior Regiment), and 10th Cdn Infantry Brigade formed from regiments that arrived in the U.K. in the summer of 1943 after serving in Newfoundland and Jamaica (The Algonquin Regt., The Argyll and Sutherland Highlanders of Canada, and The Lincoln and Welland Regt.). Its support company was The New Brunswick Rangers.

While the 27th Armoured Regiment from 3rd Cdn Armoured Brigade went to 2nd Cdn Armoured Brigade the other units were disposed as follows: 29th Armoured Regiment stayed with the 4th Cdn Armoured Division as its armoured reconnaissance regiment, 25th Armoured Regiment became the 25th Cdn Tank Delivery Regiment (The Elgin Regiment)— from March 1944, 25th Armoured Delivery Regiment (The Elgin Regiment)—and The Princess Louise Fusiliers, the motor battalion, became first a rifle battalion and then the support company of 5th Cdn Armoured Division's 11th Cdn Infantry Brigade.

5th Canadian Armoured Division retained the old 1st Cdn Armoured Brigade which was re-designated the 5th Cdn Armoured Brigade and had its original units unchanged (2nd, 5th, and 9th Armoured Regiments, and the Westminster Regiment). Its infantry brigade was the 11th Cdn Infantry Brigade formed from The Perth Regiment (ex-motor battalion), The Cape Breton Highlanders, and The Irish Regiment of Canada, with The Princess Louise Fusiliers as machine-gun support.

When armoured car regiments became corps troops, 1 Cdn. Corps had the 1st Canadian Armoured Car Regiment (Royal Canadian Dragoons) and 2 Cdn. Corps had the 18th Canadian Armoured Car Regiment (12th Manitoba Dragoons).

Each of the infantry divisions had a reconnaissance regiment, as did other infantry divisions in the British and Commonwealth armies. 1st Cdn. Inf. Div. (1st, 2nd and 3rd Cdn. Inf. Bdes.) had the 4th Cdn. Recce. Regt. (4th Princess Louise's Dragoon Guards); 2nd

By the end of the war in Europe British Firefly (17-pdr.) conversions of Shermans were more plentiful than they had been at the time of the Normandy landings when there were only enough for them to be issued on the scale of one per troop. On this parade of 5th Canadian Armoured Division at Eelde Airport, Holland, in May 1945, every second tank is a Firefly. Note the extensive use of applique armour and track shoes for added protection. The occasion was a mounted march-past with the salute taken by General H. D. G. Crerar, G.O.C.-in-C. First Canadian Army. (Canadian Official)

Amphibious Canadians in Buffaloes near Nijmegen, Holland, winter 1944. The Canadians became masters of a new art of amphibious fighting during the polders battles of the Scheldt estuary, October–November 1944. (Canadian Official)

Cdn. Inf. Div. (4th, 5th and 6th Cdn. Inf. Bdes.) had the 8th Cdn. Recce. Regt. (14th Canadian Hussars); and 3rd Cdn. Inf. Div. (7th, 8th and 9th Cdn. Inf. Bdes.) had the 7th Cdn. Recce. Regt. (17th Duke of York's Royal Canadian Hussars).

1 CANADIAN CORPS

Troops of 2nd Canadian Infantry Brigade were the main part of the force which carried out the Spitzbergen raid in August 1941, and at the end of the year two Canadian regiments (The Winnipeg Grenadiers and The Royal Rifles from Quebec City) were lost with British and Indian troops in Hong Kong. But the first Canadian tank action of the war was on August 19, 1942, when the Calgary Regiment of 1st Cdn. Army Tank Brigade with its Churchills took part in the Dieppe raid with 2nd Canadian Infantry Division.

After Dieppe the next Canadian action was in Sicily. 1st Canadian Infantry Division and 1st Canadian Armoured Brigade (as it became in August) went straight from the U.K. to join the invasion convoy off Sicily on July 10, 1943. 1st Cdn. Inf. Bde. (Royal Canadian Regiment, Hastings and Prince Edward Regiment, and the 48th Highlanders) and 2nd Cdn. Inf. Bde. (Seaforth Highlanders, Princess Patricia's Canadian Light Infantry, and The Loyal Edmonton Regiment) carried out the division's assault on the left wing of the Eighth Army. 3rd Cdn. Inf. Bde. (Royal 22nd Regiment, Carleton and York Regiment, and The West Nova Scotia Regiment) came in later with The Three Rivers Regiment of 1st Canadian Armoured Brigade. The division's support battalion was The Saskatoon Light Infantry.

The Three Rivers Regiment fought in support of 1st Cdn. Inf. Div. throughout the campaign in Sicily. The other two armoured regiments and brigade HQ had little to do. They landed at Syracuse after it was captured. The Ontario Regiment had one small action at Catania at the end of the campaign, the Calgarys had none. Nor did brigade HQ. But their turns came later in Italy.

On September 3, 1943 Eighth Army launched its assault across the Straits of Messina on to the Italian mainland. On the right was 1st Cdn. Inf. Div. with 3rd Cdn. Inf. Bde. leading and 1st Cdn. Armd. Bde., less The Ontario Regiment, under command. On the left was the British 5th Division with The Ontario Regiment under command. The Calgarys and Princess Louise's Dragoon Guards (the division's recce. regiment) with the Carleton and Yorks provided the battle group that led 1st Cdn. Inf. Div. up the toe of Italy.

In November the 5th Canadian Armoured Division came to Italy with 1 Canadian Corps. In December, 1st Cdn. Inf. Div. and 1st Cdn. Armd. Bde. fought a long and bitter battle across the Moro and into Ortona where the 1st German Parachute Division contested the town house by house and street by street. In January 1944 the whole of 1 Cdn. Corps was concentrated on the Adriatic sector of the Eighth Army line. In April it moved to the Cassino front. Here 1st Cdn. Armd. Bde. supported 8th Indian Division in 13 Corps, while the rest of 1 Cdn. Corps, supported by the British 25th Tank Brigade, pierced the Hitler Line behind Cassino and paved the way for the push down Highway 6 to Rome.

After Cassino 1st Cdn. Inf. Div. and 5th Cdn. Armd. Div. had a long rest period; 1st Cdn. Armd. Bde. fought north with 13 Corps in Fifth Army. The brigade came in to Florence on the left flank of the major thrust from the 2nd New Zealand Division and the 6th South African Armoured Division. It stayed with 13 Corps in the harsh fighting that took place in the forbidding Apennines south of Bologna while the 1st Cdn. Inf. Div. and the 5th Cdn. Armd. Div. took part in the Eighth Army's Gothic Line battle.

The 5th Cdn. Armd. Div. had by this time been reorganized. As with the 2nd New Zealand Division and the 6th South African Armoured Division it was apparent that there was too little infantry. Consequently a second infantry brigade was added to the division—and as with the other divisions that took a similar step the addition was made by creating the brigade from existing resources. Designated the 12th Canadian Infantry Brigade it consisted of The Westminster Regiment (previously 5th Cdn. Armd. Bde.'s motor battalion), The Lanark and Renfrew Scottish (converted from artillery) and the 4th Princess Louise's Dragoon Guards (previously 1st Cdn. Inf. Div.'s recce. regiment). In place of the 4th Princess Louise's Dragoon Guards the 1st Cdn. Inf. Div. was given The Royal Canadian Dragoons (previously 1 Cdn. Corps' armoured car regiment) as its recce. regiment.

The Canadians reached the Senio, but before the final assault in Italy was begun the whole Corps—1st Cdn. Inf. Div., 5th Cdn. Armd. Div., and 1st Cdn. Armd. Bde.—was withdrawn during February and March 1945 and sent to the Netherlands to join the First Canadian Army for the final operations in the North-West Europe campaign.

1st Cdn. Tank Delivery Squadron formed from "B" Squadron, the 25th Armoured Regiment, landed in in Sicily on July 17, 1943 and in Italy on September 14, 1943. When 25th Armoured Regiment was redesignated 25th Cdn. Tank Delivery Regt. (The Elgin Regt.) the 1st Cdn. Tank Delivery Squadron was re-organized as two squadrons of it. These squadrons moved to North-West Europe in March 1945.

2 CANADIAN CORPS

The assault on Normandy on June 6, 1944 brought 2nd Canadian Armoured Brigade into action in support of 3rd Canadian Infantry Division. 3rd Cdn. Inf. Div., under command of 1 British Corps, led the assault on Juno beach. It had two brigade groups up: 7th Cdn. Inf. Bde. (Royal Winnipeg Rifles, Canadian Scottish, and The Regina Rifles) on the right, landing at Courseulles, and 8th Cdn. Inf. Bde. (Queen's Own Rifles of Canada, North Shore (New Brunswick) Regiment and the Regiment de la Chaudière) on the left at Bernieres and St.-Aubin.

In the support of 7th Cdn. Inf. Bde. were assault engineers of the British 79th Armoured Division and DD tanks of 6th Armoured Regiment (1st Hussars). "A" Squadron launched ten of its tanks a mile from the shore; seven touched down on the beach. Another six were beached direct from Landing Craft. "B" Squadron launched 19 tanks at over two miles of which 14 reached the shore.

Assault engineers and DD tanks from 2nd Cdn. Armd. Bde. were also in support of 8th Cdn. Inf. Bde. The tanks were of 10th Armoured Regiment (Fort Garry Horse). None were launched; all were beached direct from Landing Craft.

The third armoured regiment of 2nd Cdn. Armd. Bde., the 27th (The Sherbrooke Fusiliers Regiment), supported the division's reserve brigade, 9th Cdn. Inf. Bde. (Stormont, Dundas and Glengarry Highlanders, North Nova Scotia Highlanders, and The Highland Light Infantry of Canada). The division's support battalion was The Cameron Highlanders of Ottawa.

The 3rd Cdn. Inf. Div. and 3rd British Inf. Div. captured Caen on July 9 with support from 2nd Cdn. Armd. Bde. The 2nd Cdn. Inf. Div. had now arrived in Normandy and on July 11, 2 Canadian Corps became operational, taking over the Caen sector, and having the two Canadian infantry divisions and the Canadian armoured brigade under its command. The Corps was in Second Army until July 31, when First Canadian became operational, taking over command of 1 British Corps as well as 2 Canadian Corps, which now also included 4th Cdn. Armoured Division and 1st Polish Armoured Division, both of which had recently arrived in Normandy. First Canadian Army, in fact, became as varied an international force as either Fifth or Eighth Armies in Italy. Belgian and Czech armoured brigade groups as well as a Dutch infantry brigade fought under its command later in the campaign.

Canadian Army's first battle as an army was the drive on Falaise which began on August 7 as Operation "Totalize", became Operation "Tractable" on August 14, and culminated in the closing of the Falaise Pocket and the destruction of the German Seventh Army.

After Falaise came the rush to the Seine and the race into Belgium, with First Canadian Army on the left of 21st Army Group. On the way several of the Channel ports were beseiged and later captured— but one fell without a fight. On September 1, the 2nd Canadian Infantry Division liberated Dieppe without firing a shot. The division consisted of the same brigades and same regiments that had suffered so grievously on the raid two years earlier: 4th Cdn. Inf. Bde. (Royal Regiment of Canada, Essex Scottish, and Royal Hamilton Light Infantry—the "Rileys"), 5th Cdn. Inf. Bde. (Regiment de Maisonneuve, Calgary Highlanders, and The Black Watch of Canada), and the 6th Cdn. Inf. Bde. (The Queen's Own Cameron Highlanders of Canada, South Saskatchewan Regiment, and Fusiliers Mont-Royal), with Toronto Scottish as the support battalion.

With the Channel ports captured First Canadian Army's next task was the clearing of the Scheldt so that Antwerp could be opened to shipping. This was followed by winter in the Nijmegen sector in Holland and Operation "Veritable" to clear the west bank of the Lower Rhine and prepare the way for the Rhine crossing on March 23–24.

During March the transfer of 1 Canadian Corps from Italy was completed and for the last six weeks of the war in Europe the whole Canadian overseas army was together under command of First Canadian Army. 1 Cdn. Corps was given the job of liberating West Holland, while 2 Cdn. Corps went north to Groningen and Oldenburg.

THE ROYAL CANADIAN ARMOURED CORPS

In August 1945, at the end of the war, the Canadian Armoured Corps was awarded the prefix "Royal" by King George VI in recognition of its outstanding war record. In five years it had raised thirty armoured units, each of which except two had a second unit in the Reserve Army in Canada. In addition there was one unit (The 19th Alberta Dragoons) in the Reserve Army only.

The thirty units were:

Regiment	
1st Armoured Car	Royal Canadian Dragoons
2nd Armoured	Lord Strathcona's Horse (Royal Canadians)
3rd Armoured (then Armoured Recce)	The Governor General's Horse Guards
4th Recce	4th Princess Louise Dragoon Guards
5th Armoured	8th Princess Louise's (New Brunswick) Hussars
6th Armoured	1st Hussars
7th Recce	17th Duke of York's Royal Canadian Hussars
8th Recce	14th Canadian Hussars
9th Armoured	The British Columbia Dragoons
10th Armoured	Fort Garry Horse
11th Army Tank Battalion (then Armoured)	The Ontario Regiment
12th Army Tank Battalion (then Armoured)	The Three Rivers Regiment
14th Army Tank Battalion (then Armoured)	The Calgary Regiment
15th Armoured	6th Duke of Connaught's Royal Canadian Hussars
16th Armoured	7th/11th Hussars
17th Armoured	The Prince Edward Island Light Horse
18th Recce (then Armoured Car)	12th Manitoba Dragoons
20th Recce (then Army Tank Battalion)	Battleford Light Infantry (16th/22nd Saskatchewan Horse)
21st Armoured	Governor General's Foot Guards
22nd Armoured	Canadian Grenadier Guards
23rd Army Tank Battalion	The Halifax Rifles
24th Army Tank Battalion (then Recce)	Les Voltigeurs de Québec
25th Armoured (then Armoured Delivery)	The Elgin Regiment
26th Army Tank Battalion	The Grey and Simcoe Foresters
27th Armoured	The Sherbrooke Fusiliers Regiment
28th Armoured	The British Columbia Regiment
29th Armoured (then Armoured Recce)	South Alberta Regiment
30th Recce	The Essex Regiment
31st Recce	15th Alberta Light Horse
32nd Recce	Royal Montreal Regiment

The two regiments without a Reserve regiment were the Royal Canadian Dragoons and Lord Strathcona's Horse (Royal Canadians). The 15th, 16th and 17th Armoured Regiments were formed in the Reserve Army only, the Active Force units mobilised by the 6th Duke of Connaught's Royal Canadian Hussars, the 7th/11th Hussars, and The Prince Edward Island Light Horse being, respectively, 5th Cdn. Armoured Division HQ Squadron, 2nd Cdn. Armoured Brigade HQ Squadron, and 1st Cdn. Armoured Brigade HQ Squadron.

Of the four recce regiments which have not been mentioned as being under command of infantry divisions in earlier sections, 24th (Les Voltigeurs de Québec) reverted to infantry and were then disbanded in the U.K., 30th (The Essex Regiment) went to the U.K. where it was later disbanded to provide reinforcements, 31st (15th Alberta Light Horse) served in Canada with the 6th Cdn. Infantry Division, went to the U.K. early in 1945 and was disbanded on arrival, 32nd (Royal Montreal Regiment) was converted to First Canadian Army HQ Defence Bn.

In the post-war reorganization of the Canadian Army 29 units were eventually included in the Royal Canadian Armoured Corps. The 1st to 11th Regiments were unchanged from the war-time list given above, the 12th Armoured was The Sherbrooke Regiment, the 13th Armoured was The British Columbia Regiment, the 14th to 18th Regiments were unchanged, the 19th was an armoured car regiment formed by the amalgamation of The Edmonton Fusiliers and the 19th Alberta Dragoons, 20th Armoured was The Saskatchewan Dragoons, 21st Armoured was Le Régiment de Hull, 22nd Recce and then Armoured was The Windsor Regiment (formerly The Essex Regiment), 23rd Armoured was The Halifax Rifles, 24th Armoured was Le Régiment de Trois-Rivières, 25th Armoured was The Queen's York Rangers, 26th Armoured was The Algonquin Regiment, 27th Armoured was The Elgin Regiment, 28th Armoured was The Grey and Simcoe Foresters, and 29th Armoured was The South Alberta Light Horse formed by the amalgamation of the 15th Alberta Light Horse and the South Alberta Regiment.

On May 19, 1958 numbers were dropped and the regiments were in future known simply by their titles e.g. The British Columbia Dragoons.

On September 16, 1958 the 6th Duke of Connaught's Royal Canadian Hussars and the 17th Duke of York's Royal Canadian Hussars were amalgamated to form The Royal Canadian Hussars (Montreal).

INDIA

The first armoured force in India was formed in 1914. Because of the large numbers of troops sent out of India to fight on the various battlefronts it became essential to increase the mobility of those remaining so that they could effectively carry out the twin tasks of maintaining internal security and repelling raiding tribesmen on the North-West Frontier. Armoured cars, organized in three-car batteries, were used for the purpose. So valuable did they prove to be in these rôles that the Indian Government proposed to include armoured cars on the establishment of India's post-war army. However, after lengthy discussions with the British Government the proposal was abandoned and the Indian Government agreed to accept nine armoured car companies of the Tank Corps on the Indian Army establishment. From 1921 to 1938 these companies, which by the end of the period had been re-equipped as light tank companies, provided the sole armoured force in India.

In 1938 the conversion of the British cavalry regiments serving in India was begun. So too was the mechanization of the Indian cavalry. Instruction in the new rôle was given by the Royal Tank Corps, which, having taught the British regiments and the first Indian regiments, left India for Egypt in 1939 before the outbreak of war.

According to a chapter on "The Royal Tank Corps in India Between the Wars" by Major E. W. Sheppard and Others which appears in Volume One of Liddell Hart's classic *The Tanks*, "it was in 1935 that the basic plan for the 'Indianization' of all the armed forces was evolved. This involved the replacement of all armoured-car and light tank companies of the British Army in India by mechanized cavalry regiments of the Indian Army, which began in 1937 and was completed in 1938-9." (p. 415). This statement is open to dispute. Certainly it is not correct to say that the replacement was completed in 1938-9, either in the sense that all British mechanized units had been replaced by mechanized cavalry regiments of the Indian Army, or in the sense that mechanization of those Indian

Indian infantry clearing a village in Eritrea with support from a Universal Carrier. Two Indian divisions, the 4th (Red Eagles) and the 5th (Ball of Fire), took part in the East African campaign in 1941.
(Imperial War Museum)

Cavalry mechanisation begins in India. Brigade Camp, Meerut, 1938. C Squadron of the 17th/21st Lancers at maintenance with troop leaders Light' Tank Mark VI between two Mark IIBs troop leader's Light Tank Mark VI beside a Mark IIB Indian pattern. Other units in the brigade were the 15th Lancers and the 21st King George V's Own Horse (Central India Horse). The C.I.H. was the first Indian cavalry regiment to go overseas in World War II. (Lt.-Col. R. L. V. Ffrench-Blake)

Retreat from Burma, Stuart tanks of 7th Armoured Brigade (7th Hussars and 2nd Royal Tank Regiment) ferrying infantry north from Prome, April 1942. (Major-General J. B. Scott)

General Sir Claude Auchinleck, Commander-in-Chief, India, reviewing the 116th (Gordon Highlanders) Regiment R.A.C. at Bolarum, 1943. The 116th R.A.C., equipped with Shermans, was at this period in 255th Indian Armoured Brigade, 44th Indian Armoured Division. (Imperial War Museum)

A Squadron, 7th Hussars, supporting a Gurkha attack at Shwegyin on the River Chindwin, during the retreat from Burma, May 1942. It was at Shwegyin that the 7th Armoured Brigade had to destroy all its tanks – with one exception. (The Seventh and Three Enemies)

"The Curse of Scotland" – the only tank of 7th Armoured Brigade that was not destroyed at Shwegyin. It was driven to Imphal and later became the command tank of the 7th Light Cavalry, re-entering Rangoon in 1945. (Lord Erroll of Hale)

cavalry regiments was complete. Two British mechanized cavalry regiments remained in India after the outbreak of war and both of them served in Indian armoured formations. These regiments were the 3rd Carabiniers (Prince of Wales's Dragoon Guards) and the 14th/20th King's Hussars. As to the mechanization of the Indian cavalry it had hardly progressed beyond the first few regiments and was not in fact completed until the 19th King George V's Own Lancers, the last to be mechanized, began its initial training as a mechanized regiment in January 1941. Brigadier J. G. Pocock in his history of the 19th Lancers *(The Spirit of a Regiment being The History of 19th King George V's Own Lancers 1921-1947*, Gale & Polden Ltd., 1962, p. 36) doubts whether the basic plan for the replacement of British units by mechanized Indian cavalry regiments "was more than under consideration at Army Headquarters, because," he writes, "it is significant that the reorganization [of the Indian cavalry in 1937], which centred on training regiments, gave no inkling of this plan."

THE INDIAN CAVALRY REGIMENTS

In 1921, the year before a similar though much less severe reduction of cavalry took place in the British Army, the number of Indian cavalry regiments was almost halved by amalgamating existing regiments. The 21 new regiments that resulted were:

1st Duke of York's Own Cavalry, Skinner's Horse
2nd Royal Lancers, Gardner's Horse
3rd Cavalry
4th Duke of Cambridge's Own Lancers (Hodson's Horse)
5th King Edward VII's Own Lancers (Probyn's Horse)
6th Duke of Connaught's Own Lancers (Watson's)
7th Light Cavalry
8th King George V's Own Light Cavalry
9th Royal Deccan Horse
10th Queen Victoria's Own Guides Cavalry, Frontier Force
11th Prince Albert Victor's Own Cavalry, Frontier Force
12th (Sam Browne's) Cavalry
13th Duke of Connaught's Own Lancers
14th Prince of Wales's Own Cavalry, Scinde Horse

15th Lancers
16th Light Cavalry
17th Queen Victoria's Own Poona Horse
18th King Edward VII's Own Cavalry
19th King George V's Own Lancers
20th Lancers
21st King George V's Own Horse (Central India Horse)

In addition there were four bodyguard units:
Governor-General's Bodyguard
Governor's Bodyguard, Madras
Governor's Bodyguard, Bombay
Governor's Bodyguard, Bengal

The 21 cavalry regiments were organized in seven

M3 Medium Lee tank of B Squadron, the 3rd Carabiniers (Prince of Wales's Dragoon Guards), moving up towards the ridge of Nungshigum, a key point eight miles north-east of Imphal, with Indian infantry of 1 Dogras on April 13, 1944. In the ensuing action B Squadron lost all their officers. The surviving tanks were commanded by the squadron sergeant-major, the infantry by a subadar. The anniversary of the capture of Nungshigum was thereafter kept by the 3rd Carabiniers as their Regimental Day. "On the ceremonial parade B Squadron forms up without its officers, and is commanded throughout by the squadron sergeant-major, in commemoration of the exceptional conduct of Sergeant-Major Craddock and the N.C.O.s and troopers who displayed such singular initiative and courage after the deaths of all their officers in this action at Nungshigum:" Lieut.-Col. L. B. Oatts in the Regimental History of the 3rd Carabiniers. (Imperial War Museum)

The tanks' job in Burma was to support the infantry, the very function for which the Americans had primarily developed medium tanks in the inter-war years in accordance with a U.S. General Staff directive of 1922 that "the primary mission of the tank is to facilitate the uninterrupted advance of the rifleman in the attack". Here a Lee (M3 Medium) carries out its "primary mission." (Imperial War Museum)

Fitting extemporised flotation gear to a carrier of 2nd British Infantry Division during the advance south to Mandalay by Fourteenth Army. (Imperial War Museum)

The jungle conditions with which the tanks had to contend – as well as with the enemy – during the re-conquest of Burma.
(Imperial War Museum)

groups of three regiments each. In 1937 this organization was changed. The aim was to achieve a uniform and possibly more economical training of recruits. The method chosen was akin to that which was used in the Indian infantry, whereby each regiment had a 10th Training Battalion which dealt with all its recruits and for which the active battalions supplied the officers and instructors. In the case of the cavalry the regiments

Sherman of Probyn's Horse (5th King Edward VII's Own Lancers), 255th Indian Tank Brigade, with Rajput infantrymen: the brigade was the armoured support of IV Corps in Fourteenth Army's offensive in Burma.

were re-organized into three groups of seven, each group consisting of six active regiments and one training regiment. For example, the third group consisted of the 6th Lancers, 7th Light Cavalry, 8th Light Cavalry, Royal Deccan Horse, 19th K.G.O. Lancers, Central India Horse, and the 20th Lancers which was the training regiment. The other training regiments were the 12th (Sam Browne's) Cavalry and the 15th Lancers.

Details of this re-organization were announced at Delhi in March 1937. Nothing was said about any plan for replacing British armoured units by mechanizing the cavalry regiments. The announcement, therefore, a year later (March 1938) that mechanization would be begun by converting the 13th D.C.O. Lancers and the Scinde Horse (14th P.W.O. Cavalry) "appeared," says Brigadier Pocock, "to be somewhat sudden."

But if the announcement of mechanization was somewhat sudden the achievement of it was anything but that. Equipment and the means to purchase it were woefully short. Reporting in 1938 a Modernization Committee under Major-General (later Field-Marshal Sir Claude) Auchinleck said that "judged by modern standards the Army of India is relatively immobile and underarmed and unfit to take the field against land or air forces equipped with up-to-date weapons." Money, especially money for cavalry re-organization, was made available by the British Government the following year as a result of the recommendations of the Chatfield Committee on the Defence of India, which came to India in November 1938 and submitted its report at the end of January 1939. But even with money for re-armament at last available there were no magicians to conjure equipment out of thin air. Among its host of detailed recommendations the Chatfield Committee suggested that the organization of an Indian cavalry armoured regiment should be: RHQ, HQ Squadron, two squadrons each of three troops of three armoured cars each, and one squadron of three troops of four light tanks each; and that an Indian light tank regiment (or a British light tank regiment serving in India) should be: RHQ, HQ Squadron, and three squadrons each of three troops of four light tanks each—a total of 41 tanks, 11 armoured carriers, and 69 wheeled vehicles, as against the armoured regiment's total of 14 light tanks, 24 armoured cars, 6 armoured carriers, and 62 wheeled vehicles. These establishments were a pipe dream for the future. The first Indian cavalry regiments to go to war had to do without tanks and armoured cars. And throughout the war, although the situation eventually improved enormously, the dependence of India on equipment from Allied factories abroad that were at the other end of a long and dangerous sea voyage meant that the Indian Armoured Corps in particular was continually being frustrated in its plans for expansion.

The first Indian cavalry regiment to go overseas in the Second World War was the Central India Horse (21st King George V's Own Horse). The C.I.H. left India in July 1940 to join the 4th Indian Division in the Western Desert as its mechanized divisional cavalry regiment. The epithet "mechanized" was barely justified. The regiment arrived in Egypt equipped only with trucks, having given up its horses only six months previously. The Bren carriers it received for training in the Desert were a novelty. But from these inauspicious

Shermans of the 19th King George V's Own Lancers of 50th Indian Tank Brigade landed at Myebon in the Arakan, south-east of Akyab Island on January 12, 1945, and moved forward in support of the infantry of 25th Indian Division, XV Corps.
(Imperial War Museum)

A chaung beachhead near Kangaw, east of Myebon, where the 25th Indian Division landed after Myebon. They fought their way inland to link up with the 81st and 82nd West African Divisions who were advancing parallel with the coast, while 26th Indian Division continued the "island-hopping" by landing on Ramree Island south of Myebon. (Imperial War Museum)

beginnings the Central India Horse went on to achieve a magnificent record and remained as the famous Red Eagles' divisional cavalry throughout the war in the Middle East, East Africa, and Italy.

The second cavalry regiment to go overseas was the 1st Duke of York's Own Cavalry, Skinner's Horse, which was the mechanized divisional cavalry regiment of the 5th Indian Division. The Ball of Fire Division, as it was known from its divisional sign, arrived in the Sudan from India in September 1940. Its divisional cavalry regiment was no better equipped than the C.I.H.

As well as the 4th and 5th Divisions in the Middle East the Indian Army in 1940 had the 11th Division in Malaya. Its expansion programme for that year involved the raising of five infantry divisions (the 6th, 7th, 8th, 9th, and 10th) and one armoured division. Units for this armoured division, called the Mobile Division until later in 1940, included both the British cavalry regiments still in India. The organization of this 1st Armoured Division, as it was re-designated, was laid down by the Commander-in-Chief on July 9, 1940. It was to consist of the 1st and 2nd Indian Armoured Brigades. Three months later he gave the order to raise a second armoured division, which was formed in 1941 as well as five more infantry divisions (the 14th, 17th, 19th, 20th, and 34th).

Meanwhile, towards the end of 1940, the Indian Government had offered four more infantry divisions and one armoured division for service overseas in addition to the 4th, 5th and 11th which had already gone. The British Government accepted the infantry divisions but was unable to accept the offer of the armoured division because no tanks could be spared from the British Army's own armoured expansion programme to equip it. India was told that no AFVs could be provided before 1942, and was asked to provide a motor brigade instead of the armoured division. This brigade, the 3rd Indian Motor Brigade, was formed by three cavalry regiments: 2nd Royal Lancers, Gardner's Horse; 11th Prince Albert Victor's Own Cavalry, Frontier Force; and 18th King Edward VII's Own Cavalry. Equipped with trucks it went overseas to the Western Desert in January 1941 and at

the beginning of April had its first action at Mechili where it suffered severe losses during Rommel's first advance. 18th Cavalry then formed part of the Tobruk garrison. The brigade again suffered grievously at Bir Hacheim at the opening of the Gazala battle in May 1942. After re-organization it went back into the battle a fortnight later at Sollum, where it was joined by the 13th Duke of Connaught's Own Lancers, one of the first two Indian cavalry regiments to be mechanized and now an armoured car regiment. From Sollum the brigade fell back to Mersa Matruh as part of the rearguard. Here it was relieved and the motorized regiments were in due course converted to their proper armoured rôle in other theatres.

In March 1941 the 9th Division joined the 11th in Malaya, and in May these two divisions came under command of III Indian Corps, whose reconnaissance regiment, which arrived in December just before the Japanese invasion, was the 3rd Cavalry. This regiment had only recently been mechanized and was far from fully trained in its new rôle. Nor was it properly equipped. Like the Central India Horse and Skinner's Horse when those regiments first went on active service, it had to make do with trucks instead of the armoured cars listed on its war establishment—although it did in fact get some armoured cars during the course of the fighting. 3rd Cavalry was heavily engaged throughout the campaign against the Japanese in Malaya.

THE INDIAN ARMOURED CORPS

On May 1, 1941, the Indian Armoured Corps was formed. It consisted of all the Indian cavalry regiments, which retained their existing numerical designations, honours and titles such as Lancers, Cavalry or Horse. But the use of the term "Indian Cavalry" was strictly forbidden! It had also been decided that an armoured corps of three armoured divisions would be formed, the third armoured division to be raised in 1942. To provide sufficient units for this, as well as for the motor brigade (which was still in existence) and the recce regiments, seven new mechanized regiments would be raised from cadres provided by existing "Indian Cavalry"(!) regiments, and one Indian States Forces

BRITISH AND COMMONWEALTH
(1939-45)
HIGHER FORMATIONS

Supreme HQ
Allied Expeditionary Force
(S.H.A.E.F.)

GHQ Home Forces

GHQ Middle East

GHQ India

Allied Force HQ
(A.F.H.Q.)

HQ Central
Mediterranean Force

Supreme Allied Command,
South-East Asia (S.E.A.C.)

Allied Land Forces
South-East Asia (A.L.F.S.E.A.)

Canadian Military HQ
(C.M.H.Q.)

New Zealand Expeditionary
Force HQ

East African Expeditionary
Force HQ

West African Expeditionary
Force HQ

HQ 11th Army Group

HQ 15th Army Group

HQ 21st Army Group

HQ Combined Operations

THE ARMIES

First

Second

Eighth

Ninth

Tenth

Twelfth

Fourteenth

First Canadian

First Australian

Second Australian

FORMATION SIGNS

THE CORPS

1
(Black Diamond For Vehicle Marking)

2

3

4

5

8
(1940–42)

8
(From 1943)

9
(Until 1942)

9
(1943)

10
(Also with Red instead of Green)

11

12

13

25

30

1
Australian

2
Australian

3
Australian

2
Canadian

1
Canadian

15
Indian

33
Indian
(also with background of Corps colours: Red, White, Red)

34
Indian

First Canadian Army Vehicles

Canadian Corps Vehicles
(Before formation of First Canadian Army)

1
Canadian Corps Vehicles

2
Canadian Corps Vehicles

While XV Corps fought its way down the coast, the rest of Fourteenth Army carried out the main offensive across the River Chindwin to Mandalay and south to Rangoon. Here a Lee tank of A Squadron, the 3rd Carabiniers, 254th Indian Tank Brigade, supports Indian infantry in an attack on a village: the brigade was 33 Corps' armoured support.
(Imperial War Museum)

Sherman of 116th (Gordon Highlanders) Regiment R.A.C., 255th Indian Tank Brigade, coming out of action near Taungtha, March 1945. Note the wire mesh protection against "sticky bombs", reminiscent of the "chicken-wire" on the early Mark Is in World War I. The 116th Regiment R.A.C. was the last regiment of the Royal Armoured Corps to come out of action when the war ended – and, incidentally, the British unit fighting furthest away from home at the time.
(Imperial War Museum)

regiment serving under the Crown would be mechanized. The new mechanized regiments were numbered 42nd to 48th Cavalry. And at the same time as these were being raised the two British cavalry regiments in India, the 3rd Carabiniers and the 14th/20th Hussars, each raised a second regiment—the 25th Dragoons from the "Carbs" and the 26th Hussars from the 14th/20th. It was at this period, it will be remembered, that some of the cavalry regiments in the United Kingdom were also providing cadres for new regiments—the 22nd Dragoons, the 23rd Hussars, the 24th Lancers and the 27th Lancers.

Late in 1941 the 1st Indian Armoured Division and its two brigades were re-numbered the 31st, the 251st, and the 252nd respectively. By this time, and despite the British Government's earlier refusal of an armoured division for overseas service, the 252nd Indian Armoured Brigade (consisting of the 14th/20th King's Hussars, 4th Duke of Cambridge's Own Lancers (Hodson's Horse), and 14th Prince of Wales's Own Cavalry, Scinde Horse, with the 1st/4th Bombay Grenadiers as its motor battalion) was in Iraq, together with the 6th, 8th, and 10th Infantry Divisions. 31st Armoured Division HQ, the divisional armoured car regiment, and 251st Armoured Brigade (3rd Carabiniers, 5th King Edward VII's Own Lancers (Probyn's Horse), and 9th Royal Deccan Horse) were still in India. From April 1941 until the end of the year the armoured car regiment was the 19th K.G.O. Lancers; despite this it was the 13th D.C.O. Lancers which went to Iraq in that rôle in 1941 before going on to the Western Desert in the emergency of 1942.

As an example of the paucity of armoured equipment at this period the 19th Lancers' history records that having started its mechanization with diverse types of civilian lorries, "whose common features were old age and battered wings", the regiment was re-equipped in April, 1941, with "an extraordinary collection of old buses" in which it moved to Sialkot to join the armoured division. Then the buses disappeared and "by the end of October the Regiment was mounted in some eighty Ford 15-cwt. trucks, one armoured carrier (made at Tatanagar) and, as an outward and visible sign of our object, eight Humber armoured cars.

Wireless sets, however, were very limited." (Pocock, op.cit. pp. 53–54). It was a story that could be matched in one armoured unit after another throughout the armies of the Commonwealth.

Under the re-numbering arrangement the second Indian armoured division became the 32nd Indian Armoured Division, with the 254th and 255th Armoured Brigades, and the third—which was to be raised in 1942—became the 43rd Indian Armoured Division, with the 267th and 268th Armoured Brigades.

As well as these armoured divisions—one embryonic, one with few tanks and at the beginning of its training, and one divided between Iraq and India— there was another armoured formation in India by the end of 1941. This was the 50th Indian Tank Brigade. It consisted of three Royal Armoured Corps regiments, formerly the 207th Infantry Brigade in the British Army, which had been converted to armour in July 1941, embarked for India on August 26, and on arrival was re-designated 50th Indian Tank Brigade. The regiments were the 146th RAC (converted from the 9th Bn. Duke of Wellington's Regiment), the 149th RAC (7th Bn. King's Own Yorkshire Light Infantry), and the 150th RAC (10th Bn. The York and Lancaster Regiment).

The outbreak of war with Japan brought the need for other theatres to help in stemming the tide of Japanese invasion. Two armoured contributions came from the Middle East. In January 1942 B Squadron of the 3rd Hussars, at that time in Cyprus, and the 7th Armoured Brigade of 7th Armoured Division which had been part of the force that had just driven Rommel back to the Tripolitanian frontier in Operation "Crusader", embarked for the East. B Squadron of the 3rd Hussars went to Java where they were lost in the Japanese conquest of that island. The 7th Armoured Brigade, consisting of the 7th Hussars, the 2nd Royal Tanks, 414 Battery (Essex Yeomanry) RHA, and A Battery 95th Anti-Tank Regiment, went to Burma where they fought their way back from Rangoon to India. "Without the 7th Armoured Brigade," General (later Field-Marshal Earl) Alexander told a former commander of the brigade, "we should not have got the army out of Burma." In the course of the retreat, at Shwegyin on the River Chindwin, it was found impossible to ferry the brigade's tanks across the river and all of them had to be destroyed—all, that is, except one Stuart belonging to B Squadron of the 7th Hussars which had got safely across but which had taken six hours to load on to a special raft and had nearly split it in the process. This tank was driven to Imphal and later became the command tank of the 7th Light Cavalry in 254th Indian Tank Brigade. In this rôle, and under its challenging name "The Curse of Scotland", the tank re-entered Rangoon in 1945.

RE-ORGANIZATION

With the Japanese at the eastern gates of India in June 1942 the Indian armoured formations were:

31st Indian Armoured Division (251st and 252nd Indian Armoured Brigades) of which HQ and 252nd Armoured Brigade, plus divisional troops (but excluding the armoured car regiment, the 13th D.C.O. Lancers, which was in Egypt), were in Iraq and Persia. The 251st Armoured Brigade, almost denuded of tanks, was in India.

32nd Indian Armoured Division (254th and 255th Indian Armoured Brigades, and 7th Armoured Brigade until it went to Iraq in September), with few tanks and still training, in India.

43rd Indian Armoured Division, about to be formed with 267th and 268th Indian Armoured Brigades.

50th Indian Tank Brigade, in India.

It was decided that the Indian armoured divisions should adopt a similar organization to the British armoured divisions i.e. one armoured brigade and one lorried infantry brigade per division instead of two armoured brigades.

As a result the 31st Armoured Division in Iraq was re-constituted with the 252nd Armoured Brigade and the 43rd Lorried Infantry Brigade of three battalions of Gurkha Rifles.

The 32nd Armoured Division was re-constituted with the 255th Armoured Brigade (consisting of the 158th RAC, converted from the 6th Bn. South Wales Borderers, the 159th RAC, converted from the 10th Bn. Gloucestershire Regiment, and the 26th Hussars, raised on February 1, 1941, from a cadre of the 14th/20th King's Hussars), and the 73rd Lorried Infantry Brigade.

The 43rd Armoured Division was now to be raised with the 267th Armoured Brigade and the 268th as its Lorried Infantry Brigade. The 267th Armoured Brigade was formed with three RAC regiments from the United Kingdom: the 116th, the 160th, and the 163rd. The 116th had left the Clyde on June 1, 1942 as the 9th Bn. Gordon Highlanders. It arrived at Bombay on July 24, moved immediately to Sialkot and there became the 116th (Gordon Highlanders) RAC on July 27. The 160th, converted from the 9th Bn. Royal Sussex Regiment, went to India in October 1942. And the 163rd, which had left the U.K. as the 13th Bn. The Sherwood Foresters in May 1942, was converted to armour at Rawalpindi in July.

The two armoured brigades which were left out of the re-constituted divisions, the 251st (from 31st Armoured Division) and the 254th (from the 32nd), were re-designated Indian Tank Brigades.

The equipment of the various formations was to be —when tanks became available—Grants or Lees for the 32nd and 43rd Armoured Divisions, Valentines for the 50th Indian Tank Brigade, and Grant/Lees and Stuarts for the 251st and 254th Indian Tank Brigades. The 31st Armoured Division was equipped with Stuarts, later to be replaced by Shermans.

CONTRACTION

In the event this re-organization of India's armoured forces was changed before it materialized. Shortage of available men of the high standard necessary for a mechanized force and a decline in the intake of personnel from the United Kingdom, added to the shortage of shipping for bringing tanks and weapons from the United States, forced the abandonment (announced in September 1942) of a proposal to raise a heavy armoured brigade in 1943, and at the end of 1942 brought the decision to amalgamate the 32nd and 43rd Armoured Divisions. This was effected in February 1943, the resulting new division being numbered the 44th Indian Armoured Division, consisting of the 255th Armoured Brigade and the 268th Lorried Infantry Brigade. The 267th Armoured Brigade was broken up. The 160th RAC reverted to infantry, the 163rd RAC went into the 255th Armoured Brigade in place of the 159th RAC which reverted to infantry, and the 116th RAC, having been warned of disbandment to provide men for Wingate's Special Force, survived as an armoured regiment. By the end of 1943 it too, equipped with Shermans, was in 255th Armoured Brigade of 44th Indian Armoured Division.

Thus, in June 1943, the Indian Army was left with the 31st Armoured Division in the Middle East, and 44th Armoured Division plus three tank brigades (50th, 251st, and 254th) in India. As well as these armoured formations India had the 4th, 6th, 8th, and 10th Infantry Divisions in the Middle East, and the 5th, 7th, 14th, 17th, 19th, 20th, 23rd, 25th, 26th, 36th, and 39th Infantry Divisions in India. The 34th Infantry Division in Ceylon had just been broken up and the 9th and 11th Infantry Divisions had been lost in Malaya.

The contraction of the armoured forces continued. In October 1943 the 251st Tank Brigade was disbanded. Probyn's Horse and the Royal Deccan Horse replaced the 26th Hussars and the 163rd RAC in the 255th Armoured Brigade, and the 3rd Carabiniers were transferred to the 254th Tank Brigade. The 26th Hussars and 163rd RAC were transferred to Wingate's Long Range Patrol and went to Central India Command for special training; in December 1943 the 163rd reverted to infantry. All but two (43rd and 45th Cavalry) of the newly-raised Indian regiments were disbanded.

Early in 1944 the 44th Armoured Division (to which since the beginning of the year the 19th K.G.O. Lancers, equipped initially with Stuarts and then with Shermans, had been the armoured reconnaissance regiment) was broken up. Divisional HQ and certain divisional troops were used for the Indian Airborne Division which took over the 44th's divisional number as well. The 255th Armoured Brigade became an independent tank brigade organized for the maintenance, training and operation of detached armoured regiments working with infantry divisions, while 268th Infantry

BRITISH AND COMMONWEALTH
(1939-45)
ARMOURED DIVISIONS

1st
(and 2nd Armoured Brigade
until the end of the war)

1st
(in Italy 1944)

2nd

6th

7th
(First Style)

7th
(Second Style)

8th

9th

10th
(also with Yellow instead of
Black)

11th

Guards

42nd

79th

1st Australian

2nd Australian

3rd Australian

2nd New Zealand
(Not designated as an Armoured
Division but included its own
integrated Armoured Brigade
from 1943)

4th Canadian

5th Canadian

31st Indian

44th Indian
(and 1st Indian Armoured
Brigade in 1946)

6th
South African

No. 1 Armoured Replacement
Group, Central Mediterranean
Force

ARMOURED FORMATION SIGNS

ARMOURED BRIGADES AND (ARMY) TANK BRIGADES

1st (Army) Tank

4th Armoured

6th Guards Tank

7th Armoured

8th Armoured

9th Armoured

20th Armoured

21st (Army) Tank
(First Style)

21st Tank
(Second Style)

22nd Armoured

23rd Army Tank

23rd Armoured

24th Army Tank

25th (Army) Tank

25th Armoured Engineer

27th Armoured

31st (Army) Tank
later Armoured

33rd (Army) Tank
later Armoured

34th (Army) Tank

35th (Army) Tank

36th (Army) Tank

3rd Australian
Army Tank

4th Australian Armoured

1st Canadian Army Tank

1st Canadian Armoured Vehicles

2nd Canadian Armoured Vehicles

(Personnel's Badges were
Horizontal Diamonds in above
colours but without Maple
Leaf)

2nd Indian Armoured
(1946)

3rd Indian Armoured
(1946)

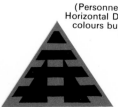
50th Indian Tank

254th Indian Tank

255th Indian Tank

Three Indian infantry divisions fought in the Italian campaign: the 4th, 8th, and 10th. Infantry of 8th Division are here being carried on DD Shermans of B Squadron, 7th Hussars, 9th Armoured Brigade, in the pursuit at the end of the campaign. Note the track "grousers". (Imperial War Museum)

Staghound armoured cars of 2nd New Zealand Divisional Cavalry Regiment moving up to the division's first action in Italy on the Sangro in November 1943. (New Zealand Official)

Brigade became a GHQ reserve brigade.

ACTION

By this time armoured units were in action again in Burma on both fronts. In the Arakan the 25th Dragoons fought under command of XV Corps from January to July 1944, by which time the monsoon rains had started and the regiment was withdrawn to

Sherman ARK. The New Zealanders formed an assault squadron to operate specialised armour; it worked with the British 25th Armoured Engineer Brigade. (New Zeland Official)

India. On the main front in the north IV Corps at Imphal had 254 Indian Tank Brigade, consisting of the 3rd Carabiniers in Grant/Lees, the 7th Light Cavalry (Stuarts), and C Squadron of 150 RAC. At Dimapur-Kohima 33 Corps had 149 RAC and 150 RAC (less C Squadron) from 50th Indian Tank Brigade, 11th P.A.V.O. Cavalry (formerly of 3rd Indian Motor Brigade and now equipped with armoured cars), and 45th Cavalry (Stuarts).

Having defeated the Japanese offensives in the Arakan by June and around Imphal by December 1944, the Fourteenth Army under General (later Field-Marshal Viscount) Slim began its main counter-offensive by crossing the River Chindwin on December 3. On the right flank XV Corps began a supporting offensive on December 12. In the main offensive IV Corps' armoured support was the 255th Indian Tank Brigade, 33 Corps' was the 254th Indian Tank Brigade, while in the Arakan XV Corps had the 50th Indian Tank Brigade. There had been changes in the tank brigades: 50th had 146 RAC, 19th K.G.O. Lancers, and 45th Cavalry; 254th had the 3rd Carabiniers, 149 RAC, 150 RAC, and 11th P.A.V.O. Cavalry; 255th had 116 RAC (which entered the campaign near Pakkoku on the Irrawaddy on February 10, 1945), Probyn's Horse, the Royal Deccan Horse, 7th Light Cavalry (with "The Curse of Scotland"), and 16th Light Cavalry (armoured cars). "A" Squadron of the 25th Dragoons returned to the campaign in Central Burma in May 1945.

While the Fourteenth Army was pushing south to Mandalay and Rangoon other Indian cavalry regiments were in action in Italy as divisional reconnaissance units. The 4th, 8th, and 10th Indian Infantry Divisions fought in Italy, the Central India Horse still part of the Red Eagles, the 6th Lancers (Watson's) with the 8th. The 31st Indian Armoured Division was still on duty in the Levant, Iraq and Iran, although by now it was without the 43rd Gurkha Lorried Infantry Brigade which was fighting in Italy. Early in 1945 the 14th/20th King's Hussars left the division and went to Italy where, after converting one of its squadrons to Kangaroos, it came under command of the 43rd Gurkha Brigade.

After the end in Burma the 50th Indian Tank Brigade, now consisting of 11th P.A.V.O. Cavalry (equipped with Stuarts), 13th D.C.O. Lancers

(Shermans), and 19th K.G.O. Lancers (Shermans), took part in the occupation of Malaya which took place on September 9, 1945, the date originally planned for its invasion. While 19th K.G.O. Lancers remained in Malaya, P.A.V.O. Cavalry and 13th Lancers went to Java with the 5th "Ball of Fire" Division.

At the end of 1945 the 31st Indian Armoured Division went back to its original designation of the 1st Indian Armoured Division and returned to India in 1946. The 252nd Indian Armoured Brigade was re-numbered 2nd Indian Armoured Brigade, the 255th Indian Tank Brigade was re-designated the 1st Indian Armoured Brigade, and the 254th Indian Tank Brigade was re-designated the 3rd Indian Armoured Brigade.

On August 15, 1947, two years to the day after the end of the war with Japan, the old Indian Army was divided into the armies of the two countries, India and Pakistan, that succeeded the British Raj. Nor was this a simple division. Most regiments and battalions were composed of different classes, recruited from both India and Pakistan; squadrons and companies had to be sent away to other units—and sent at a time when communal hatred was at its height.

NEW ZEALAND

At the outbreak of World War II New Zealand raised a division, the 2nd New Zealand Division, for service overseas. It was raised in three contingents, or echelons. The 1st Echelon left New Zealand for Egypt in January 1940; the 2nd left for Egypt in May, but was diverted to England, where it formed part of 7 British Corps for the defence of the U.K. after Dunkirk, and then went on to Egypt, arriving there in January 1941; and the 3rd left New Zealand for Egypt at the end of August 1940. The division had the 4th, 5th, and 6th Brigades, each having a battalion from each of the three military districts in the islands: 4th—18, 19, and 20 battalions (Northern, Central, South Island (Southern) districts respectively); 5th—21, 22, 23 battalions; 6th—24, 25, 26 battalions. In addition the 5th Brigade had the 28th Maori Battalion. The division saw action in Greece and Crete before going into the Desert campaign as part of the newly-named

M10 of 7th Anti-tank Regiment, RNZA, 2nd New Zealand Division, moving through San Casciano, south of Florence, Italy, its gun to the rear.　(New Zealand Official)

Eighth Army and fighting in Operation "Crusader" (November-December 1941) when it was involved in the grim battle at Sidi Rezegh. It fought at Alamein and right through to Tunisia, and then took part in the Italian campaign as a "mixed" division with two brigades of infantry and one of armour.

As well as the famous 2nd Division which earned a tremendous reputation for itself in North Africa and Italy, New Zealand raised four* other infantry divisions and one army tank brigade. The 1st, 4th, and 5th Divisions were for home defence, the 3rd served in the Pacific operations against the Japanese. The tank brigade was originally intended for the Middle East, but when Japan entered the war in December 1941 it was held in New Zealand as the nucleus of home defence. Designated the 1st New Zealand Army Tank Brigade it consisted of the 1st, 2nd, and 3rd Army Tank Battalions, and was equipped with Valentines. The N.Z. War Cabinet, after much heart-searching

---

*Five for a short period. When Rommel was threatening Egypt in 1942 a 6th Division was made up from units not forming part of 2nd Division's order of battle. When the threat disappeared 6th Division was disbanded.

Sherman of 19 Armoured Regiment, 4th NZ Armoured Brigade, 2nd NZ Division, the tank which accompanied the first New Zealanders into Florence, August 1944. Note the fern leaf divisional sign in front of the driver.　(New Zealand Official)

Sherman Kangaroos carrying men of 27 Battalion, 9th Infantry Brigade, 2nd NZ Division, before the Senio crossing, April 1945. The 9th was the third infantry brigade in the division and was formed in February 1945.　(New Zealand Official)

debate, agreed to release one tank battalion and reinforcements to join the 2nd Division. The 3rd Tank Bn. was selected. It went to the Middle East and was distributed among the battalions of 4th Brigade which was converted to an armoured brigade in October 1942.

The 3rd Division, which had previously been named the Pacific Section 2nd New Zealand Expeditionary Force, served in New Caledonia from November 1942 to August 1943, during which time it had no tank support. The division, consisting of the 8th, 14th, and 15th Brigades, was retained in New Zealand for most of 1942, the 8th Brigade having been in Fiji from November 1940 until it was relieved by American forces when the United States entered the war. When the division moved north from New Caledonia to the Solomon Islands 15th Brigade was disbanded because of manpower shortage. The division now had tank support. In July 1943 the whole 2nd Tank Bn. had been warned for service with it, but in the event only one squadron accompanied it to the Solomons. Designated Tank Squadron 3rd Division the squadron was equipped with 25 Valentine IIIs (three-man turret) of which nine were converted to close support tanks by mounting 3-in. howitzers from Matilda IV CS tanks in place of the normal 2-pdrs. which did not have an adequately effective H.E. shell. Among its actions the Tank Squadron supported 14th Brigade (30, 35, and 37 Bns.) at Vella Lavella and Green Islands.

As well as the 4th Armoured Brigade and the Tank Squadron 3rd Division, there was another armoured unit in New Zealand's Expeditionary Force. This was the Divisional Cavalry Regiment of 2nd Division. Personnel for this unit were volunteers from the Mounted Rifles regiments, of which there were nine—three in each military district:

1st Mounted Rifles (Canterbury Yeomanry Cavalry)
2nd Queen Alexandra's (Wellington West Coast) Mounted Rifles
3rd (Auckland) Mounted Rifles
4th (Waikato) Mounted Rifles
The Otago Mounted Rifles
6th (Manawatu) Mounted Rifles
9th (Wellington East Coast) Mounted Rifles
10th (Nelson) Mounted Rifles
11th (North Auckland) Mounted Rifles

Until 1921 there had been twelve Mounted Rifles Regiments. The old 8th Canterbury Mounted Rifles was incorporated in the 1st to become the 1st (Canter-

bury Yeomanry Cavalry), and the old 5th (Otago Hussars) 7th (Southland), and 12th (Otago) were amalgamated into the (5th) Otago Mounted Rifles.

On January 1, 1942 all nine Mounted Rifles regiments added the words "Light Armoured Fighting Vehicles Regiment" to their title—which resulted in something of a mouthful! For example, 2nd Queen Alexandra's (Wellington West Coast) Mounted Rifles Light Armoured Fighting Vehicles Regiment. These regiments were in the New Zealand Armoured Corps.

On March 29, 1944 the N.Z.A.C. was re-organized into three regiments:

1st Armoured Regiment—3rd, 4th, 11th L.A.F.V. Regiments
2nd Armoured Regiment—2nd, 6th, 9th L.A.F.V. Regiments
3rd Armoured Regiment—1st, 5th, 10th L.A.F.V. Regiments

After the war these armoured regiments inherited the battle honours of the battalions (armoured regiments) in 4th Armoured Brigade. The 1st inherited the honours of 18 Bn., the 2nd inherited the honours of 19 Bn. and the Tank Squadron 3rd Division, and the 3rd inherited the honours of 20 Bn. The battle honours of the 2nd N.Z. Divisional Cavalry Regiment were inherited by the 1st Armoured Car Regiment which was formed after the war by the New Zealand Scottish Regiment, machine-gunners during the war.

On July 12, 1947, the New Zealand Armoured Corps was granted the prefix "Royal".

2nd NEW ZEALAND DIVISION

The 2nd New Zealand Division, which fought in Greece, Crete, the Western Desert, Tunisia and Italy, was originally an infantry division consisting of three brigades. The only armour that was an integral part of the division was its own 2 N.Z. Divisional Cavalry regiment, equipped with light tanks and carriers. Tank support for the division in the Desert battles in 1941 and 1942 was provided by British armoured formations. The New Zealanders were not always happy with the results of this arrangement. At one stage the state of ill-feeling was such that, according to Major-General Sir Howard Kippenberger in his book *Infantry Brigadier,* "there was throughout the Eighth Army, not only in the New Zealand Division, a most intense distrust, almost hatred, of our armour." The New Zealanders decided to have their own tank support and to adopt the "new model" organization

Across the Adige with umbrella. Sherman of 4th NZ Armoured Brigade crossing the last river obstacle in the Italian campaign by pontoon ferry, April 1945. (New Zealand Official)

The 2nd New Zealand Division enters Trieste, May 2, 1945. A Sherman of 4th NZ Armoured Brigade.
(New Zealand Official)

with two infantry brigades and one tank brigade.

Rather than release the whole of the 1st N.Z. Tank Brigade from its home defence rôle it was eventually decided to convert one of the division's three infantry brigades and to supplement this with the 3rd Tank Bn. and reinforcements from New Zealand. 4th Brigade was withdrawn from the division after suffering severe casualties on Ruweisat Ridge in July 1942 and at Maadi Camp, near Cairo, began its training and re-equipment as an armoured brigade. Meanwhile 5th and 6th Brigades and the rest of the division fought at Second Alamein and along the North African shore into Tunisia. For Alamein the division was allotted 9th (British) Armoured Brigade from 10th Armoured Division and thus took part in the battle as a "new model" division with one armoured and two infantry brigades.

After Alamein there was a strong possibility that the 2nd N.Z. Division, like the last of the three Australian divisions in the Middle East, would be withdrawn for service against the Japanese in the South Pacific. Eventually, in June 1943, the New Zealand Parliament after much debate acceded to the request of Churchill and the Combined Chiefs of Staff—the 2nd N.Z. Division, one of the finest in Eighth Army, would be left in the Mediterranean theatre.

Its future having been decided the division now returned from Tunisia to Maadi Camp. There followed four months of re-equipment, re-organisation and training. The key change was the return to the division of 4th Brigade as an armoured formation. The reunion meant that the division had to re-think its tactical doctrine and re-structure its administration in order to transport, recover, repair, refuel and munition the tanks. Every arm was affected by the integration of an armoured brigade. 4th Armoured Brigade, equipped with 150 Shermans, consisted of 18th, 19th, and 20th Armoured Regiments (previously Battalions), 22nd (Motor) Battalion, Forward Delivery Squadron, Band, and its own E.M.E. 4th Armoured Brigade Workshops and Recovery Unit.

The Divisional Cavalry regiment was re-equipped with Staghound armoured cars instead of Honeys and carriers.

Summing up the potentiality of this "new model" division with its 4,500 vehicles and 20,000 men, the official New Zealand War History (N. C. Phillips *Italy Vol. I The Sangro to Cassino*, p. 35) says:

"It was capable of moving fast, of hitting hard while it moved and, as an enemy that forced it to deploy would quickly discover, of hitting harder still when it halted. Its mixed character, neither a purely infantry nor a purely armoured division, fitted it for operations needing adaptability and some measure of independence for, where the terms of battle were at all equal, it possessed within itself the means of breaking into a defensive position, piercing it and exploiting its own success by flooding its armour through the gap. But positional, as distinct from mobile warfare, in which the Division would have to merge its identity into a larger mass, would rob it of these advantages and search out its latent weakness—a shortage of infantry." This was the weakness of all "new model" divisions and the reason why this divisional organisation was abandoned in the British Army.

Shortage of tanks at the beginning of the war – a problem shared by all Commonwealth countries – led New Zealand to experiment with this "Bob Semple" tank, named after the N.Z. Minister of Defence. Also known as the "Mobile Pillbox" tank it had an armoured superstructure on an International Harvester agricultural tractor chassis. Only four were built, the design proving to be unsatisfactory. (New Zealand Official)

After its preparation at Maadi the division sailed for Taranto in October and moved up to its first action in Italy on the Sangro in mid-November 1943. In January 1944 it went west to Cassino where it fought until April. It was then moved to the Apennine mountain sector and in May advanced up the Liri to Avezzano. After the fall of Rome the division was in the battles for Arezzo and Florence, then Rimini and into the Romagna. On October 26 it was withdrawn into Eighth Army reserve.

By now the shortage of infantry was abundantly manifest. The immediate task in reserve was to increase the division's infantry strength and this at the expense of the armour for, as Freyberg, the GOC, cabled home "there is a shortage of infantry . . . while at the same time there seems to be more armour than can be employed." The two infantry brigades were each increased from three to four battalions by converting the Divisional Cavalry to infantry (which caused volcanic reactions in the regiment) and by 22nd (Motor) Battalion reverting to a normal infantry battalion.

The division returned to the line a month later, took part in the drive to the Senio and then manned a sector of the Winter Line. In February 1945 a third infantry brigade (9th) was formed with the Divisional Cavalry, 22nd Battalion and 27th (Machine-Gun) Battalion which was converted to infantry. The division took part in the spring offensive across the Senio. For this a new unit was formed to operate the "funnies"— Sherman dozers, Churchill AVREs, Churchill ARKs, Valentine Bridge-layers, and Kangaroos. Designated 28 Assault Squadron its two troops worked with E Squadron of the British 25th Armoured Engineer Brigade. The assault on the Senio Line began on April 9. It was the beginning of the end of the Italian campaign. On April 21 the division was at Budrio, a few miles east of Bologna; on May 2 it had reached Trieste.

On July 29, 1945, HQ Eighth Army was re-designated HQ British Troops in Austria. It had been in existence since midnight on September 26–27, 1941 when its name had been changed from HQ Western Army, which itself had been formed in Cairo earlier that month and then moved to the Western Desert. The 2nd New Zealand Division was the only original formation of Eighth Army still with it when it ceased to exist.

SOUTH AFRICA

At the outbreak of war in September 1939 South Africa's armoured force consisted of two Vickers Medium tanks and two Crossley armoured cars, all four vehicles dating from 1925. The two Crossleys formed the armoured car section of the Union Defence Force and in August 1932, a year after the section had been formed, they took part in a punitive expedition in South West Africa—the first operational use of armour by the U.D.F.

That armoured cars would be needed in future operations if war broke out had been made apparent from the Minister of Defence's training policy statement issued to the U.D.F's General Staff in 1938, in which he said that "the organization, equipment and training of the Defence Force were to be based on meeting an enemy on African soil, in bush warfare." According to Lieutenant-General George Brink*, who commanded the 1st South African Division from 1940 to 1942, "tanks were not even dreamed of, but the organization made liberal provision for armoured cars as the most suitable type of armoured fighting vehicle for bush warfare and the open country to be encountered in parts of East and Central Africa" where the theatre of war was likely to be.

Efforts were therefore made to get armoured cars from Britain and the United States. But neither country had any available. The South Africans in

---

*In the Foreword to Harry Klein's *Springboks in Armour*, Macdonald, 1965.

South African armoured car crew maintaining the guns of their Marmon-Herrington, East Africa, 1941. Note the large double doors at the rear. This is a riveted hull version of the Mark II.
(S.A. National War Museum)

consequence decided to build their own. From this decision came the South African Marmon-Herringtons, designed and built in the Union from imported chassis and armament and home-produced armour plate. Quantity production began in July 1940 and from then until it ended in April 1944 a total of 5,746 armoured cars were delivered, 4,566 to the Union Defence Force and 1,180 to the United Kingdom Government which had asked South Africa to supply armoured cars for use in the Middle East.

While the production of the armoured cars was being organized in the first half of 1940 the South African Tank Corps came into being. On January 31 authority was given for the establishment of No. 1 Armoured Car Company with 22 armoured cars (when they became available), six officers, and 161 other ranks. To begin with the only armoured cars available for training—when they were not in the repair shop— were the two old Crossleys which had spent a few weeks at the turn of the year on patrol in South West Africa, the area they had visited on the punitive expedition seven years previously. Apart from these the company had a section of Dragon troop carriers for mobile exercises.

In April the formation of four more armoured car companies was authorized, and in May the raising of three motor-cycle companies.

By this time the German blitzkrieg was striking across Flanders and Mussolini was poised to attack in Africa—from Cyrenaica eastwards into Egypt, from Eritrea westwards into the Sudan, and from Abyssinia south into Kenya.

In South Africa the personnel of No. 1 Armoured Car Company were abruptly transferred to No. 1 Light Tank Company which was formed, almost overnight, for service in East Africa. No. 1 Armoured Car Company was reconstituted, and at the end of May took delivery of the first Mark I Marmon-Herringtons. No. 1 Light Tank Company, Nos. 1 and 2 Armoured Car Companies, and Nos. 1, 2, and 3 Motor-Cycle Companies were the six companies of the 1st Battalion South African Tank Corps which was formed on May 23, 1940.

On June 1, No. 1 Light Tank Company sailed from Durban for Kenya where it took over 12 Light Tanks Mark III which had been sent from Egypt together with Royal Armoured Corps instructors. On June 10, when Italy declared war, No. 1 Armoured Car Company was sent with the 1st Battalion Transvaal Scottish to the frontier with Portuguese East Africa.

By the end of June five armoured car and two motor-cycle companies had been formed. A fortnight later, on July 15, the South African Tank Corps was reorganized into Nos. 1 and 2 Armoured Fighting Vehicles (AFV) Battalions, each with three armoured car companies and one motor-cycle company, with No. 1 Light Tank Company and the third motor-cycle company unattached. In the event only one platoon of this third company was raised. The idea had been to use motor-cycle companies in the rôle of mounted riflemen, but experience in East Africa showed that the armoured car had less limitations and no more motor-cycle units were formed.

Each of the five armoured car companies had 22 armoured cars, 14 motor-cycles, 7 motor-cycle combinations, 1 motor car, 11 one-ton lorries, and 10 three-tonners. Each motor-cycle company had 93 motor-cycles, 30 motor-cycle combinations, 2 one-tonners, and 8 three-tonners. Later in the year the strength of an armoured car company was increased to 7 officers and 296 other ranks, with 38 armoured cars. It was at this strength that the South African Tank Corps went "Up North", Nos. 2 and 3 Armoured Car Companies and No. 1 Motor-Cycle Company arriving in East Africa in October, and No. 1 Armoured Car Company and No. 2 Motor-Cycle Company in December, to join 1st South African Division.

The division consisted of:

> 1st South African Infantry Brigade (1st Transvaal Scottish, 1st Royal Natal Carbineers, and 1st Duke of Edinburgh's Own Rifles (The Dukes))
> 2nd South African Infantry Brigade (1st Natal Mounted Rifles, 1st Field Force Battalion, and 2nd Field Force Battalion)
> 5th South African Infantry Brigade (3rd Transvaal Scottish, 2nd Regiment Botha, and 1st South African Irish).

No. 1 Armoured Car Company was attached to 5th S.A. Brigade, No. 2 Armoured Car Company to the 2nd S.A. Brigade, and No. 3 Armoured Car Company to the 1st S.A. Brigade (which served with the 11th (African) and 12th (African) Divisions during the Abyssinian campaign, its place in 1st South African Division being taken by 25th (East African) Brigade). The two motor-cycle companies were divisional troops.

As well as the South African armoured car companies Lieut.-General Sir Alan Cunningham's East Africa Force also had the East African Armoured Car Regiment equipped with Marmon-Herringtons. Although the training manual defined the duties of armoured cars as reconnaissance and stated that they "will not be used in the rôle of tanks for frontal attacks" Colonel Klein's view was that "either the South African armoured-car commanders in Abyssinia had not studied their tactics, or they had set out to write a new handbook of their own. From the very first clash with the enemy they . . . took on the rôle they were obliged to undertake throughout the campaign—that of infantry tanks." (op.cit. p. 21). Called "Garri Kifarru" ("Rhinoceros Cars") by the Italian colonial infantry the armoured cars time after time paved the way for successful attacks and kept down infantry casualties.

The battle for Abyssinia began in earnest on January 28, 1941, and, apart from the capture of the northern fortresses, was over on May 16, less than four months later. The three South African armoured car companies and the 1st S.A. Light Tank Company then moved to Egypt, leaving a Light Armoured Detachment from the Light Tank Company (equipped with three light tanks and four Bren carriers) to take part in the battle for Gondar and the other northern fortresses in October and November. The Kenya Armoured Car Regiment also took part in these actions with the 12th African Division.

During the time when the armoured car companies were in East Africa the South African Tank Corps had been further expanded and re-organized. Personnel of the 1st Mounted Brigade were transferred to the Tank Corps and formed the 1st and 2nd AFV (Commando)

Marmon-Herrington Mark II – welded version – being used as a Field Dressing Station by South African medical detachment in the Desert, 1942. (S.A. National War Museum)

Regiments. Recruits from the South African Railways and Harbours Regiment formed the nucleus of a new armoured car company. Four regiments (the 2nd Royal Natal Carbineers, the 2nd Imperial Light Horse, the Regiment Westelike Provinsie, and the Regiment Suid-Westelike Distrike) were converted to armoured car companies. In March 1941 it was decided that the companies should be formed into armoured car regiments and armoured car reconnaissance battalions. The outcome was: the 1st and 2nd Regiments (whose designation was later changed to Armoured Car Commandos, a squadron of the 1st serving in the Madagascar campaign), the 4th, 5th and 6th Regiments, the 3rd and 7th Reconnaissance Battalions, No. 8 Armoured Car Commando (later re-designated as an armoured car regiment), No. 12 Armoured Car Commando, and, writes Colonel Klein, "the famous 'phantom' 13th Armoured Car Regiment, which was at all times the make-or-break training and special duties regiment."

The 3rd Reconnaissance Battalion was formed from Nos. 1, 2, and 3 Armoured Car Companies, and detachments of Nos. 1 and 2 Motor Cycle Companies, from the East African campaign. "3rd Recce" served in the Western Desert together with the 4th and 6th Armoured Car Regiments and the 7th Reconnaissance Battalion. The 5th Regiment went to the Middle East but was broken up on arrival to provide reinforcements.

Marmon-Herrington Mark III with its turret removed and mounting a 2-pdr. This car, of the 4th South African Armoured Car Regiment, is on "stand to" in Cyrenaica.
(S.A. National War Museum)

3rd Recce (which was re-designated 3rd S.A. Armoured Car Regiment in July 1942, though the change was ignored except in official documents!) served with the 1st S.A. Division. The 7th Reconnaissance Battalion served with the 2nd S.A. Division and was lost with the division and the British and Indian troops under its command in the fall of Tobruk in June 1942. On the eve of the Battle of Alamein the 4th and 6th Regiments were amalgamated into the 4th/6th S.A. Armoured Car Regiment and operated with the 1st (British) Armoured Division. Together with the Royal Dragoons (a British armoured car regiment) the 4th/6th broke through in the van of the British armour.

6th SOUTH AFRICAN ARMOURED DIVISION

At the end of 1942 the South Africans, including the armoured car regiments, returned home on leave. A few months later the South African Tank Corps was disbanded. The reason was that the Active Citizen Force regiments which had been selected to make up the newly-formed 6th South African Armoured

Division were below strength, and it was proving extremely difficult to bring them up to strength. The 6th S.A. Armoured Division was being raised for service in Europe.

In April 1943 the South African Tank Corps regiments from the Middle East ceased to exist: the 3rd Armoured Car Regiment (the "3rd Recce") was absorbed by the Natal Mounted Rifles, the 4th/6th by the Royal Natal Carbineers and the Imperial Light Horse.

The 6th South African Armoured Division arrived in Italy in April 1944 and came under command of Fifth U.S. Army. It consisted of:

11th South African Armoured Brigade (Prince Alfred's Guard, Pretoria Regiment, and Special Service Bn. Regiment, with the combined Imperial Light Horse/Kimberley Regiment as its motor battalion)

12th South African Motorized Infantry Brigade (1st Royal Natal Carbineers, combined battalion 1st City/Cape Town Highlanders, and combined battalion Witwatersrand Rifles/De La Rey)

The armoured reconnaissance regiment was the Natal Mounted Rifles.

The division went into the line at Cassino, fought its way into Florence, and took part in the breaching of the Gothic Line. As with other formations in Italy the shortage of infantry for the type of fighting involved made it necessary to add another brigade to the division. From May 1944 until February 1945 this was the 24th (British) Guards Brigade. When the Guards left a new South African infantry brigade, 13th Brigade, was formed from divisional troops, including the Royal Durban Light Infantry, and the 1st Royal Natal Carbineers which was transferred from the 12th Brigade. With this order of battle the division took part in the final assault through Bologna and into the Po Valley in April 1945.

"Through the mud . . ." Marmon-Herrington armoured car of the South African Tank Corps in Central Abyssinia, 1941. The cars, called "Garri Kifarru" ("Rhinoceros Cars") by the Italian colonial infantry, were generally used as infantry tanks in this campaign.
(S.A. National War Museum)

Major-General Poole, GOC 6th South African Armoured Division, (beside the jeep) among South African armour in a suburb of Bologna, which the South Africans entered on April 21, 1945. The tank behind the jeep is a Grant converted for command purposes. Note the chair beside the gun barrel.
(Imperial War Museum)

Cruiser Mark IVA – the up-armoured A13 mounting a co-axial Besa 7.92mm machine-gun (A13 Mark IIA) – on training in the United Kingdom. The bracket on the side of the turret carried two dischargers which projected a 4-inch smoke canister about 150 yards. The A13 was the first British tank to have Christie suspension. · (R.A.C. Tank Museum)

Survey of AFVs in British and Commonwealth Service during World War II

by Duncan Crow

IN 1936, before rearmament began in earnest, the British Army had 375 tanks, of which 209 were light tanks and the remainder mediums. Of these 375, all but 71 were officially classed as obsolete—the "moderns" being two Medium IIIs, 22 Mark V Lights, and 47 Mark VI Lights, a mark that was just being introduced into service.

During the three years that elapsed before the outbreak of the Second World War in September 1939 several hundred more Mark VI Lights of various models were produced, together with the first of the new cruiser and infantry tanks that were to replace the old mediums. The two classes of cruiser and infantry, or I, tank were the outcome of the conflict of views about a tank's purpose—whether it was purely an infantry support weapon, or whether its prime purpose was in mobile operations as the successor to the horsed cavalry.

The pilot model of the first of the new tanks, the A9 Cruiser Mark I, appeared in April 1936, and the first deliveries were made in January 1939. Also in 1936 the

pilot A10 Cruiser Mark II appeared, but the first delivery was not made until December 1939. The A13 Cruiser Mark III had a speedier development period. The order for two pilots was given at the end of 1936 and two years later, December 1938, the first deliveries of the production series were made. By the beginning of September 1939, 79 cruisers (Marks I and III) had been produced and 77 were in service.

The pilot model of the first I tank, the A11 Infantry Tank Mark I, appeared in September 1936. While production was beginning on this first Matilda the design of its successor was under way. The pilot model of the A12 Infantry Tank Mark II (sometimes called "Matilda senior" until the Mark I went out of service after Dunkirk when it formally took over the name Matilda) was ready in April 1938. By the outbreak of war only two "Matilda seniors" were in service. The total pre-war production of I tanks was 67.

Thus by September 1939 only 146 cruiser and I tanks had been produced, compared with several hundred light tanks, mainly Mark VIBs. The three categories of

283

Light Tanks Mark VIB of the 1st Royal Tank Regiment, 7th Armoured Division, in the Desert. Cruisers in the background. (Imperial War Museum)

A10s (Cruisers Mark II) in the Desert: 170 A10s were built.

A9 (Cruiser Mark I), of which 125 were built, mounted the new 2-pdr. with a co-axial .303 Vickers MG and two other .303 MGs one in each sub-turret on each side of the driver's compartment. The A9 was the first British tank to have a power-traversed turret.

Light Tank Mark VIB had round cupola, one-piece radiator louvre, and return roller attached to hull side.

Light Tank Mark VIC had a 15-mm Besa as its main armament.

A10 Mark I with Vickers .303 MG co-axially in turret. Most A10s were Mark 1A with a Besa 7.92-mm instead of the Vickers.

Covenanter was the A13 Mark III (Cruiser Mark V). Four marks of Covenanter were produced. (Imperial War Museum)

The A14 was an experimental "heavy cruiser" with Horstmann-type suspension and forward hull machine-gun auxiliary turrets.

tank—light, cruiser, and infantry—remained current in the British and Commonwealth Armies throughout the war.

LIGHT TANKS

Light tanks were the backbone, albeit a somewhat fragile one, of the British armoured forces at the outbreak of the war and for the next year. There were about 1,000 in service.* Light tanks, together with carriers, were the equipment of the seven Mechanized Divisional Cavalry regiments in the B.E.F. They also formed the main fighting vehicle equipment of the armoured brigades in England and Egypt. Other light tanks were in India, a few were in Australia and Canada. When the 1st Armoured Division went to France in May 1940 almost half its tanks were still light tanks, despite the substantial increase in cruiser production in the previous nine months.

Light tank production from the beginning of the war until the end of June 1940 was 320, of which 180 were produced in the first four months, 80 in the first quarter of 1940, and 60 in the second quarter. The tanks produced were Mark VIBs and Mark VICs, the latter mounting the 15-mm Besa as well as the 7·92-mm coaxial.

The campaign in France in 1940 showed up the failings of the light tanks. After Dunkirk there was a loss of interest in them on the part of the General Staff who now favoured armoured cars for the reconnaissance rôle. Consequently only 35 were produced in the last six months of 1940 as against 140 in the first half. Nevertheless British light tank production was not finished. The Mark VII Tetrarch was just going into production when the change of policy occurred. The first four were delivered for test in November 1940. No light tanks were produced in the first quarter of 1941, but 73 were built during the rest of the year—all Tetrarchs. In 1942 a further 100 Tetrarchs brought the total for this tank to 177 at which production ceased. Tetrarchs were used in the Madagascar landing in May 1942, and by the 6th Airborne Reconnaissance Regiment of 6th Airborne Division in the Normandy

* Table 25 of M. M. Postan's *British War Production* (H.M.S.O. London 1952) gives the total pre-war light tank production as 1,002. Though some of these were on their last legs they survived in service into the war.

The A16 was an experimental "heavy cruiser" developed from the A13 with Christie suspension. It had auxiliary machine-gun turrets on each side of the driver's compartment like the A9 and the experimental A14.

landing in June 1944. Some were also sent to Russia with Matildas and Valentines in 1942.

The last light tank to be produced was the Mark VIII Harry Hopkins of which 102 were built, the main production order of 99 being carried out after the Tetrarch and completed in 1944. The Harry Hopkins was not used operationally. Various marks of the Alecto self-propelled weapon were built on Harry Hopkins' chassis until the Alecto project was abandoned in 1945.

CRUISER TANKS

Cruiser tank production from the outbreak of war until the end of June 1940 was 322, the rate going up from 71 in the last four months of 1939 to 92 in the first quarter of 1940 and 159 in the second quarter. It then dropped in the two succeeding quarters to 147 and 78 respectively, before growing rapidly throughout 1941 to reach 479 in the last quarter of the year. This growth was in response to a War Office programme of December 1940 which raised the proportion of cruisers required from 45 to 78 per cent and reduced the I tank requirement from 55 to 22 per cent. Even so, from the third quarter of 1940 right through 1941 the output of I tanks continued to be higher than the output of cruisers:

There were three marks of Crusader. Mark I had a 2-pdr. as its main armament and a 7.92mm Besa in a forward sub-turret (which was sometimes removed): II was up-armoured from 40mm (maximum) to 49mm (maximum): III had a 6-pdr. as its main armament and 51mm (maximum) of armour. All three had a 7.92mm Besa co-axial machine-gun. (Imperial War Museum)

Cromwell crossing Nijmegen Bridge, Holland, shows the exhaust flame deflector – the "Normandy cowl" – fitted on all Cromwells in the North-West Europe campaign to conceal exhaust flames at night.   (Imperial War Museum)

This three-quarter rear view of a Centaur AA tank shows the flush top of the rear decking which distinguished the A27(L) from the A27(M). The A27(M) Cromwell had a raised armoured louvre.

| | Production of | |
	Cruisers	I Tanks
1939 Sept –Dec.	71	63
1940 1st qtr.	92	46
2nd	159	121
3rd	147	227
4th	78	354
1941 1st	184	469
2nd	347	566
3rd	406	942
4th	479	1,375
	1,963	4,163

Indeed the cruiser output never reached that of the I tanks and in total over the six years of the war the proportion was about two cruisers to three I tanks.

Both the A9 (Cruiser Mark I) and the A10 (Cruiser Mark II) were interim tanks that only went into limited production. Of the A9 125 were built, including a number of close support tanks with a 3·7-inch mortar as the main armament instead of a 2-pdr. gun. The A9 had two forward sub-turrets with Vickers ·303-in machine-guns. Of the A10 170 were built, all but a few being Cruiser Mark IIAs which had a 7·92-mm Besa coaxial instead of a Vickers ·303-in, and another Besa in the hull front. This was the first British tank to mount a Besa. There was also a close support version of the A10. The A9 had 6 mm. to 14 mm. of armour and weighed 12·5 tons, the A10 had 6 mm. to 30 mm. of armour and weighed 1·25 tons more.

Originally the A10 was supposed to be an infantry support tank. Then it was re-designated as a "heavy cruiser". This classification was part of the pre-war canon that proliferated the designations and characteristics of armoured fighting vehicles to make a variety in which each closely defined type was intended to perform a closely defined rôle. The A13 (Cruiser Mark III) with 6 mm. to 14 mm. of armour was looked upon as a "light cruiser" which would need the support in action of a "heavy cruiser". Because the A10 was only an interim type three other heavy cruisers were embarked upon.

The first of these, the A14, was designed at Woolwich by the Chief Superintendent of Design and built in 1939 by the L.M.S. Railway Company. Like the A9 it had two forward hull machine-gun sub-turrets. It had Wilson epicyclic step-down steering and Horstmann-type suspension.

The second project was given the designation A15, but this did not go beyond the design stage and the "A"

number was transferred to an entirely different project that became the Cruiser Mark VI.

The third project, also with two forward hull machine-gun sub-turrets, was the A16 which was built in 1938 by Nuffield Mechanisations and Aero Ltd., a newly created armaments firm that had built the first A13 the previous year. The A13 was the first British tank to have Christie suspension, and the A16 was a development of it. The Chief Superintendent of Design and Thompson Taylor co-operated with Nuffields in the building of the single vehicle, which was the first to have Dr. H. E. Merritt's double differential steering mechanism. Used in conjunction with a Maybach propulsion gearbox this was called the Merritt-Maybach transmission. It was superseded in general use in British tanks by the Merritt-Brown transmission which had Merritt's later-developed triple differential system.

The specification for the "heavy cruiser" had called for a 2-pdr. as the main armament, two forward hull machine-gun sub-turrets, 30 mm. of armour (maximum), a cross-country speed of 25 m.p.h., and a weight of 25 tons. While the A14 and A16 were being built a second mark of A13 was produced with 30 mm. of armour (maximum) which increased the tank's weight from 14·2 to 14·75 tons. Nevertheless it could still do almost 40 m.p.h. There appeared to be no advantage in the A14 and A16 over the up-armoured A13 and they did not go beyond the experimental stage.

The up-armoured A13 (A13 Mark II) with spaced armour on its turret was Cruiser Mark IV. The Mark IVA had a Besa instead of a Vickers machine-gun. Total production of A13 Marks I and II was 665.

Cruisers Marks I, II, IIA, III, IV, and IVA saw action in France in 1940 with the 1st Armoured Division and in the Western Desert in 1940 and 1941 with the 7th Armoured Division. The A9s and A10s left the battlefield on the Egyptian frontier during Operation "Battleaxe" in June 1941; the A13s, which still formed half the strength of 7th Armoured Brigade for Operation "Crusader" in November 1941, went after the fighting at Sidi Rezegh during that Operation.

The next tank in the cruiser series, the A13 Mark III (Cruiser Mark V), better known by its name Covenanter, began its design life as a "heavy cruiser" project in succession to the A14 and A16. The first deliveries were made in the summer of 1940 and production continued until January 1943 by which time 1,365 Covenanters had been produced in four marks, including some close support tanks with a 3-inch howitzer and a few special purpose tanks (bridge-layers, command, OP, and ARV). The Covenanter weighed 18 tons, had 7 mm. to 40 mm. of armour, and was armed with a 2-pdr. and a co-axial Besa. Apart from a Covenanter bridgelayer used by the Australians on Bougainville Island the Covenanter was used for training purposes only and was never in action. It formed a major part of the AFV equipment of the 1st Polish Armoured Division and the Guards Armoured Division during their training and of the 9th Armoured Division.

Almost simultaneously with the Covenanter the next mark of cruiser was developed. The Covenanter design was accepted for production in April 1939, and in August Nuffields' own proposal for a "heavy cruiser" developed from the A13 was accepted. This was given the ordnance designation A15, which it took over from the earlier defunct project already mentioned. This new A15, Cruiser Mark VI, was named Crusader. It became the standard British tank of the armoured brigades in action in North Africa until replaced by the American Grants and Shermans. It was first in action in Operation "Battleaxe" in June 1941 and continued in service until the end of the North African campaign, with the Sherman gradually replacing it as the Eighth Army moved westwards after the Second Battle of Alamein. Almost as many Crusaders were produced as all other cruisers put together. Its total was 4,350 gun tanks plus 1,373 for special rôles (command, OP, anti-aircraft, ARV, gun tractor, and bulldozer). There were three marks of Crusader: Mark I weighed 18·8 tons, had 40 mm. of armour (maximum), and was armed with a 2-pdr. and two Besas—one co-axial, the other in a forward sub-turret (this gun and turret were sometimes removed); Mark II was up-armoured to 49 mm. (maximum) and weighed 19 tons; Mark III had a 6-pdr. as its main armament and only the co-axial Besa; its armour was 51 mm. (maximum). All three marks had a minimum of 7 mm. of armour. Some specialist Crusaders remained in service after the gun tanks had been withdrawn in May 1942.

Cruisers Marks I to VI inclusive were all tanks that had started their design life pre-war. The later cruisers were war-time designs. In 1941 a specification was laid down for a cruiser with front armour of 75/65 mm., weighing 24 tons, and mounting a 6-pdr. (57-mm.) on a 60-inch turret ring. The tanks that resulted from this were the A24 Cruiser Mark VII Cavalier (weight 27 tons) and the A27 Cruiser Mark VIII (27·5 tons). Fitted with a Liberty engine the A27(L) was called the Centaur, with a Meteor engine the A27(M) was the Cromwell. Cavaliers, of which 500 were built, were not used in action as gun tanks but about half were converted to armoured OPs for artillery regiments of armoured divisions in North-West Europe 1944–45. Cromwells, on the other hand, equipped the 22nd Armoured Brigade of 7th Armoured Division as well as five armoured reconnaissance regiments of armoured divisions in 21 Army Group. There were four marks of Centaur and eight marks of Cromwell. Main differences were: Centaurs I and II had a 6-pdr. as the main armament, Centaur III had a 75-mm., Centaur IV, which was a support tank, had a 95-mm. Cromwells I, II, and III were 6-pdr.-armed, IV, V, and VII had a 75-mm., and VI and VIII had a 95-mm. for close support. Cromwells VII and VIII had the armour increased (mainly on the front) from 76 mm. maximum as on all Cavaliers, Centaurs and other Cromwells to 101 mm. Minimum armour was 20 mm. on Cavaliers and Centaurs and 8-10 mm. on Cromwells. The first production Centaurs were delivered at the end of 1942, the first Cromwells in 1943. There were a number of Centaur and Cromwell special purpose tanks—OP, anti-aircraft, bulldozer, ARV. Contracts for 3,500 Cromwells were placed. It is not clear whether these were all carried out in full, but it seems doubtful that they were.

Lengthened Cromwell chassis were used in 1943–44 for the production of 200 Challengers (A30) mounting a 17-pdr. The Challenger had the rôle of a tank destroyer in support of the other cruisers, a troop typically consisting of three Cromwells and one Challenger. An alternative version of the A30 was developed as a self-propelled anti-tank gun; it was called Avenger. The order for 230 Avengers was not fulfilled until 1946, because by the time the pilot model was ready in 1944 the American M10 had been adopted for service in British tank destroyer regiments.

The next tank in the cruiser line was the Comet, a development of the Cromwell designed to overcome the weaknesses of the Challenger which were attribu-table mainly to mounting a big gun on a comparatively small hull. Developed under the ordnance specification A34 the first production Comets were delivered in

The 11th Armoured Division were re-equipped with Comets early in 1945. Comets of A Squadron, 15th/19th The King's Royal Hussars, cross the Weser at Petershagen on April 7, 1945. The Comet was the last of the cruiser series.
(Imperial War Museum)

The Challenger with lengthened Cromwell chassis and mounting a 17-pdr. was a tank destroyer in support of other cruisers. Seen here at St. Anthonis, Holland, in October 1944 is a Challenger of B Squadron, 15th/19th The King's Royal Hussars, which was the armoured reconnaissance regiment of the 11th Armoured Division.
(Imperial War Museum)

Centurion Mark I. This is one of the six pilot models, armed with a 17-pdr. gun and Polsten cannon in ball-mount, that were rushed to the 22nd Armoured Brigade in Germany in May 1945.
(Imperial War Museum)

Australian Cruiser Mark IV prototype with 17-pdr. gun. The basic design of the tank was such that it was possible to up-gun it from the 2-pdr. of the Mark I to the 17-pdr. of the Mark IV.
(Australian War Memorial)

September 1944 and sent to Belgium in November. The armoured units of the 11th Armoured Division, including the divisional armoured reconnaissance regiment, were the only ones to be re-equipped with Comets before the fighting in Europe was over. Their re-equipment, begun in December, was interrupted by the Ardennes offensive and completed in March. The Comet weighed 32·7 tons with maximum armour of 101 mm. and minimum of 14 mm.; its main armament was a 77-mm. gun which was, in fact, a slightly less powerful version of the 17-pdr. (76·2-mm.) with a calibre of 75-mm. but which was re-named to avoid confusion with other British and American guns in service. The Comet remained in service with the Regular Army until 1959.

The Comet was really the last of the cruiser tanks. Although the Centurion which succeeded it (and to which it contributed in development) was designed as a cruiser, by the time it came into production in 1945 the idea of a multi-purpose "capital" tank had taken the place of the previous two-type concept (cruiser and I tanks). The Centurion, developed under the ordnance designation A41 with a 17-pdr. and armour thickness of 17–152 mm. was regarded as meeting the "capital" tank requirement and thus became the first of what are now called main battle tanks. Although six Centurions were rushed to the 22nd Armoured Brigade of 7th Armoured Division in May 1945 they arrived too late for testing in action and the Centurion had to wait for the Korean War to prove its worth. That it did so is evidenced by the fact that the Centurion was still in service more than a quarter of a century after its first marks were produced. In the 1930s such a length of service would simply have indicated parsimony in defence spending; in the post-1945 world it is proof of military effectiveness!

The Australians and the Canadians both built cruiser tanks from their own designs. The Australian tank was the Sentinel, Australian Cruiser Tank Mark I (AC I). It combined American automotive practice (as demonstrated in the M3 Medium) with British configuration, and added some new features of its own. Its hull was cast as one unit, something that had never been attempted anywhere before with a tank of this size. The Sentinel weighed 28 tons with maximum armour of 65 mm. and minimum of 25 mm. It was powered by three Cadillac 75 engines arranged in clover-leaf pattern with a combined power of 330 b.h.p. Its suspension was copied from the French Hotchkiss design with horizontal volute springs. It was armed with a 2-pdr. and two Vickers ·303 machine-guns, one co-axial, the other in a forward hull mounting. Production of AC I was 65.

Australian Cruiser Mark II (AC II), which was to be a lighter tank, was abandoned at the design stage; but Mark III (AC III), which mounted a 25-pdr. instead of the 2-pdr., was put into production. A fourth Mark (AC IV) was projected, mounting a 17-pdr. In July 1943 the Australian Government ordered work on the Australian Cruiser to stop because the availability of American tanks had removed the need for it. Apart from the 65 completed AC Is there were 25 uncompleted AC IIIs—and these were never finished. The Sentinel was used for training only; but it should not be dismissed without comment on this account. Whereas British designers were unable to mount a 17-pdr. in a tank without going to a new hull, the Australians so designed the Sentinel that it could be up-gunned without radical alteration.

The Canadian cruiser was the Ram. It was based on the M3 Medium chassis but had a newly designed superstructure and a layout and armament to British standards. The first 50 built had a 2-pdr. as the main armament and were designated Ram I. The remainder of the production run—another 1,899 vehicles—had a 6-pdr. and were called Ram II. Secondary armament in both cases was a co-axial ·30 Browning, a front hull ·30 Browning, and a third ·30 Browning for AA defence. Ram weighed 29 tons with a maximum armour thickness of 87 mm. and minimum of 25 mm. The majority of the Rams built came to Britain as the equipment of the Canadian armoured divisions, but they were not used by them in action, being replaced by Shermans. Rams, however, did see action. With their turrets removed they became armoured personnel carriers, known as Kangaroos (see under section on

Matilda (Infantry Tank Mark II) "Glenorchy" of Major K. P. Harris, M.C., 7th Royal Tank Regiment, with an Italian flag captured àt Tobruk, January 22, 1941. "The most striking sequence of successes achieved by any regiment – in . . . the British Army – during the war." (Imperial War Museum)

Valentine with track sand guards and auxiliary fuel tank for desert operations. Note revolver port on the turret side. More Valentines were built than any other British tank.

Self-Propelled Weapons), and equipped two APC regiments in 79th Armoured Division during the North-West Europe campaign. Ram variants included the Ram OP/Command tank of which 84 were built from Ram IIs and Ram ARVs.

A second cruiser built by the Canadians was the Grizzly. This was basically the M4A1 Medium with Canadian tracks and British wireless equipment. Grizzly production was 188. An AA variant of the Grizzly known as the Skink was also designed, but only three were produced before Allied air superiority over Europe in 1944 made a large number of AA tanks unnecessary.

INFANTRY TANKS

The first Matilda, Infantry Tank Mark I, of which 140 were built, weighed 11 tons with a maximum of 65 mm. of armour and was armed only with a Vickers machine-gun. It formed the greater part of the strength of the two infantry tank battalions (4th R.T.R. and 7th R.T.R.) of the 1st Army Tank Brigade in the B.E.F. in 1940. It went out of service after Dunkirk.

"Matilda senior", Infantry Tank Mark II, was altogether a more impressive and important tank. Looking at the Matilda thirty years later in the Imperial War Museum one may be astonished at the use of such epithets, but in its day, which lasted for

almost two years—a long time in war—it was a world-beater. It was the tank of the 4th and 7th Royal Tank Regiment which set the Germans back on their heels at Arras in May 1940 and, in the hands of the same units among others, had signal successes in the Desert campaign. Of the 7th R.T.R.'s actions at Sidi Barrani, Bardia, and Tobruk in the campaign that culminated in the defeat of the Italians at Beda Fomm in February 1941, the regimental history of the Royal Tank Regiment (*The Tanks* by Captain B. H. Liddell Hart, Volume II, p. 55) says that it was "the most striking sequence of successes achieved by any regiment—in the R.T.R., or in the R.A.C., or in the British Army—during the war. Indeed, the history of warfare shows no case of a single fighting unit having such a great effect in deciding the issue of battles, and of a campaign." A peerless record indeed.

The Matilda was produced at the Vulcan Foundry in Newton-le-Willows, Warrington, where the present writer spent a week in March 1942 on one of the courses designed to introduce tank users to tank builders. Whether the result was quite what was intended is debatable—but it was certainly a memorable week! Matilda weighed 26·5 tons with a maximum of 78 mm. of armour and a minimum of 13 mm. It was armed with a 2-pdr. and a Vickers ·303-in. machine-gun (in the case of Matilda I) or a 7·92-mm. Besa (in

Valentines (Infantry Tank Mark III) of either 17th/21st Lancers or 2nd Lothians and Border Horse, 26th Armoured Brigade, 6th Armoured Division, on the road from Thala to Kasserine to stem the German breakthrough, Tunisia, February 19, 1943.
(Imperial War Museum)

Churchill IVs of 1st Canadian Army Tank Brigade drawn up for inspection by H.M. King George VI "somewhere in England", February 11, 1943. The brigade went to Sicily in July.
(Canadian Official)

the case of later marks). Infantry Tank Mark II and Mark IIA (Matilda II) had two A.E.C. engines, Mark IIA* (Matilda III) and Mark IIA** (Matildas IV and V) had two Leyland engines. Matilda IV and V had the No. 19 wireless set instead of the No. 11 set. There was a close support Matilda III and IV with a 3-inch howitzer instead of the 2-pdr. There were also specialized Matildas including: Scorpions I and II, Barons, and Anti-mine Roller Attachments for sweeping paths through minefields, C.D.L. tanks (see under Grant C.D.L. Tanks), Matilda with Carrot carrying a demolition charge on the Anti-mine Roller Attachment, and Matilda Frog with flame-throwing equipment in the turret of a Matilda IV. Total production of Matildas was 2,987 before a halt was called in August 1943.

As well as the 4th and 7th R.T.R. in France, Egypt and Cyrenaica other units with Matildas were the 42nd and 44th R.T.R. (Egypt, Cyrenaica). A squadron of 4th R.T.R. was in Eritrea with the 4th Indian Division and half a squadron of the 7th R.T.R. was lost in Crete. Detachments from 6th, 42nd, and 44th R.T.R. with Matilda Scorpions were at the Second

A column of Churchill AVREs of 79th Armoured Division near Coch, towards the end of Operation "Veritable" which cleared the Reichswald and broke through the Siegfried Line, March 1945. AVREs were Churchills III or IVs, armed with Petards. First two in the column are Churchill IVs, third and fourth are carrying fascines.
(Imperial War Museum)

Battle of Alamein, October 1942. By this time Matilda gun tanks had been withdrawn from the Desert battlefield after a stand at El Alamein in July 1942 when the retreat from Gazala was halted. But the Matilda's service was not yet finished: many were sent to Russia, others were used by the Australians in the Pacific theatre. It was the Australians who developed the Matilda Frog and used it in Borneo in 1945.

Infantry Tank Mark III, the Valentine, was produced in far greater numbers than any other British tank. The first Valentine, built by Vickers and based on elements of their three earlier tanks—the A9, the A10, and the A11, came off the production line in May 1940. By the time production ceased early in 1944, 6,855 Valentines (including special vehicles on Valentine chassis) had been built in the U.K., plus 1,420 built in Canada, bringing the grand total to 8,275. There were eleven basic marks of Valentine; the main differences were:

Mark I	A.E.C. petrol (gasoline) engine, two-man turret mounting a 2-pdr. and a co-axial Besa machine-gun.
Mark II	as I except for A.E.C. diesel engine.
Mark III	as II except for three-man turret.
Mark IV	as II except for General Motors diesel engine.
Mark V	as IV except for three-man turret.
Mark VI	Canadian Valentine like Mark IV, but with Browning ·30 instead of the Besa and nose plate cast not bolted.
Mark VII	Canadian Valentine, improved Mark VI.
Mark VIIA	Canadian Valentine, improved Mark VII.
Mark VIII	A.E.C. diesel engine, two-man turret mounting a 6-pdr. only.
Mark IX	Mark VIII except for General Motors diesel engine.
Mark X	Up-rated General Motors diesel engine, two-man turret mounting a 6-pdr. and a co-axial Besa machine-gun.
Mark XI	as X, but with 75-mm. gun instead of 6-pdr.

Valentines were used in a number of special rôles. The first production DD "swimming" tanks were adaptations of Valentines Marks V, IX, and XI; 625 were converted to this rôle. Valentine DD tanks were

The 78-ton Tortoise (A39) with its 32-pdr. gun at the R.A.C. Tank Museum. Note twin-Besa cupola for AA defence. One track is missing. (Duncan Crow)

Crocodile in action. Crocodiles were Churchill VIIs with flame-throwing equipment. The flame projector took the place of the hull machine-gun and was operated by the hull gunner. (Imperial War Museum)

used for training in the U.K., Italy, and India; a few were used operationally in Italy in 1945. Valentines were used in tank flamethrower experiments, as bridgelayers, and with various mine-clearing devices including Scorpion and Snake, the latter being a long tube of explosive pushed across a minefield by the tank and then exploded by remote control to clear a path. There was also a Valentine OP tank, a Valentine Dozer, and a few Valentines were converted to C.D.L. (armoured searchlight) tanks. The Bishop and the Archer self-propelled weapons were on Valentine chassis (see section on Self-Propelled Weapons).

The Valentine weighed 17 tons and had an armour thickness of 65 mm. maximum, 8 mm. minimum. Although designed as an infantry tank and used in service as such by Army tank brigades, it was also issued to many armoured regiments in 1941 instead of cruiser tanks which were in short supply. Despite the different classification there was no real contradiction in this because the Valentine was essentially an improved version of the A10 "heavy" cruiser. Valentines were issued to the 20th and 26th Armoured Brigades of 6th Armoured Division, to the 23rd and 24th Armoured Brigades of 8th Armoured Division (both of which had originally been formed as Army tank brigades), to the 29th and 30th Armoured Brigades of 11th Armoured Division, and to the 1st Polish Armoured Division which was formed in Scotland. Of these formations the 23rd and 26th Armoured Brigades took Valentines into action, the former fighting in them from First Alamein in July 1942 until the end of the North African campaign, the latter, with mixed squadrons of Valentines and Crusaders, in Tunisia from November 1942 until the end of February when its units were re-equipped with Shermans. Valentines were first used in action by 8th R.T.R. of 1st Army Tank Brigade in the attack on Capuzzo on November 22, 1941, in Operation "Crusader", and they equipped the same unit in the brigade's great night attack under Brigadier Bill Watkins in support of 2nd South African Division against the Bardia fortress on January 1, 1942. 4th and 44th R.T.R. were also equipped with Valentines later in the Desert campaign, while 7th R.T.R. took over some Valentines (and five Grants) to add to its remaining Matildas before joining the ill-fated Tobruk garrison with 4th R.T.R. in June 1942. 42nd R.T.R.

also had a proportion of Valentines at one stage.

Valentines were used for a time by 50th Indian Tank Brigade, by the New Zealand Tank Squadron 3rd Division in the Solomon Islands, by a Special Service Tank Squadron in Madagascar, and, extensively, by the Russians who were sent all but 30 of the Canadian Valentine output plus 1,300 British-built Valentines—a total of 2,690, of which some 400 were sunk en route.

Second only to the Valentine in numbers produced was the Churchill, Infantry Tank Mark IV (A22). The first batch of Churchills came off the Vauxhall Motors production line in June 1941. Ten companies as well as Vauxhall ultimately formed the Churchill Tank Production Group as well as a host of sub-contractors. Production lasted as long as the war and 5,640 Churchills were built. There were a large number of basic marks and variants. But all were powered by a Bedford twin-six 350 b.h.p. engine. Weight was 39 tons with maximum armour of 102 mm. and minimum of 16 mm. in the earlier marks, and 40 tons with a maximum of 152 mm. and minimum of 25 mm. in Marks VII and VIII. The main characteristics of the different marks and variants were:

Mark I	3-in. howitzer in the front hull and a 2-pdr. gun with co-axial 7·92-mm. Besa in the cast turret.
Mark II	3-inch howitzer replaced by Besa.

Three-quarter front view of the T14 Assault Tank at the R.A.C. Tank Museum. Beyond it is a late production Sherman with horizontal volute spring suspension. The T14, too, had HVSS and incorporated components from the Sherman as well as features from the M6 Heavy. 8,500 were ordered, but only two were built. This one is seen at the R.A.C. Tank Museum, Bovington. (Duncan Crow)

Stuart I (M3 Light Tank) modified by the British by addition of track sand-shields, extra stowage boxes and fuel tank, and track shoes on hull sides. (Imperial War Museum)

Mark IICS	as I but with 3-inch howitzer in the turret and 2-pdr. in the nose.
Mark III	6-pdr. and co-axial 7·92 mm. Besa in welded turret and Besa in nose.
Mark IV	as III but with welded turret.
Mark IV (NA 75)	IV with 6-pdr. replaced by M3 75-mm. gun from salvaged Sherman: 120 Mark IVs converted by 21st Tank Brigade workshops in North Africa (=NA).
Mark V	as IV but with 95-mm. howitzer instead of 6-pdr.
Mark VI	as IV but with British-built dual-purpose (HE/AP) 75-mm. gun.
Mark VII (A22F, re-designated A42 in 1945)	a largely re-designed Churchill with thicker armour, a new cast/welded turret with cupola, circular (instead of square) escape doors on the sides of the hull, five- instead of four-speed gearbox, improved suspension, 75-mm. gun.
Mark VIII	close support version of VII with 95-mm. howitzer in place of 75-mm. gun.
Mark IX	III or IV re-worked to contemporary standards of protection by addition of appliqué armour and by fitting VII's turret though retaining 6-pdr.
Mark IX LT	as IX but with original III or IV turret (LT=Light Turret).
Mark X	VI re-worked as IX but with 75-mm. gun.
Mark X LT	as X but with original VI turret.
Mark XI	V re-worked as VIII.
Mark XI LT	as XI but with original V turret.

Churchills were converted for a number of special rôles, notably as recovery vehicles, AVREs (Armoured Vehicles, Royal Engineers) and Crocodiles (flame-throwing tanks). AVREs, which were Churchill IIIs or IVs armed with Petards and modified to allow the fitting of various devices for demolishing, bridging, or making a passage through anti-invasion defences, equipped the 1st Assault Brigade, R.E., of 79th Armoured Division for the North-West Europe campaign, and were also used by 25th Armoured Engineer Brigade in Italy. Crocodiles were Churchill VIIs with flame-throwing equipment; 31st Armoured Brigade of 79th Armoured Division was the Crocodile brigade, and there were Crocodiles in 25th Armoured

Engineer Brigade. 7th R.T.R., one of the units in 31st Armoured Brigade, used Crocodiles again in the Korean War. Churchills were also widely used as bridgelayers and as ARKs (Armoured Ramp Carriers) for spanning defence ditches or climbing sea walls.

The Churchill first saw action on August 19, 1942 when the Calgary Regiment of 1st Canadian Army Tank Brigade with Mark Is and IIIs was part of the 2nd Canadian Infantry Division Group that assaulted Dieppe. A trio of Churchill IIIs were used as command vehicles at 7th (Motor) Brigade HQ during the Second Battle of Alamein, but it was not until the Tunisian campaign that Churchills were used in strength over a period of time. Two tank brigades of Churchills were part of First Army in Tunisia. The first of these, 25th Tank Brigade, arrived in February 1943 and within twenty-four hours of reaching its concentration area west of Le Kef it found itself preparing for action: the Germans had advanced from the Faid Pass, broken through the Americans at Sidi Bou Zid, and had captured Sbeitla; the whole southern front was wide open. Churchills of 142nd (Suffolk) Regiment, R.A.C. were hurried down from Le Kef to Sbiba and fought their first action in support of 2nd Coldstream Guards, 1st Guards Brigade, to the east of the Sbiba-Sbeitla road at 17.00 hrs. on February 21. The second tank brigade to arrive in Tunisia was the 21st Tank Brigade which landed between March 23 and 27 as the third brigade in 4th Infantry Division which was a "mixed" division with one tank and two infantry brigades. Both tank brigades subsequently fought in the Italian campaign, though they were not completely equipped with Churchills throughout. In the North-West Europe campaign 34th Tank Brigade was equipped with Churchills as well as 31st Tank (later Armoured) Brigade (which started with one Crocodile unit and two ordinary Churchill units and ended with three Crocodile units), and 6th Guards Tank Brigade. A few Churchills were also used (though not in action) by the Australians in New Guinea.

The Churchill was the last "I" tank to be produced in quantity. But it was not the last to be developed. One of the later designs stemmed from the Valentine, another from the Churchill itself. The Valentine development was the A38 Valiant which weighed 27 tons, had maximum armour of 114 mm. (10 mm. minimum), and mounted a 75-mm. gun with a co-axial Besa 7·92-mm. machine-gun. The first pilot model (Valiant I) had a General Motors 210 b.h.p. diesel engine; the second (Valiant II) had a Rolls-Royce 8-cylinder Meteorite engine designed for petrol (gasoline) or diesel fuel. The Meteorite fore-shadowed the post-war multi-fuel tank engines. Valiant I was completed in mid-1944, but before Valiant II was finished interest in this type of tank had declined and the A38 project was dropped.

The Churchill development was Black Prince (A43), originally called "Super Churchill", of which only six were built. This tank arose from a General Staff request to the Tank Board in September 1941 to develop both cruiser and infantry tanks mounting large calibre high velocity guns that would be able successfully to engage the largest German tanks. In the cruiser field the Challenger was in due course produced with a 17-pdr.; for the heavier-armed "I" tank the Churchill 3-inch Gun Carrier was improvised

Churchill III (left) and Churchill I (right) near Medjez-el-Bab, Tunisia, April 1943. Two tank brigades fought in Tunisia with Churchills – 25th Tank Brigade (51st R.T.R., North Irish Horse, 142nd (Suffolk) Regiment, R.A.C.) which arrived in February, 1943; and 21st Tank Brigade (12th R.T.R., 48th R.T.R. 145th (Duke of Wellington's) Regiment, R.A.C.) which arrived as an integral part of 4th Division at the end of March.
(Imperial War Museum)

Stuart, and three of its crew, of the 8th King's Royal Irish Hussars in the Desert. The 8th Hussars were the first British regiment to receive M3 Light Tanks – in August 1941.
(Imperial War Museum)

by mounting a 3-inch 21-cwt. AA gun with limited traverse on a Churchill chassis, and at the same time the idea was considered of modifying the Churchill design to take a 17-pdr. in a turret. This was rejected in 1941 because the Churchill was too narrow to accept a turret wide enough to take a 17-pdr. Increasing the width was precluded by the old-established War Office requirement that tanks must be within standard loading gauge limits on British railways. The 3-inch Gun Carrier project was beset by changes of policy and "file-mongering" including the argument as to whether it was a tank or self-propelled artillery. In late 1942, when 50 had been built, the 3-inch Gun Carrier was abandoned. A year later the idea of the 17-pdr. Churchill was resurrected. The width restriction had by now been lifted. Vauxhall's were asked to produce the A43, which would be an interim vehicle to fill the gap until the new "universal chassis" multi-purpose tank, the A41 Centurion, was ready. In the event the first pilot models of both Black Prince and Centurion were ready at the same time as the war in Europe ended, and although full tests were carried out with the Black Prince (which was essentially a Churchill VII scaled up to take the bigger gun) no production order was placed. The future belonged to the Centurion.

HEAVY ASSAULT TANKS

At the outbreak of war in 1939 there were powerful voices in favour of building heavy tanks for crossing shelled areas to assault the enemy's fortifications. This was the type of warfare envisaged—a repeat performance of the 1914–18 Western Front. One attempt to meet this presumed need was the A20, which was a revised Infantry Tank Mark I weighing 43 tons with an armour basis of 80 mm. and mounting a 2-pdr. and coaxial Besa. After two pilot models had been built the A20 was abandoned in favour of the A22, the Churchill.

Another attempt was the TOG tank—TOG standing for The Old Gang of World War I tank pioneers who were brought together again to design and build this "shelled area" assault tank. Two TOG tanks

were built, the second being completed in March 1941 by which time the Churchill had been accepted as the standard heavy infantry tank, despite initial short-comings, and TOG was used only for trials. In this capacity, incidentally, it was fitted with the turret mounting a 17-pdr. gun which was intended for the Challenger and was thus the first British tank to be armed with this gun. TOG 2 weighed 80 tons with a maximum of 86 mm. armour and minimum of 25 mm.

By the end of 1942 British tank policy was undergoing a fundamental change. Influenced by the American Medium tanks which came into British service from early 1942, and by the all-important opinion of General Montgomery, there was a strong move away from the "two types of tank". Montgomery had decided that he wanted a single type of tank, a "capital" tank he called it, which would combine the advantages of a cruiser and infantry tank and could fill both rôles. This gave rise to the idea of a "universal" chassis capable of adaptation for different AFV rôles. Until such a chassis could be specially designed it was hoped that the Cromwell chassis would be suitable as the basis for a heavy assault tank to replace the Churchill which had so far shown itself to be mechanically unreliable. This assault tank on the

Stuart of the 8th Hussars camouflaged with a "sun shield" to make it look like a lorry on the approach march to Sidi Rezegh where the Stuarts went into action for the first time, November 19, 1941. The 3rd and 5th R.T.R. were also equipped with Stuarts for this battle.
(Imperial War Museum)

Grant squadron of the Royal Tank Regiment in the Desert, May 1942, when this tank first went into action in the Gazala battle.
(Imperial War Museum)

Cromwell chassis was projected in three designs, two by Rolls-Royce (the A31 and A32), the third (A33) by English Electric. The A31 was simply an up-armoured Cromwell, the A32 was up-armoured to Churchill standard and had stronger suspension to carry the extra 4·5 tons. Neither design was taken up. The A33, on the other hand, weighing 45 tons with 114 mm. maximum armour (20 mm. minimum) progressed to pilot model stage. But the A33 was overtaken by events. The Churchill proved itself in Tunisia and Italy and remained in production, and with the Comet narrowing the gap between cruiser and "I" tank the A33 had nothing outstanding to offer that would warrant a production order.

One man who disagreed strongly with Montgomery's views about a single type of tank was Lieutenant-General Sir Giffard Le Q. Martel, until early in 1943 the Commander of the Royal Armoured Corps. "It was quite impossible at that time to build a tank to fill this dual rôle," he wrote in his autobiography in 1949. "We all agreed that a really good cruiser tank with a good gun and reasonably heavy armour was an essential necessity for the mobile operations which we would have to carry out in France and Germany in 1944–45, but in addition we were convinced that we needed a limited number of far heavier tanks to force

our way through the defences against the Tigers and Panthers which we knew we would meet in the initial stages in France. I had always pressed for this and it would have been quite possible to construct a limited number of these heavy tanks." (*An Outspoken Soldier,* Sifton Praed & Co., 1949, p. 273).

The heavy tank in question was the Tortoise (A39). It was designed by Nuffield Mechanisations and Aero Ltd. and was strongly backed by Duncan Sandys, then Parliamentary Secretary to the Minister of Supply. It had a crew of seven, weighed 78 tons with 225 mm. maximum armour and 35 mm. minimum, was 10 ft. high, 12 ft. 10 in. wide, and 33 ft. long including its gun which was in a limited traverse mount. This gun was a 3·7-in. 32-pdr., the largest gun fitted to any British tank of World War II design. It had a muzzle velocity of 3,050 ft./sec. The secondary armament was three Besa 7·92-mm. machine-guns, two in an independent turret on the roof for AA defence and the third to the left of the 32-pdr. The armour thickness was proof against any known German anti-tank gun. The huge superstructure was cast in one piece.

Work on the Tortoise drifted along without any high priority being given to it (according to Martel, because the C.I.G.S., Sir Alan Brooke, supported Montgomery's views) until the German Royal Tiger

The "world's highest tank" – M3 Medium Lee of the 3rd Carabiniers, C Squadron, on Kennedy Peak (8871 ft.), Chin Hills, Burma, November 1944. (Imperial War Museum)

M3 Medium Lee with infantry clearing a village in Central Burma. (Imperial War Museum)

and Jagd Tiger were met in Normandy, where the British and American tanks were indeed blown off the battlefield by the Tigers and Panthers. Six pilot models were then ordered with the delivery of the first scheduled for August 1945. In fact the pilots were not delivered until 1946-47, by which time they had a curiosity value only. Though the Tortoise's armour and armament would have been a Godsend in many of the Normandy actions the sight of its huge width on the Tank Park of the Royal Armoured Corps Tank Museum at Bovington is striking witness of the transportation problem inherent in its strength.

There was one other assault tank project. This was the T14, built for the British by the Americans. The requirement for this tank was discussed in September 1941 when an American Ordnance Mission was in the U.K. to continue the exchange of views that had begun in June the previous year when a British Tank Mission went to the United States to buy tanks for the British Army. The U.S. Ordnance Department were disposed towards heavy tanks and were currently working on the M6 Heavy. In December they began studies for a tank that would accord with British requirements and would incorporate as many components as possible of the new M4 Medium (the Sherman) while using features from the M6 Heavy. It was designated the T14 Assault Tank. In March 1942 another British Tank Mission arrived in the U.S.A. As part of its procurement work it ordered 8,500 T14s. But only two pilot vehicles were ever completed. One of these was sent to Britain in 1944. By then—as happened in the case of other assault tank and infantry tank developments—interest had shifted to the heavily armed cruiser which would be a multi-purpose tank, and the T14 was dropped without going into production. The T14 weighed 37·5 tons with armour thickness ranging from 19 mm. minimum to 133 mm. maximum. It was 20 ft. 4 in. long, 10 ft. 3 in. wide, and 9 ft. 1 in. high, with tracks that were 25·75 in. wide as on the M6 Heavy. It had horizontal volute spring suspension and was powered by a Ford GAZ V-8 gasoline engine of 520 b.h.p., which gave it a maximum speed of 22 m.p.h. Its main armament was a 75-mm. M3 gun, but provision was made for mounting a 76-mm. or 105-mm. gun instead. Secondary armament was a ·50 Browning machine-gun for AA defence, and two ·30 Brownings, one in the hull front, the other co-axial.

Thus, in the long run, heavy tanks got nowhere in British service during World War II. Nor were they much more successful in American service: the U.S. Ordnance Department fought what was in the main a losing battle against Army Ground Forces' reluctance to take into service tanks with thicker armour and heavier guns. Who was right? The battlefields of Europe gave the hard answer.

THE AMERICAN TANK ARSENAL

Though the T14 was an abortive exercise in British procurement of tanks from the United States it was the exception that proved the rule. And the rule was that from 1941 onwards the British and Commonwealth armoured forces depended heavily for their tanks on the huge output of the United States. This is not to say that British tank production fell away. For the first nine months of the war, from September 1939 until the end of May 1940, the average monthly rate of

Challenger turret with 17-pdr. mounted on TOG 2 tank, which is preserved at the R.A.C. Tank Museum, Bovington Camp, Dorset. TOG 2 was the first British tank to be armed with this gun – though for experimental purposes only. (Duncan Crow)

British tank output was 82. During the last quarter of 1940 it rose to 150. A year later, during the last quarter of 1941, it was 626. And it continued to rise the following year.

An average monthly production rate of 626 is equivalent to producing enough tanks to equip more than three armoured brigades or three tank brigades a month, allowing that the tanks were of the right type for the formation concerned. British tank production during the six years of war totalled about 27,000, slightly more than Germany produced. But American tank production was far greater than British and German production combined. From a total annual

Grant of The Governor General's Horse Guards, 5th Canadian Armoured Division. Until sufficient Rams were available Grants and Lees made up the numbers in Canadian armoured regiments. In Canadian service the M3 Mediums had a number of modifications including jettisonable fuel tanks and mud chutes above the bogies, as shown here. (Canadian Official)

Sherman and one of its opponents. On the left a Tiger tank captured intact by 22 Battalion of 2nd New Zealand Division at La Romola south of Florence, Italy, in July 1944, dwarfing a Sherman of the 4th New Zealand Armoured Brigade.
(New Zealand Official)

Sherman of the 13th/18th Royal Hussars (Queen Mary's Own), 8th Armoured Brigade, beside the River Waal near Nijmegen, Holland, in October 1944. (Imperial War Museum)

production of some 4,000 tanks in 1941, American tank output rose to an average monthly rate of 2,083 in 1942 and 2,458 in 1943 when it was at its peak. In total during the five years 1941-45 the United States produced 88,000 tanks.

STUART/HONEY

The first American tank in service with the British was the M2A4 Light which was used for training only. The first American tanks to go into action with British crews were the M3 Lights, called by the British, Stuarts or "Honeys".

In August 1941 the 8th King's Royal Irish Hussars of 4th Armoured Brigade, 7th Armoured Division, received the first M3 Lights, 84 of which had arrived in Egypt in the first Lease-Lend shipment in July. A total of 280 out of the 538 produced in the United States in April, May and June 1941 were in fact shipped to Suez and Massawa.

By the end of August the 8th Hussars had 36 Stuarts and on October 1 they paraded at full strength with their new tanks. The regimental history notes with implicit astonishment that "they arrived complete even to the wireless, and it was decided to name each after a famous race-horse." The other armoured units in 4th Armoured Brigade, the 3rd R.T.R. and 5th R.T.R., were also equipped with Stuarts.

Other Stuarts were issued to units in the U.K. and some were brought out to Egypt by the 1st Armoured Division. The 9th Lancers of 2nd Armoured Brigade who sailed for the Middle East at the end of September 1941 took with them seven Crusaders and 17 Stuarts, the balance of 28 AFVs to be delivered to them when they arrived.

When the 9th Lancers received their Stuarts they were dismayed. But "it must be owned," records the regimental history, "that we did the M3 (or 'Honey' as it came to be known) a great injustice. It was old-fashioned and uncomfortable, the spluttering of its rotary engine filled the hearer with apprehension, but the little tank hardly ever broke down and later performed miracles of endurance. Its 37-mm. gun was no worse then the Crusader's 2-pdr., though, by German standards, both were inadequate." This was being sadly and abundantly proved in the Western Desert at the very time that the 9th Lancers were steaming up the Red Sea. Operation "Crusader" to relieve Tobruk began on November 18 and the following day at Sidi Rezegh came the first action of the Honeys. They had to take on Panzer IIIs with 50-mm. guns and Panzer IVs with 75-mm. guns. They were severely mauled. The 8th Hussars were reduced to a single squadron as a result of casualties.

Stuarts of all Marks were used as gun tanks for the rest of the North African campaign, though on a declining scale as the M3 and M4 Mediums (Grants and Shermans) became available. Stuarts were also used extensively as gun tanks in Burma. In the other theatres after 1943 they were only used as gun tanks by armoured recce regiments of armoured divisions. With their turrets removed, however, they equipped the recce troops of armoured regiments ("a tremendous improvement on the Daimler Scout car" comments the 9th Lancers' History), and were also used for reconnaissance by infantry units.

The British Mark designations for Stuarts and the U.S. equivalent designations, with the year in which the tank first appeared, were:

Year	U.S. Service Designation	Engine	British Designation	Remarks
1940	M2A4 Light Tank	Continental	Some used; loosely call "Stuart"	Introduced 37-mm. gun in M1–M5 Light Tank series
1941	M3 Light Tank	Continental	Stuart I	Improved M2A4 with trailing idler from earlier M2 Combat Car (M1A1 Light Tank)
1941	M3 (Diesel)	Guiberson	Stuart II	Sometimes called Stuart Hybrid
1942	M3A1 Light Tank	Continental	Stuart III	Improved version of M3
1942	M3A1 (Diesel)	Guiberson	Stuart IV	Sometimes called Stuart Hybrid, as other tank with diesel motor
1942	M3A3 Light Tank	Continental	Stuart V	Improved hull shape
1942	M5 Light Tank	Twin-Cadillac	Stuart VI	Modified hull shape (originally M4, but changed to avoid possible confusion with M4 Medium Tank)
1942	M5A1 Light Tank	Twin-Cadillac	Stuart VI	Improved turret

The M3s weighed 12 tons, the M5s 14·75 tons. Armour thicknesses were: M3—10 mm. minimum, 51 mm. maximum, M5—12 mm. minimum, 67 mm. maximum.

Commonwealth Armies

Stuarts as gun tanks were used in action by Australian forces in the Middle East (by divisional cavalry regiments) and in New Guinea (by armoured regiments). The 31st Indian Armoured Division in Iraq and Persia was equipped with Stuarts until these were later replaced by Shermans; and Indian mechanized cavalry regiments used Stuarts in action in Burma. Stuarts were supplied to the New Zealand Army and used in action in the Middle East (by the divisional cavalry regiment) as well as for home defence.

LEE/GRANT

The second American tank to go into service with the British was the M3 Medium, which they called the Grant or the Lee, depending upon which version it was: The Grant had a turret specially built for British requirements so that it would take the wireless instead of having it in the hull as was the American practice at that time; the Lee was the standard American version of the M3, including the prominent machine-gun cupola which was absent on the Grant's re-designed turret.

British designations for the M3 Medium series and the basic characteristics of each Mark were:

U.S. Service Designation	British Designation	Characteristics
M3	Lee Mk. I	Wright R975 (Continental) engine and all-riveted construction
M3 (Diesel)	Lee Mk. I	Guiberson diesel engine
M3A1	Lee Mk. II	Identical mechanically to M3, but with cast hull
M3A1 (Diesel)	Lee Mk. II	Identical mechanically to M3 (Diesel), but with cast hull
M3A2	Lee Mk. III	Similar to M3, but with welded instead of riveted hull. None were delivered to the British
M3A3	Lee Mk. IV	Welded and with Continental R975
M3A3	Lee Mk. V	M3A3 with twin General Motors 6–71 diesel engines
M3A4	Lee Mk. VI	Similar to M3 but with the Chrysler A–57 Multibank engine
M3A5	Grant Mk. II	As M3A3 but with riveted instead of welded hull. Original U.S. type turret

The Grant Mark I was the M3 with special turret to meet British requirements—distinguished from other variants by the lack of a cupola. M3, M3A1 and M3A2 weighed 27 tons, M3A3 28 tons and M3A4 and M3A5 28·5 tons. Armour thicknesses were: 12 mm. minimum, 37 mm. maximum.

The Grants began to be sent from the United States to the British Eighth Army in the Western Desert early in 1942. By this time Operation "Crusader" was over, having driven Rommel back to Agedabia. Attempts to advance further were repulsed and on January 21 Rommel launched a counter-offensive which forced the Eighth Army to withdraw to the Gazala line.

The Grants at Gazala

After a lull of three and a half months a new and almost decisive battle opened in the Western Desert on May 26, 1942. Rommel's forces feinted against the

Sherman Crab Mark I south of Caen on its way to take part in Operation "Tractable", the drive for Falaise, Normandy, August 1944. The Crab Mark II had a hydraulic cylinder on the right hand side only. (Canadian Official)

northern part of the Gazala line and then, under cover of darkness, the Axis armour drove south and rounded the southern end of the line beyond Bir Hacheim. Their initial progress was spotted and reported by British aircraft but the reports were misinterpreted by Eighth Army command.

Rommel's plan was for his armoured divisions (the Trieste, the Ariete, the 21st Panzer, and the 15th Panzer) to drive up north behind the British line destroying the dispersed British armoured formations one by one, while 90th Light Division was to bear north-east towards the British rear areas and there, in best blitzkrieg fashion, attack command centres and capture supply dumps.

The Trieste division strayed into a minefield and the Ariete was unable to keep up with the Panzers, but the Panzers themselves were round Bir Hacheim and driving north by first light on May 27. They destroyed 3rd Indian Motor Brigade, drove off 7th Motor Brigade, overran 7th Armoured Division HQ, and caught the 8th Hussars of 4th Armoured Brigade before the regiment had had time to deploy. Then, unexpectedly, there was a check. The other armoured regiments in 4th Armoured Brigade were the 3rd and the 5th R.T.R. The 3rd R.T.R. had just had time to deploy when it ran into the path of 15th Panzer Division; the 5th, some four miles to the north, were just moving off from leaguer when they became engaged with 21st Panzer Division driving past their flank.

The battle between the 3rd R.T.R. and 15th Panzer Division was not as one-sided as might have been expected, because two squadrons of the 3rd R.T.R. were equipped with the Eighth Army's new "secret weapon" —the Grant. In an epic fight the 3rd R.T.R. (under "Pip" Roberts who was later to command 11th Armoured Division) held up the advance, to the amazement of the Germans. Instead of meeting Stuarts or Crusaders they found to their dismay that they were under fire from British-manned tanks at a range too great for retaliation.

But the British too were at a disadvantage because the Grant, with its main armament in the hull-front, could not be fought from a hull-down position. Furthermore the sponson mounting of this 75-mm. gun gave only a limited traverse. Nevertheless the Grants inflicted heavy casualties before the Germans

Sherman V (Guards) of 1st (Armoured) Battalion Coldstream Guards, Guards Armoured Division, fitted with Typhoon aircraft rocket projectors on the sides of the turret.

Sherman Fireflies. Apart from the nearest tank almost all the others in view are Fireflies armed with the 17-pdr. gun. The occasion for this line-up was the Guards Armoured Division's last mounted parade on June 9, 1945, when they said "Farewell to Armour." The tanks were painted in shiny battleship grey, with white hatches, black knobs, red tow-ropes, and gaily striped aerials. (Major G. B. Mackean)

eventually dislodged the isolated 3rd R.T.R. "The advent of the new American tank had torn great holes in our ranks," Rommel wrote ruefully in his journal. "Our entire force now stood in heavy and destructive combat with a superior enemy."

While the remnants of 4th Armoured Brigade withdrew eastwards the Panzers pressed on and successfully engaged 22nd Armoured Brigade of 1st Armoured Division before being counter-attacked by 2nd Armoured Brigade (also of 1st Armoured Division) and then by 1st Army Tank Brigade which between them destroyed many German tanks.

By May 29 Rommel's armour was in a parlous position and even he admitted to being uneasy. But in the end he was let off the hook and by the beginning of July the Eighth Army found itself pushed back to El Alamein.

Sherman OP of Eighth Army in Italy, July 1944. Note extra aerials and cable reels. (Imperial War Museum)

Both sides started the Gazala battle with a new asset: the Germans had the Panzer III (J) Special mounting a long 50-mm. gun; the British had the Grant. Quantitatively the advantage of these new assets was all on the side of the British. There were only 19 Panzer III (J) Specials in the Panzer Divisions and a further 19 in Tripoli; but there were 167 Grants in the Eighth Army and another 250 in reserve in Egypt.

The 167 Grants were allotted to 4th Armoured Brigade of 7th Armoured Division on the scale of two squadrons of Grants to one of Stuarts, and to the regiments of 1st Armoured Division roughly on the scale of one Grant squadron to two Crusader squadrons. Throughout the Gazala battle, at Knightsbridge and in The Cauldron, the Grants played a leading part and in the withdrawal to Alamein they staved off more than one disaster, especially on July 3 when Rommel with his last 26 tanks made a final attempt to break through the fragile line forming at Alamein and to drive through to Alexandria. Indeed the Grant acquired the nickname of "ELH", or "Egypt's Last Hope."

First to Second Alamein

On July 3 all available Grants were in 1st Armoured Division which had about 100 tanks in all, 38 of them Grants. By July 16, 1st Armoured Division had 170 tanks of which 60 were Grants. During August British tank strength rose to 935 of which 194 were Grants. Of these, 713 (including 164 Grants) were immediately available to the Eighth Army. More than half of the Grants were in 22nd Armoured Brigade which had now come under command of 10th Armoured Division.

For the battle of Alam Halfa, which lasted from August 31 to September 7, British armour consisted of 10th Armoured Division with two armoured brigades —the 8th and the 22nd, and a third (23rd Armoured Brigade) in Army reserve; and the 7th Armoured Division giving mobile cover on the southern flank. The 164 Grants were in 8th Armoured Brigade (72 Grants out of 84 tanks in three regiments) and 22nd

Armoured Brigade (92 Grants out of 166 tanks in four regiments).

Between Alam Halfa and Second Alamein, which started on October 23, the number of tanks in Eighth Army rose to 1,441 of which 210 were Grants and 270 were the newly-arrived Shermans. It was at Second Alamein that the Sherman first went into action and gradually thereafter as the Eighth Army advanced into Tunisia the Shermans replaced the Grants. So the main fighting period of the Grants in the Western Desert was the five months from the end of May to the end of October 1942.

Lee/Grants in Burma

The other theatre of war in which the Lee/Grants played a crucial part was Burma. While the M3 Medium was being declared obsolete by the American Army in April 1944 one regiment equipped with Lee/Grants was fighting in the Arakan and another at Imphal. This latter regiment was the 3rd Carabiniers (Prince of Wales's Dragoon Guards), part of 254th Indian Tank Brigade, which also had the Indian 7th Cavalry mounted in Stuarts. The "Carbs" arrived at Imphal in December 1943, first went into action in March 1944, and from then until their arrival in Rangoon on May 28, 1945 fought their way in their Lee/Grants for 1,100 miles "with battles all the way and over ground at which," says the regimental history, "the imagination boggles." Included in this

Locust (M22 Light Tank) with Littlejohn Muzzle Adapter fitted by the British.

journey, after the capture of Tiddim, was the ascent of Kennedy Peak by tanks of C Squadron. At nearly 9,000 feet Kennedy Peak is the highest point in the Chin hills, and it was the highest ever reached by tanks up to that time (November 4, 1944).

Grant C.D.L. Tanks

The use of a searchlight in an armoured housing mounted on a tank to dazzle and blind the enemy was suggested during the First World War by Captain de Thoren. Major Martel carried out a trial on Salisbury

Bishop – officially "Carrier, Valentine, 25-pdr. gun Mk. I" – in Tunisia, May 1943. The gun was mounted in a simple armoured box structure with its ammunition carried in a towed limber. (Imperial War Museum)

299

Archer – "S.P. 17-pdr. Valentine" – with its rearward facing gun, driving on to a raft to cross the Rhine, March 1945.
(Major-General N. W. Duncan)

Plain in 1927 when he was commanding the mechanized Field Company R.E. in the Experimental Mechanized Force. In 1933 a syndicate was formed under Mr. Miczakis to develop the idea. Advice was taken from Major-General J. F. C. Fuller and from the Duke of Westminster, of armoured car fame. The rights of the Thoren light were acquired and the apparatus was sold to the War Office in 1937, eventually appearing for service use under the name, adopted to maintain secrecy, of C.D.L. (standing for Canal Defence Light).

The first C.D.L. tanks were Matildas and enough were constructed to equip two army tank brigades—the 35th in the U.K. and the 1st in the Middle East. The disadvantage of the Matilda C.D.L. was that it was unarmed because the original turret had to be replaced by the special C.D.L. turret which contained the light and no gun. When Shermans had replaced Grants in the Eighth Army by early in 1943 it was decided to re-equip the 1st Tank Brigade with some of the spare Grants converted to the C.D.L. rôle. These had the advantage over the Matildas of retaining their 75-mm. gun in the sponson and of thus being able to take offensive action. They also had a machine-

Priest – "105-mm. S. P. Priest" – was the American M7, which had an M3 Medium chassis. Priests were Eighth Army equipment from Second Alamein to the end of the Italian campaign and some were initially used in Normandy by British armoured divisions. This vehicle is seen in Sicily in July 1943.

gun mounted in the front of the armoured searchlight housing, and, for camouflage purposes, later conversions had a dummy 37-mm. gun as well.

The 1st Tank Brigade returned to the U.K. in 1944 to take part in the forthcoming operations in North-West Europe and replaced 35th Tank Brigade which was disbanded. In the event, however, only a few C.D.L. tanks were used during the crossings of the Rhine and the Elbe in 1945, and the brigade was never used in action on the scale for which it had trained. One occasion did arise in Normandy, when it was decided to use it in the Canadian attack south of Caen, but it proved impossible to move the brigade up in time to take part. Other Grant C.D.L. tanks, of 43rd R.T.R., were sent east in 1945 to take part in the invasion of Malaya, but were never used.

Other Grant Special Purpose Types

The British converted Grants for mine clearing, using the Scorpion flailing device also mounted on the Matilda and the Valentine. There were two Scorpions used on the Grant—III and IV. Scorpion III was produced at the start of the Eighth Army's Tunisian campaign in January 1943 to provide a faster flailing tank than the Matilda. Scorpion IV was an improved version of III, having a second Bedford engine at the left rear to give more powerful rotor-drive.

Grants were also converted to armoured recovery vehicles, and a few Grants were fitted as command tanks with extra radio equipment and with the 37-mm. gun replaced by a dummy barrel.

Commonwealth Armies

As well as being used in the Burma theatre, as already mentioned, Lee/Grants were extensively used by the Australians for equipping their three armoured divisions in the Commonwealth. Indeed even at the end of the war in 1945 the Grant was the most numerous type of tank in Australian service: 752 Lee/Grants, 409 Matildas, 373 Stuarts, 65 Sentinels, and 51 Churchills. The Australians produced their own special Grant armoured recovery vehicle.

The Canadians, too, used Grants; primarily to make

up tank numbers in their first armoured division until sufficient Rams had been produced.

SHERMAN

In his autobiography, appropriately entitled *An Outspoken Soldier*, Lieut.-General Sir Giffard Martel, wrote that it was as a result of President Roosevelt's intervention that the U.S. Army was persuaded to let the British have a considerable number of Shermans "to tide us over" until the Cromwell was coming off the production lines in quantity. "The Sherman tank was a dual purpose tank and was a very sound and reliable machine, but it was not as good as either the Cromwell or the Churchill for their respective rôles. We were most grateful for the use of these tanks to cover this period and in fact we continued to use some Sherman tanks up to the end of the war."

To say only "some Sherman tanks up to the end of the war" is seriously to under-value the importance of the Sherman in the British and Commonwealth armoured forces. The Sherman in fact, far from being a stop-gap, became the most important tank in British service. From 1943 until the end of the war in 1945 it was more widely used in the British and Commonwealth armies than any British designed or British produced tank. It was chosen as the tank with which to equip the British, Canadian, New Zealand, and South African armoured divisions from 1943 on. Some idea of its dominant use can be gained from counting up the number of armoured regiments in 21 Army Group alone which were equipped with it as against those equipped with Cromwells or Churchills —taking "armoured regiments" to include "armoured reconnaissance regiment" and "tank battalion/ regiment". There were 32 Sherman-equipped regiments at the maximum in 1944 (reduced to a minimum of 25 in 1945), compared with 12 Churchill regiments (including AVREs) and 9 Cromwell regiments, one of which became a Comet regiment as did three Sherman regiments.

This proportion of Shermans was even higher in Italy where there were no Cromwells or Comets (which were issued to 21 Army Group only) and only half the number of Churchill units—and even these had two Sherman troops in each squadron after mid-1944. Shermans were also well represented in Burma and 31st Indian Armoured Division had them as replacements for their earlier Stuarts.

Shermans began to be issued to British Eighth Army armoured regiments early in September 1942. Among the first to receive them were the 9th Lancers of 2nd Armoured Brigade, 1st Armoured Division. Two squadrons were equipped with 16 Shermans each, the third squadron ("A") continued to have Crusaders. The 9th Lancers' tanks were mainly Sherman IIIs (M4A2s) with "two immense General Motors Diesels" which made them faster and easier to maintain than the Lancers' previous tanks. "Their greatest blessing," records the regimental history (p. 108), "was their slowness to catch fire when hit. The Grants had been driven by radial aero engines running on high-octane aviation spirit and they went up in flames in seconds, usually exploding as well." Furthermore, the 75-mm. gun in the turret made hull-down firing positions possible, while "the telescopes were better and the gun was longer and more accurate."

Unfortunately this slowness to catch fire was only relative. It was the general experience that the tank burnt very easily because the ammunition storage was unprotected. Indeed the Shermans burnt so easily that the German anti-tank gunners nicknamed them "Ronsons". "Wet stowage" for ammunition was a design improvement introduced into Shermans in 1944 to try to obviate this weakness, but few "wet stowage" vehicles were made available to the British.

In the matter of the gun, however, there was no doubt about the absolute improvement. The 17th/21st Lancers of 26th Armoured Brigade, 6th Armoured Division, who were re-equipped with Shermans in Tunisia, found that the best feature of their new tanks compared with the Valentines they had fought with up to then was the 75-mm. gun. The elevating gear of the 75-mm. was operated by hand-wheel, thus eliminating human error when shooting at the halt, and for shooting on the move the gun was stabilised in elevation. Apart from the ease with which the Sherman burnt, the 17th/21st's criticisms of the tank were that its cross-country performance was only moderate owing to the short track base and the high silhouette, dictated by the fact that the drive was carried to the front axle.

By the time the Second Battle of Alamein opened on October 23, 1942, some 300 Shermans had arrived in Egypt and 270 of these were with Eighth Army ready for the battle. A large proportion of them were the cast hull, Continental-engined M4A1s. As the advance along the North African littoral continued the balance between Shermans, Grants, Valentines, Stuarts, and Crusaders progressively altered in the Shermans' favour. The switch to Shermans proceeded

Sherman Kangaroo of the 4th Queen's Own Hussars in Italy, 1945.

even more rapidly after the conclusion of the North African campaign as American production reached its zenith and the Mediterranean was opened for shipping. For the Sicilian campaign (Operation "Husky") even the Valentine addicts of the all-R.T.R. 23rd Armoured Brigade were converted to Shermans, and after they had got over their sense of loss at parting with tanks that had travelled "several thousand miles apiece on their own tracks" they welcomed the advantages of their M4A2s.

The Sherman, they found, "was to be cherished above all things for its big gun (75-mm.). It was to be prized also for its speed, its space (almost its comfort) and for its simplicity. There was plenty of room in it for the three men in the turret—commander, gunner and wireless operator—and for the driver and bow-gunner forward in the hull; there was room even, either within or lashed outside, for most of their worldly possessions." (Captain M. A. Ash, *The History of the 23rd Armoured Brigade.*)

The "big gun" on the Sherman was made even bigger with the arrival of the 76-mm. gun in a new turret designed originally for the T23 Medium tank. Compared with the 75-mm. M3 gun which had a length of 40 calibres (the 75-mm. M2 mounted in the Grant was 31 calibres long), the 76-mm. had a length of 50 calibres. The 9th Lancers, who were issued with 76-mm. gun tanks at Ortona, Italy, in July 1944 found the new tank "an impressive weapon with its gun protruding several feet in front of the tank. The turret was larger and incorporated all-round vision slits in the commander's cupola. The guns were targeted on

the 25th of July. Tests showed that the recoil action damaged the end of the deflector guard and might even break the wireless set, but the guard was strengthened and the trouble stopped."

British units also received Shermans mounting the 105-mm. M4 howitzer for close support.

Sherman Firefly

The biggest gun fitted to the Sherman was the British 17-pdr., a 76-mm. calibre gun with a length of 60 calibres and a muzzle velocity of 2,980 ft./sec.* This was a British adaptation and was not adopted for service by the U.S. Army. In order to fit it into the turret the gun was mounted on its side and adapted for left-hand loading. Various modifications had to be made to the turret including the welding of an armoured box to its outside rear to house the wireless set. When armed with the 17-pdr. the tank was called the Sherman Firefly.

The pilot Firefly conversion was ready in November 1943. This was done as an insurance against the failure of the Challenger programme to come up to expectations, the Challenger, which was the first tank to mount the 17-pdr., having revealed shortcomings in its trials. Firefly conversions went ahead as rapidly as possible from February 1944 onwards. Because of

* Comparative muzzle velocities were: British 2-pdr. 2,600, 6-pdr. Mk. II 2,340, 75-mm. 2,050, 77-mm. 2,575, U.S. 37-mm. 2,600-2,900, 75-mm. M2 1,850, 75-mm. M3 2,050, 76-mm. 2,600, 90-mm. 2,700, German 3·7-cm. 2,445, 5-cm. L/42 2,247, 5-cm. L/60 2,700, 7·5-cm. L/24 1,263, 7·5-cm. L/43 2,428, 7·5-cm. L/48 2,461, 7·5-cm. L/70 3,068, 8·8-cm. L/56 2,657, 8·8-cm. L/71 3,340.

M10 – "3-in. S.P. Wolverine" – of 5 Corps, Eighth Army crossing the River Savio, Italy, on a causeway of Churchill ARKs. (Imperial War Museum)

Sexton – "25-pdr. S.P. Tracked" – self-propelled gun crossing a "two-storey" Churchill ARK II (Italian pattern) bridge near the bank of the River Senio, Italy, April 1945. (Imperial War Museum)

Humber Scout Car.   (The Eleventh at War)

Fantail ferrying men of 56th Division across the River Po, Italy, on April 26, 1945. The division was supported by 12th RTR and 48th RTR of 21st Tank Brigade.
(The Seventh and Three Enemies)

the shortage of 17-pdrs. available for fitting to tanks there were only sufficient Fireflies by the time of the Normandy landings in June 1944 for them to be issued on the scale of one per troop. Later this scale increased considerably. Altogether about 600 Fireflies were produced, compared with 200 Challengers.

The Sherman (M4 Medium) Series

British designations for the M4 Medium series and the basic characteristics of each Mark were:

U.S. Service Designation	British Designation	Characteristics
M4	Sherman I	Welded hull, Continental engine
M4 (late production)	Hybrid I	Combination cast/rolled hull front
M4A1	Sherman II	Cast hull, Continental engine
M4A2	Sherman III	Welded hull, General Motors 6046 diesel engine
M4A3	Sherman IV	Welded hull, Ford GAA engine
M4A4	Sherman V	Lengthened rear hull to accommodate Chrysler Multibank engine
M4A6	Sherman VII	Lengthened rear hull to accommodate Caterpillar D-200A (Ordnance designation RD-1820) diesel engine

NOTE: There was no M4A5 as such; the designation was a "paper" one for the Ram which was developed and built in Canada.

To the basic designations the British added suffixes to differentiate between the various main armaments carried: A=76-mm. gun, B=105-mm. howitzer, C=17-pdr. gun. Absence of suffix A, B, or C meant that the tank mounted a 75-mm. gun. A further suffix Y was added if the tank had horizontal volute spring

suspension and wide track. Thus, for example, Sherman IIIAY was M4A2 with 76-mm. gun and HVSS with 23-inch wide track; Sherman VC was M4A4 with 17-pdr. gun, a Firefly. There was also a variant called Sherman V (Guards) which was M4A4 fitted with Typhoon aircraft rocket projectors on the turret as well as having its main armament. This was an addition made in the Guards Armoured Division.

The M4 and M4A1 weighed about 29·5 tons, M4A2 and M4A3 about 30 tons, and M4A4 and M4A6 31·25 tons. Armour thicknesses were: 12 mm. minimum, 75 mm. maximum (turret), 50 mm. (hull).

The major type of the M4 series supplied to British and Commonwealth forces was the M4A4—the Sherman V. More than 1,600 were supplied to the Eighth Army in Italy in 1943 alone. The second most numerous type was the M4A2, then the M4, the M4A1, and finally the M4A3 of which very few were supplied because this type was mainly used by the U.S. Army.

Sherman Specials

As well as their dominant importance as gun tanks in British armoured formations in the later stages of World War II the Shermans also played a key rôle in the "funnies" of 79th Armoured Division in North-West Europe and of 25th Armoured Engineer Brigade in Italy. The Sherman and the Churchill were the two tanks used for the special purpose equipment of those formations. The main uses of the Sherman were as a D.D. swimming tank and as the

M10A1 with 3-in. gun replaced by a 17-pdr. became "17-pdr. S.P. Achilles Mk. IIC." The M10 similarly converted was the Achilles Mk. IC. The gun in this photograph (not shown at full length) is at maximum elevation.

Marmon-Herrington armoured cars of The King's Dragoon Guards in the Desert near Tobruk, November 1941.
(History of the K.D.G.s)

Universal Carrier Mark II with Stacey towing attachment – standard on Mk. IIs – towing a 6-pdr. anti-tank gun near Geilenkirchen, north of Aachen, Germany, November 1944. The Universal Carrier was the most ubiquitous tracked vehicle in the British and Commonwealth armies. It was used in a variety of roles. (Imperial War Museum)

mine clearing Crab. The Sherman Crab, which was developed from the Scorpion, became the standard British mine clearing vehicle. The whole of 30th Armoured Brigade in 79th Armoured Division was equipped with these flail tanks which retained their main armament so that they could act as normal gun tanks when required.

Shermans were also used operationally as recovery vehicles, for anti-mine explosive devices, and for bridging devices, the latter in Italy only. Also unique to the Eighth Army in Italy was the Sherman Kangaroo, an armoured personnel carrier that copied the idea of the Ram Kangaroo used in 79th Armoured Division. Turrets were also removed from Shermans to make fascine carriers. Another British conversion was the Sherman OP for use as a command tank or as an armoured OP. As with the Grant command tank the main armament was replaced by a dummy gun barrel.

Commonwealth Armies

The 1st and 5th Canadian Armoured Brigades in Italy were equipped with Shermans as were the 2nd and 4th Canadian Armoured Brigades in 21 Army

Daimler armoured car of the 11th Hussars with Littlejohn Adapter for increasing the muzzle velocity of the 2-pdr. gun. (The Eleventh at War)

Group. The 4th New Zealand Armoured Brigade of 2nd New Zealand Division and the 11th South African Armoured Brigade of 6th South African Armoured Division in Italy were Sherman-equipped. So too was the 252nd Indian Armoured Brigade (of 31st Indian Armoured Division), as well as a number of armoured units in Burma including Probyn's Horse, the Royal Deccan Horse, the 19th K.G.O. Lancers, and the 116th Regiment (Gordon Highlanders) R.A.C. which, it so happened, was the last regiment of the Royal Armoured Corps to come out of action when the war ended—and, it may be added, the British unit fighting furthest away from home at the time. Thus it was a Sherman that was the last British-crewed tank in action in World War II.

LOCUST AND CHAFFEE

Two other American tanks were used by British forces, both of them classified as light tanks though the second of them, the Chaffee, was equivalent to the early British cruisers in weight and superior to them in armament.

The M22 Light, called by the British the Locust, was designed as an airborne tank. In appearance it was rather like a miniature Sherman. Weighing just over 7 tons, with armour thickness from 9 mm. minimum to 25 mm. maximum, it was armed with a 37-mm. gun and a coaxial ·30 Browning machine-gun. Altogether 830 were built, between April 1943 and February 1944, and of these several hundred were sent to Britain for use by U.S. and British forces. But none were used in action by the Americans and only a handful by the British. Those that were, were carried in Hamilcar gliders in the Rhine crossing operations of the British 6th Airborne Division in XVIII U.S. Airborne Corps on March 24, 1945. Some Tetrarchs were also used.

One of the Locusts received by the British was modified by having a Littlejohn Adapter fitted to

Humber armoured car of the 11th Hussars in Tunisia.
(The Eleventh at War)

increase muzzle velocity of its main armament.

The Chaffee (with armour thickness the same as the Locust) replaced the Stuart/Honey in some British units at the end of the war. Its American designation was M24 Light Tank, but it weighed just over 17·5 tons (the Covenanter, for example, weighed 18 tons) and it had a 75-mm. gun as its main armament. This gun was basically the same as the cannon fitted in the Mitchell bomber; it weighed only half as much as the earlier 75-mms. used in the Lee and Sherman and yet it had exactly the same performance. The coaxial and hull machine-guns were ·30 Brownings.

SELF-PROPELLED WEAPONS

Of the five self-propelled weapons mainly used by British and Commonwealth forces in World War II two were British, two American, and one Canadian. The British SPs were both on Valentine chassis. The first of these, on a Valentine II chassis, mounted a 25-pdr. gun with all round traverse. Officially designated "Carrier, Valentine, 25-pdr. gun Mk. I," it was known as the Bishop. It was produced in response to an urgent request from Eighth Army HQ for equipment similar to that which was being so effectively used by the Afrika Korps. Bishops were used in action in North Africa from mid-1942 through to the end of the campaign in Tunisia in May 1943. They were then used in the Sicilian campaign two months later.

The second British-designed SP weapon was the

Archer ("S.P. 17-pdr., Valentine"). This mounted a rearward facing 17-pdr. gun with limited traverse in an open topped superstructure over the fighting compartment of a Valentine. The first production model was completed in March 1944 and Archers, of which 665 were built compared with 100 Bishops, equipped anti-tank regiments of British armoured divisions in North-West Europe from October 1944 and in Italy in 1945. The Archer remained in service for some time after the war.

Of the two American designed weapons the first was the M7, called by the British the Priest because of its "pulpit" with ·5-in. Browning for anti-aircraft defence. Officially designated "105-mm. SP, Priest", in British service, the M7 had an M3 Medium tank chassis. The first 90 of a large order placed by the British Tank Mission in the United States arrived in Egypt in September 1942 in time to take part in the Second Battle of Alamein which was the M7's baptism of fire. Hundreds more were later delivered. The Priests supplemented and soon replaced the British-designed Bishops as the main Eighth Army SP weapon; they remained in service throughout the Italian campaign. Priests also equipped some artillery regiments in British armoured divisions in the Normandy landings but were withdrawn in favour of Sextons early in the campaign. The redundant Priests were converted into armoured personnel carriers by the removal of their 105-mm. howitzers and used in the First Canadian Army attack south of Caen in August 1944. These "Unfrocked Priests", or Priest Kangaroos, were replaced in 21 Army Group by Ram Kangaroos which equipped two APC regiments. The Kangaroo idea was taken up by the Eighth Army in Italy where both converted Priests and Shermans were used in the APC rôle.

The Sexton, officially designated "25-pdr. SP, Tracked", was the Canadian self-propelled weapon. It had a Ram (i.e. M3 Medium) chassis and mounted a 25-pdr. and was thus virtually the M7 anglicized. Production continued from early 1943 until the end of 1945 during which time 2,150 were built. Over this period modifications were made so that the Sexton which started with the equivalent of the M3 Medium

Prototype Armoured Car, A.E.C., Mark I. This differed from the production vehicles principally in having a direct vision port for the driver in addition to a single periscope. (A.E.C. Ltd.)

Yugoslav Partisans with A.E.C. Mark II armoured cars supplied to them by Britain in 1944. The Mark II had a three-man turret with 6-pdr. gun and co-axial Besa machine-gun.
(Imperial War Museum)

Daimler scout car Mark II. This mark had front-wheel steering only. (Imperial War Museum)

Armoured Car, Coventry Mark II, which had a 75mm gun instead of a 2-pdr. as in the Mark I. (Imperial War Museum)

chassis ended up with one similar to the M4 Medium. (The M7, too, was given the improved chassis of the M4 Medium, becoming the M7B1 and M7B2, neither of which was used in British service). Sextons were in widespread use in British and Canadian divisions in 21 Army Group, their replacement of Priests being carried out in order to make more 105-mm. ammunition available to the American sector of the invasion force and to standardize ammunition in the British and Canadian sector. The Sexton remained in service until the late 1950s.

The second American SP gun was the M10 and M10A1. Both mounted a 3-inch gun, the M10 on an adapted diesel-engined M4A2 Medium chassis, the M10A1 on a Ford-engined M4A3 chassis. In British service they were designated "3-in. SP, Wolverine." M10s replaced towed 17-pdrs. in some batteries of anti-tank regiments. Thus, for example, 75th Anti-Tank Regiment of 11th Armoured Division had two batteries of M10s and two of towed 17-pdrs. in North-West Europe in 1944–45. From late 1944 most Wolverines were converted to Achilles by the replacement of the 3-inch gun with a British 17-pdr. M10s thus converted were designated "17-pdr. SP, Achilles Mk. IC", M10A1s became Achilles Mk. IIC. Some vehicles were converted to gun towers by the removal of the open-topped turret. Achilles remained in British service for many years after the war.

CARRIERS, BUFFALOES AND FANTAILS

The most ubiquitous tracked vehicle in the British and Commonwealth armies was the Universal Carrier of which 33,987 were built in Canada alone, this number supplying more than one fifth of Britain's carrier needs. The majority of carriers were built in the U.K., but there was also substantial production in Australia and New Zealand (about a third of the Canadian output), and a large number of carrier engines were built in the United States. Some carriers were made in India at Tatanagar.

For amphibious work there was the Terrapin, which was the British equivalent of the American DUKW, and the American Landing Vehicle Tracked. British and Commonwealth forces used two marks of LVT which they called Buffalo Mk. II (U.S. LVT (A) 2) and Buffalo Mk. IV (U.S. LVT 4) in the North-West Europe campaign and Fantail in Italy. Armament fitted to these vehicles were two Brownings and a 20-mm. Polsten cannon. The 33rd Armoured Brigade in 79th Armoured Division was equipped with Buffaloes

and the Canadians became masters of the art of amphibious fighting in the polders battles of the Scheldt estuary in October–November 1944. In Italy there were two Fantail units under control of 9th Armoured Brigade.

ARMOURED CARS

British and Commonwealth forces were far less dependent on the American arsenal for armoured cars than they were for tanks—not surprisingly, perhaps, because armoured cars have never been as popular in the United States as they have been in many other countries. Britain built some 9,000 armoured cars, 11,000 scout cars, and 8,750 light reconnaissance cars; South Africa built 5,746 Marmon-Herrington armoured cars; Canada built some 200 armoured cars, 3,255 scout cars, and 1,761 light reconnaissance cars; a grand total of approximately 40,000 vehicles.

The armoured cars used in action by British regiments in the early stages of World War II were the Morris CS9/LAC (used by the 12th Lancers in France 1939–40 and by the 11th Hussars in the Western Desert and Cyrenaica until 1941), the Guy (six used by Phantom in France 1939–40), and the 1924 pattern Rolls-Royce with open-topped turret and faceted armour (used by the 11th Hussars until 1941). The first Indian armoured car regiment to go overseas on active service, the 13th D.C.O. Lancers of 31st Indian Armoured Division, went to Iraq in 1941 with Chevrolets. These had pre-war Crossley armoured

A.E.C. Mark I armoured cars of The Royal Dragoons near Enfidaville Tunisia. The Mark I had a Valentine tank turret with 2-pdr. gun and co-axial Besa machine-gun.
(Major K. G. Balfour, M.C.)

Staghound Mark I (U.S. designation Armoured Car T17E1). A jettisonable fuel tank fitted on to the hull side above the stowage box. Armament was a 37mm gun and co-axial .30 MG in the turret, a .30 MG in the right hull front, and a pintle for a third .30 MG on the turret roof. (History of The K.D.G.s)

Greyhound (U.S. designation Light Armoured Car M8) in British service. The Greyhound had a "magnificent cross-country performance." (Imperial War Museum)

bodies on Chevrolet 4 × 2 track chassis, the conversion being made in 1939–40.

The first South African built Marmon-Herringtons to reach the Middle East arrived at the end of 1940 and 20 were issued to the King's Dragoon Guards at Tahag Camp on January 4, 1941, when that regiment began its conversion to armoured cars. A total of 1,180 Marmon-Herringtons were supplied to British and Indian armoured car regiments in the Middle East and India, while 4,566 were delivered to the Union Defence Force and used by South African armoured car units in East Africa and the Middle East.

The next armoured cars to come into battle were the Humber in November 1941 and the Daimler in June 1942. Later in the year came the Humber Mark III and the A.E.C. There were four marks of Humber, two of Daimler, and three of A.E.C. built before the war ended, as well as a few Coventry Marks I and II, which were designed to combine some of the best features of the Humber and Daimler. The first three marks of Humber had a 15-mm. Besa and a co-axial 7·92-mm. Besa; Mark IV had a 37-mm. gun instead of

the 15-mm. Besa. The Daimlers had a 2-pdr. gun and a coaxial 7·92-mm. Besa. The A.E.C. Mark I had a 2-pdr., the Mark II had a 6-pdr., and the Mark III had a 75-mm. gun; in each case there was a co-axial 7·92-mm. Besa. The Coventry Mark II also had a 75-mm. gun with co-axial Besa, while the Mark I had a 2-pdr. instead of the 75-mm. The Canadian-built armoured car, the Fox, was a counterpart of the Humber Mark III, but with Brownings instead of Besas.

Reconnaissance regiments of infantry divisions included armoured cars and light reconnaissance cars in their equipment. By 1944 the armoured cars were generally Humber Mark IVs, although sometimes they were Daimlers. The light reconnaissance car most widely used was the 4-wheel drive Humber Mark III or IIIA.

The American armoured car most used by British and Commonwealth units was the Staghound (U.S. T17E1). It was first received about July 1943, too late to take part in the North African campaign for which it had been intended. The terrain of Italy, which was the next location for action, was less well suited to an

An armoured car troop in the latter part of the war typically consisted of two Daimler armoured cars and two Daimler scout cars. A troop of The Royal Dragoons setting out on patrol to Celle, Germany, April 1945. (Major K. G. Balfour, M.C.)

Armoured White half-track mounting a 75mm gun in British service. Each of the four squadrons of an armoured car regiment had two of these SP 75s. (Major K. G. Balfour, M.C.)

armoured car of some 14 tons—twice as heavy and more unwieldy than the Daimler and Humber which formed the mainstay of the sabre squadrons of the armoured car regiments. However, other qualities of the Staghound—notably its roominess—made it acceptable as a regimental and squadron headquarters car. The crew of five provided a useful reserve of wireless operators and spare drivers in this rôle.

Some regiments were fully equipped with Staghounds, others had them on a scale of three in each of the four squadron headquarters and three in RHQ. The Divisional Cavalry regiment of the 2nd New Zealand Division which was equipped with Staghounds in Italy found them "tough and sturdy but of a somewhat conspicuous silhouette." Staghounds were used in Italy by British, Canadian, Indian, and New Zealand units and by British and Canadian units in 21 Army Group in North-West Europe. The 1st Belgian Independent Armoured Brigade in 21 Army Group also had them.

Included in the Staghounds at squadron headquarters were a proportion of British-converted Staghound IIs with a 3-inch close support howitzer in place of the standard 37-mm. gun. The hull machine-gun and assistant driver's seat were removed to give extra ammunition space, and 4-inch smoke dischargers were fitted to the turret sides instead of the 2-inch bomb thrower on the turret roof. In Staghound III the original turret was replaced by a Crusader turret with a British 75-mm. dual-purpose gun and a co-axial 7·92-mm. Besa. Staghound AA armoured cars (U.S. T17E2) were alternatives to Humber AA armoured cars of which four were on the strength of RHQs. There was also a Staghound Command car which had the turret removed, and a Staghound was used experimentally with Lulu mine-detecting equipment. The Americans developed the T17E3 for the British; this had a 75-mm. howitzer for the close support rôle, but it was never put into production and Staghound II was used instead.

The Greyhound (U.S. Light Armored Car M8), the other main type of U.S. armoured car supplied to Britain, did not reach units on the battle fronts until late in the war. This was a 6-wheeled vehicle (the Staghound had 4 wheels). The 12th Lancers received some in Italy in September 1944 and commented on their "magnificent cross-country performance", also approving of the fact that they could cross the class 9

bridges with which it was planned to replace those blown in coming operations. However, it was at the same time noted that the Greyhound was difficult to reverse (an important feature in a reconnaissance vehicle likely to be the first to encounter opposition) and hard to protect against mines.

Britain also received 30 Boarhounds. These were heavy 8-wheel drive armoured cars (U.S. T18E2) with a 6-pdr. and co-axial ·30 Browning. They were designed for the Desert but, like the Staghound, were too late to take part in that campaign. They were used for trials only. Two other American armoured cars were allocated names by the British but neither came into service. The Deerhound (U.S. T17) was a 6×6 vehicle with a 37-mm. M6 gun and a co-axial ·30 machine-gun. The total production of 250 was offered to the British, rejected by them, and then issued to the U.S. Military Police. The Wolfhound (U.S. Light Armored Car M38) never arrived in Britain, the end of the war and the number of M8 Greyhounds available restricting the output of the Wolfhound to a few pre-production vehicles. But the Wolfhound was not without its importance. Though the United States turned away from armoured cars and back to tanks for reconnaissance tasks the M38 seems undoubtedly to have had a significant influence on Britain's post-war Saladin.

The American wheeled armoured vehicle most widely used by British forces in World War II was the Scout Car, M3A1—the White Scout Car—which was neither a true scout car by British standards nor an armoured car. It was employed extensively in motor battalions of armoured formations from 1941 onwards and in most units of the armoured divisions, variously as an armoured personnel carrier, command vehicle, or armoured ambulance. The White Scout Car was in use right to the end of the war, although latterly tending to be replaced by half-tracked vehicles, also supplied by the United States. These half-tracks were used in armoured car regiments to mount 75-mm. guns, there being two SP 75s in each of the four squadrons, though they were generally employed as a regimental battery.

Finally, a word of tribute must be paid to the American vehicle, unarmoured though it was, without which, one feels on reflection, the Allied armies would hardly have been able to manage at all! The mere mention of its name is enough to conjure up the remembrance of its versatility: salute to the jeep.

Staghound Mark III was a British development which had a Crusader turret mounting a British 75mm dual-purpose gun and a co-axial Besa MG. (Imperial War Museum)

Boarhound (U.S. designation Armoured Car T18E2). This heavy armoured car mounted a 6-pdr. and co-axial .30 Browning. It had 8-wheel drive. (Chris Ellis)

INDEX *(References are to text and captions)*

1. BRITISH AFV's   2. BRITISH AND COMMONWEALTH ARMIES   3. GENERAL

1. AFVs INDEX

(Armoured Cars, Self-Propelled
Weapons, Tanks and Tracked
Carriers)

ARMOURED CARS 197–216, 238,
258, 265, 306–8
A.E.C. 205, 210, 211, 212, 214, 215,
305, 306, 307
A.F.V. W.19, 208
Alvis 202, 203
Alvis-Straussler 228–32; A.C.3 230;
A.C.3D 230–32; Type A 231, 232
Armament 212
Armstrong-Siddeley 197

Basilisk flamethrower 215
Beaverbug I 236
Beaverette 233–36
Boarhound 308
Breda 219
B.S.A. 202, 203
B.S.A.-Daimler 208

Classification 201
Coventry 211, 215, 306
Crossley 197, 280

Daimler 203–4, 205, 207, 208, 209,
214, 215, 236, 296, 304, 306, 307
Daimler Ferret 202
Deerhound 308
Dingo 203
Dodge 235, 236

Ford 208
Ford Lynx 203, 212

"Garri Kifarru" 281, 282
General Motors Fox 212
Greyhound 307, 308
Guy 199–210, 306
Guy Ant 197

Hillman Gnat 236
Humber 200–5, 207–9, 212, 214,
215, 226, 233–36, 243, 272, 303,
305, 307
Humberette 233, 234

In service 214
Ironside I 233

Lanchester 197
Light Reconnaissance Cars 201,
233–36

"Malcolm Campbell" 235, 236
Marks, variants and special
versions 212–14, 216
Marmon-Herrington 214, 217–27,
280, 303, 307; Mk. I 218–19, 220,
221; Mk. II 218–19, 220, 221, 227,
239, 280, 281; Mk. III vi, 220–23,
282; Mk. IV 222–23; Mk. IVF 223,
224; Mk. VI, VII and VIII 224–25
Morris 197, 198, 201, 203, 214,
234, 306
Morris Salamander 236

Otter I 227, 236

Production 208

Rolls-Royce 197, 214, 306

Scout cars 201–3, 208, 209, 236,
238, 257, 308
"SOD" 205
Specifications 216
Staghound 276, 279, 307–8
Standard 233
Steyr-Daimler-Puch 197, 198, 199,
202
Straussler, A.C.1 and A.C.2 228–29;
articulated chassis 229; LAC 229

Technical descriptions 209–12
39M Csaba 232
Trials 197

Vickers Wolseley wheel-cum-track
182–88

White 307
Wolfhound 308

SELF-PROPELLED WEAPONS
305–6
Achilles 303, 306
Alecto 285
Archer 291, 300, 305
Avenger 287

Bishop 291, 299, 305

Carden-Loyd 45

M10 306
M10A1 303, 306

Priest 300, 305

Sexton vii, 302, 305

TANK(S)
A9 (Cruiser Mk. 1) vi, 2, 3, 15–16,
283, 284, 286
A9 E1 3
A10 (Cruiser Mk. II) vi, 3, 4, 15–16,
283, 284, 286
A10 Mk. I 284
A10 E1 3
A11 see Infantry Tank Mk. I
A12 see Infantry Tank Mk. II
A13 15–16
A13 (Cruiser Mk. IIA) vi, 4
A13 (Cruiser Mk. III) 4, 283, 286

A13 (Cruiser Mk. IV) 4, 5
A13 E1 2
A13 E2 4
A13 Mk. I (Cruiser Mk. III) 5
A13 Mk. II 286
A13 Mk. III (Cruiser Mk. V) see
    Covenanter
A14 284, 286
A15 (Cruiser Mk. VI) see Crusader
A16 285, 286
A20 87
A20/E1 86
A20E1, A20E2, A20E3, A20E4 87
A22 see Churchill
A22F 96
A24 see Cavalier
A27 (Cruiser Mk. VIII) 22, 287;
    series data 30
A27 (L) see Centaur
A27 (M) see Cromwell
A30 see Challenger
A33 Assault 27
A33 (1) Assault 27
A34 see Comet
A39 see Tortoise
A41 22
A43 see Black Prince
AC1 (Australian Cruiser Mk. 1)
    65–69, 73, 74, 288 (see also
    Sentinel)
AC2 67
AC3 68–72
AC4 69, 72, 73
American vii, viii ARV 177
Avenger 26, 27
AVRE vi, vii, 61, 129, 137, 174;
    carpet-laying 149; with SBG 138,
    156, 171; with fascine 171

Badger 61
Baron 290
BARV 181
Black Prince (A43) 98, 103, 292,
    293
"Bob Semple" 279
Bystrokhodnii 2

Cavalier (Cruiser Mk. VII, A24) vi,
    8, 22, 23, 24, 27, 287
CDL 128, 134, 144, 172, 173, 249,
    253, 290
Centaur vi, 23, 27, 286, 287; Mk. IV
    22; AA 26; ARV 181; Bulldozer 26
Centurion viii, 22, 258, 288, 293;
    Mk. I 288
Chaffee 304, 305
Challenger 25, 26, 27, 28, 31, 287,
    295
Charioteer 27
Chieftain 190, 191
Christie 2, 4, 12

Churchill (Infantry Tank Mk. IV,
    A22) vii, 85–104, 242, 248, 258,
    259, 260, 291–93; Mk. I, 86, 87,
    92, 293; Mk. II 88–92; Mk. III, 85,
    90–93, 97, 101–4; 125, 293; Mk.
    IV 92, 96, 113, 125, 137, 141, 244;
    Mk. V 93, 100; Mk. VI 93, 99; Mk.
    VII 96, 101, 104, 157; Mk. VIII 96,
    102; Mk. IX, X and XI 96; Mk. IX
    LT, X LT and XI LT 96; Mk. X 104;
    Ardeer Aggie 109; ARK Mk. I 125,
    146; ARK Mk. II 125, 146; ARV
    Mk. I 177, 178; ARV Mk. II 179

Churchill AVRE 97, 106, 107–9,
    116, 139, 140, 248, 250, 290, 292;
    AVRE sledge 144; Bangalore
    torpedoes 112; carpet-layers 107,
    109, 110; Conger 2 inch Mk. I 111;
    Elevatable Goat 110, 112;
    explosive charge devices 110,
    112; fascine carrier 109; Goat 138;
    Goat Mk. III 111, 112, 139; log
    carpet 111; mat laying 108, 110;
    S.B.G. 106, 109, 141; Snake 108,
    111

Churchill, basic marks 92–97;
    Bridgelayer 124, 127; Bullshorn
    Mark IIIc 120; Carpet-Layer Mark
    III 143; CDL 128; conception and
    birth 86–89; Crocodile vii 97,
    113–16, 137, 155, 157, 160, 161,
    162, 248, 251, 291, 292;
    description of 89–92; Great
    Eastern Ramp 126, 254; Hudnott
    ARK 126; in service 99–101;
    Mobile Bailey 127; Mobile Brown
    Bridge 127; Mobile Dalton Bridge
    127; "N.A.75" 93; production
    group 88; scissors bridging 176;
    special purpose 97–99, 105–28,
    special purpose roles 292; 3-inch
    gun carrier 97, 98, 103; Woodlark
    126; Woodpecker 109

Comet (A34) 29, 31–44, 287;
    commentary on 43; description of
    39–40; in service 40–43;
    specification 44; Type A 35, 41;
    Type B 41

Covenanter (A13 Mk. III, Cruiser
    Mk. V) vi, 5–6, 14–16, 284, 286,
    287; Mk. I 5; Mk. II 6; Mk. III 6;
    Mk. III Bridgelayer 7; Mk. IV 6, 7,
    14; Mk. IV Bridgelayer 15

Crab, see Sherman Crab
Crocodile, see Churchill Crocodile

Cromwell v, vii, 12, 18, 21–30, 246–
    49, 286, 287, 293; description of
    23–26; development history 22–
    23; tactical employment 27;
    variants 26; Mk. III 23; Mk. III D
    24; Mk. IV 21, 22, 24, 28–30; Mk.
    IV F 24; Mk. IV F 0P 30; Mk. V 23;
    Mk. VI 24; Mk. VII 23, 24; Mk. VIII
    23; Mk. X 23; AOP 26; ARV 26

Cruiser vi, 2, 21, 48, 258, 285–89;
    Australian 65–84; Canadian 45–
    64; disguised as lorries 11, 14;
    series data 20; Mk. I see A9; Mk. II
    see A10; Mk. III see A13; Mk. IVA
    283; Mk. V see Covenanter; Mk.
    VI see Crusader; Mk. VII see
    Cavalier; Mk. VIII vi, see also
    Centaur and Cromwell; Chassis
    ARV 179; see also Ram, Sentinel,
    Sexton

Crusader (Cruiser Mk. VI) vii, 1–20,
    240, 256, 285, 286, 287; armoured
    recovery vehicle 14, 18;
    command tank 12; description of
    8–12; gun tractor 14; specialist
    roles 12; tactical employment
    16–18; Mk. I 7, 13, 287; Mk. II 7,
    11, 12, 14, 18–20, 287; Mk. II CS 1,
    15; Mk. III 7, 8, 9, 11, 13, 16, 17,
    18, 287; Mk. III AA Mk. I 19;
    Mk. III AA Mk. II 19; Mk. III AA
    Mk. III 19; Mk. III (OP) 13; Mk. IV
    7; Mk. VI 286; ARV 181;
    bulldozer 14; Dozer 19

DD 132, 135, 136, 142, 146, 147,
    149, 150, 153, 162, 170, 171, 172,
    176, 232, 245, 264, 276, 290, 303

Firefly 261, 262
Flail 121–22, 143, 151, 164, 171,
    180, 248, 262
Flame-Throwing vii, 83, 113–18,
    137, 155, 159, 248, 251, 257

Grant viii, 17, 18, 48–52, 65, 76,
    256, 273, 282, 294, 297–301;
    special-purpose 300; ARV Mk. I
    179, 180; ARV Mk. II 181; CDL
    147, 168, 169, 299; Scorpion 300
Grizzly 62, 63, 289

Heavy assault 293–95
Honey see Stuart

Infantry (I) vi, vii, 2, 21, 289–93;
Mk. I see Matilda; Mk. II see
Matilda; Mk. III see Valentine;
Mk. IV see Churchill

Lakeman ARK (Gun Churchill) 126
Lee 253, 267, 272, 294, 297–301
Light 285; Mk. VI 283; Mk. VIB 283,
284, 285; Mk. VIC 284, 285;
Mk. VII Tetrarch 285; Mk. VIII
Harry Hopkins 285; Marmon-
Herrington Type CTL-1 190; see
also Stuart (or Honey)
Locust 299, 304;
M22 air-portable 154

M3 Light see Stuart (or Honey);
M3 Medium see Grant (or Lee);
M4 Medium see Sherman; M4A1
63; M4A4 see Sherman Mk. V;
M7 62; M10 302; M13/40 255;
M24 Chaffee 258; M19 17, 46, 47

Matilda (Infantry Tank Mk. I and II)
vii, 4, 76–84, 256, 257, 283, 289;
Mk. I (A11) 289; Mk. II (A12) vii,
260, 289; Mk. II-V 290; post-war
use 84; specialised equipments
83; C.D.L. 300; Dozer 82, 83, 257;
Frog 75, 77, 80, 82, 83, 257;
Hedgehog 82, 84, 257; Scorpion
151, 290; Senior 283, 289; with
Carrot 290
"Mobile Pillbox" 279

Production vii

Ram vii, 50–61, 107, 158, 288;
description of 51–53; experimental
versions 61; in service 57–58;
production changes 53–57;
searchlight carrier 61; specification
64; variants 58–61; Mk. I 48, 49,
50, 259, 288; Mk. II 51, 52, 53, 54,
57, 58, 259, 288; ARV 61, 289;
ARV Mk. I 60, 179; ARV Mk. II
179; Kangaroo 304; OP 58, 60
R.E. 132, 137, 149

Schofield Wheel and Track 185,
188
Sentinel vii, 65–74; commentary on
72; description of 70–71;

specification 73; ACI 288;
ACII 288; ACIII 288; ACIV 288
Sexton 54, 62–64; GPO 63

Sherman vii, viii, 18, 146, 243, 258,
261, 268, 269, 272, 273, 276, 277,
278, 296, 301–4; British
designations 303; special-purpose
105–28, 303; Mk. III AY, DD III
133; III D.D. Rocket Egress 119;
Mk. V 147, 261, 298; AMRCR
120; Ark II 126; ARV I 177, 178,
180; ARV II 179, 180; Badger
flame-thrower 118; BARV 180;
C.I.R.D. with Flying Bangalore
torpedoes 108, 111; C.I.R.D. with
Tapeworm 111; Conger 149;
Conger 2 inch Mk. I 111; Crab 105,
122, 135, 151, 153, 154, 156, 164,
171, 174, 248, 250, 262, 304;
Crab Mk. I 123, 152; Crab Mk. II
116, 122, 152, 153; Crib Carrier
128; Crocodile flame-thrower 115;
DD 119, 135, 136; DD Mk. II 132,
133; Mk. II Ginandit 119; DD Mk.
III 134; BELCH 119; Fascine
Carrier 128; 170; Firefly v, 298,
302; Kangaroo 128, 277, 301, 304;
Kangaroo APC 128; Marquis 122;
Lobster 122; Octopus 126;
OP 128, 298, 304; Pram Scorpion
122; Snake 108, 111; Tankdozer
128

Skink AA 63, 289
Special-purpose 105
Stuart (or Honey) (M3 Light) viii,
76, 238, 256, 257, 266, 273, 292,
293, 296–97
Super Churchill 292

T14 Assault 291, 295
TOG 293
Tortoise (A39) 291; 294
TT 144

Valentine (Infantry Tank Mk. III)
vii, 4, 46–48, 142, 146, 237, 241,
260, 289–91; DD 131, 132;
Dozer 291; OP 291
Valiant 292
Vickers Medium 182, 280; Mk. I
184, 185; Mk. II 123; Mk. VIA 255;
Wheel-cum-Track 183, 184, 185

Tank entraining and detraining 182
Tank wagons 182

TRACKED CARRIERS
Armoured Personnel Carrier 158
Bren Carriers 256
Buffalo 162, 164, 166, 167, 170,
171, 172, 173, 175, 252, 263, 306

Carden-Loyd Mk. V 183
Fantail 303, 306
Kangaroo 59, 61, 158, 252
LVT 160, 166, 306; LVT4 165
Priest Kangaroo 59, 305
Ram Kangaroo 163
Terrapin 306
Universal Carriers viii, 240, 242,
265, 304, 306
Wallabies 61
Weasel 170

2. BRITISH AND COMMON-WEALTH ARMIES INDEX

(NOTE: This index does not go
below brigade level. Main
references to the units in a brigade
or higher formation will be found in
the formation narratives on
pp. 237–282)

BRITISH ARMY
ARMY GROUP 21st 59–60, 62,
109, 126, 128, 144, 173, 175,
287, 304, 308

ARMIES First vii, 17, 92; Second
157, 164, 172, 173, 175, 264;
Fifth 263; Eighth 17, 62, 125, 126,
127, 128, 263, 279–80, 287, 301;
Fourteenth 276

CORPS 4th 276; 12th 172; 30th
172, 173

DIVISIONS Airborne 6th 285, 304;
Armoured v, 27; organization 237;
1st v, 11, 16, 17, 240, 241; 2nd v,
241; 6th v, 11, 17, 18, 237, 239,
240, 242; 7th v, 16, 21, 28, 29, 36,
42, 172, 242; 8th v, 243; 9th v, 6,
15, 128, 244; 10th v, 245; 11th v,
18, 28, 42, 129, 162, 238, 246,
288; 42nd 247; 79th vii, 6, 59, 83,
109, 110, 114, 116, 120, 122, 125,
128, 129–76, 247, 254, 303, 304;
Guards 15, 28, 33, 100, 246, 249,
287

BRIGADES Armoured v, 240, 249;
1st 249; 2nd 249, 301; 3rd 249;
4th 76, 249, 253; 5th Guards 250;

6th Guards 250; 7th 1, 17, 244, 250; 8th 54, 250; 9th 246, 250; 10th (later Tank) 250; 11th (later Tank) 40, 250; 20th 250; 22nd 17, 42, 249, 251, 288; 23rd 241, 244, 251; 24th 251; 26th 251, 301; 27th 6, 131, 139, 146, 147, 245, 251; 28th 251; 29th 40, 251; 30th 122, 131, 142, 147, 154, 251, 304; 33rd 171; 74th 253; 137th 253; Assault (RE) 1st 131, 141, 153, 160; Motor, 7th 85, 243, 297; Tank v, 2, 239, 240; 1st 131, 134, 147, 249; 21st 251; 25th (later Armoured Engineer) 242, 251 252, 303; 31st (later Armoured) 251; 32nd 242, 252; 33rd (later Armoured) 252; 34th 252; 35th 131, 147, 253; 36th 253

AUSTRALIAN ARMY 255–58, 297, 300

CORPS 256

DIVISIONS 256; Armoured 255–58; 6th Infantry 16

BRIGADES Armoured 75, 76, 78, 83, 256, 257

CANADIAN ARMY 45, 109, 118, 164, 166, 169, 227, 258–65, 288, 290, 295, 300, 304, 306, 308

CORPS 263; 1st 263, 264; 2nd 162, 264

DIVISIONS Armoured 240, 260, 262, 263, 264; Infantry 130, 260, 263, 264

BRIGADES 264; Armoured 260, 262, 263, 264, 304; Army Tank 50, 260; Infantry 262, 264; 1st Motor Machine-gun 258

INDIAN ARMY 222, 251, 265–77, 297, 304, 308

CORPS 3rd 269; 15th 269, 272, 276

DIVISIONS Armoured 269, 272, 273, 276, 277, 304; 4th (Red Eagles) Infantry 265, 268–269, 276; 5th (Ball of Fire) Infantry 265, 268–269, 277

BRIGADES Armoured and Tank 269, 272, 273, 276, 277, 304; 3rd Motor 269, 297

NEW ZEALAND ARMY 277–80, 297, 304, 308

DIVISIONS 277–80; 2nd 123, 245, 278–280, 304

BRIGADES 277–79, 304

SOUTH AFRICAN ARMY 219–222, 240, 280–82, 304

DIVISIONS 1st 281; 2nd 282; Armoured, 6th 240, 282, 304

BRIGADES 281, 304

3. GENERAL INDEX

Abyssinia 2, 281
Adder flame-thrower 115
Aerials 13, 178
African Colonies 222
Alam Halfa 298
Aleppo 239
Alexander, Field-Marshal Earl 272
Ammunition 19, 25, 28, 44, 64, 73, 102
Andrews, Lt.-Col. Johnny 258
Anti-mine explosive devices 7, 15, 111, 120, 147, 148, 290
Antwerp 162, 164
Anzio beach-head 244
Arakan 276
Ardennes 164, 288
Arezzo 279

ARMAMENT 18, 28, 44, 73, 102, 107
Anti-aircraft 88 mm vii
Anti-tank: Boys 201, 219, 221, 222; 6-pdr. 7, 17
Armoured Cars 212
Bofors (40-mm.) 13
Howitzer: 77; 3-inch 17; 95-mm. 100; Lorraine Schlepper 13
Machine-guns 258; ·30 cal 52; Besa 7, 8, 9, 83, 86, 93, 178, 204, 211, 225, 283, 285, 286, 292, 307, 308
Bren 12, 14, 18, 26, 178, 201, 219, 221, 222, 233
Browning 48, 222, 224, 305, 306, 308

Vickers 13, 69, 71, 212, 221, 222, 225, 288
Oerlikon (20-mm.) 13, 19
OQF 6-pdr. Mk. III 57; Mk. V 57
Petard mortar 107, 109, 153
Polsten cannon 288, 306
Q.F. 75-mm. 96
Rocket projectors 298
Scout Cars 212
75-mm. gun 23, 25, 27, 31, 42, 50, 58, 78, 98, 211, 258, 307, 308
76-mm. gun 31, 302
77-mm. gun 42
88-mm. gun 15, 17, 31
2-pdr. gun 7, 16, 47, 49, 68, 77, 204, 211, 215, 222, 224, 285, 286
6-pdr. gun 7, 16, 22, 23, 25, 31, 50, 53, 86, 99, 285, 308
17-pdr. gun 31, 67, 72, 73, 96, 98, 262, 288, 295
25-pdr. gun 17, 62, 66, 68, 69, 71, 299, 302
32-pdr. gun 291

Armour 19, 30, 44, 64, 73, 102
Armour plates 15, 23, 24

ARMY
Belgian 308
British and Commonwealth see British and Commonwealth Armies Index; Dutch East Indies 230; German v, vii, 16, 21, 297, 298; Afrika Korps 1, 16, 17, 305; Hungarian 232; Irish 104, 223, 246, 251, 296; Italian 16; Polish 5, 15, 28, 250, 287; Portuguese 230; Royal Jordanian 104; U.S. 105, 122, 164, 172, 304

"Army Tank Battalion (Special)" 253
Arnhem 173, 196
Arromanches 143
Ash, Capt. M.A. 302
Atherton Jack 14
Auchinleck, Field-Marshal Sir Claude 266, 268
Australia 65
Avezzano 279

Badger flame-thrower 118
Badges: Armies 270; British and Commonwealth, Armoured Divisions 274; British and Commonwealth, higher formations 270
Balcombe 256
Balikpapan 79, 83, 257

Bangalore torpedoes 111, 112
Bardia 16, 255, 289
Battle of Mareth 17
Beach Armoured Recovery Vehicles
    see Tank(s), BARV
Beda Fomm 16, 289
Benghazi 220
Bir Tengeder 222
Blerick 164
Borneo 83, 256, 257
Bougainville 79, 84, 256
Boulogne 158
Bovington 45
Brakes 210
Brancaster 149
Bremen 173
Bremerhaven 173
Breskens 162
Brest 160
Bridge, mobile 123
Bridgehead 153
Bridging devices 123–27
Brink, Lieut.-Gen. George 280
Brooke, Sir Alan 294
Brown, Capt. B. S. 127
Brunei 83, 257
Brussels 249
Brutinel, Maj. Raymond 258
Bull's Head 175
Bullshorn plough 120, 147
Burma 238, 253, 266, 267, 294, 299

Caen 134, 157
Calais 16, 158
Cambrai 109
Camouflage 25
Camouflage unit 253
Camp Borden 45, 47
Campbell, Brig. "Jock" 1
Campbell, Sir Malcolm 236
Canadian Indestructible Roller
    Device (CIRD) 121
Canadian Pacific Railway Co. 46
Canal defence lights 128, 134, 248,
    249, 253
Capuzzo 238
Carden, Sir John 3
Carden-Loyd 188
Carpet laying devices 107, 109, 110,
    141, 149
Carter, Col. E. J. 46
Cassino 244, 282
Centipede 170
Cerignola 243
Chamberlain, A. 65
Cherbourg 16, 153
Christie, J. Walter 1, 189
Churchill, Winston S. 6, 33, 88
Cleves 175
Cobra flame-thrower 115
Cockatrice device 113
Code, A. R. 67
Communications 19, 30, 44, 64, 73,
    102

Conger 149, 150
Cooking arrangements 12
Courage, Maj. G. 44
Crab 147
Crab flail 122
Crerar, Gen. H. D. G. 262
Crete 290
Crocker, Gen. Sir John 237
Cunningham, Lieut.-Gen. Sir Alan
    281
"Curse of Scotland" 266, 273
Cyrenaica 251, 282

D-Day 181, 245, 246
Dalton, Maj. T. R. 127
Desert 253
Desert Rats 21, 238
Desert Tank Delivery Organization
    253
de Thoren, Capt. 299
Dieppe vii, 64, 91, 92, 105, 114,
    125, 130, 131, 137, 258, 259, 264
Dill, Gen. Sir John 88
Donovan, Lieut. J. J. 105
Douvres 157
Dredge, Sergeant T. W. 33
Dummy units 251, 253
Dunkirk 182, 234, 254
du Toit, Maj. A. S. 121

Egypt 242, 244, 281
El Alamein viii, 15, 17, 92, 97, 240,
    241, 279, 287, 290, 298, 301, 305
Elbe 173, 175
Electrical system 20, 30, 44, 71, 73,
    104
Emmerich 172

ENGINES

Alvis 230; Bedford 87, 91, 104;
    Cadillac 66, 70, 71, 73, 288;
    Daimler 209; Ford 224, 229, 295;
    Harland and Wolff 86; Hercules
    model RXLD 211; Humber 233;
    Liberty 19, 22, 23; Meadows 86,
    87; Meteor 22, 23, 27, 30, 40, 44;
    Meteorite 194, 292; Perrier-
    Cadillac 70, 71; Riley 236; Rolls-
    Royce Merlin 22; Wright 51, 52,
    63, 64

Evatt, Dr. H. V. 6

Falaise 155, 157, 248, 261, 264,
    297
Fascines 109, 142
Fascine, roller 123
Flame deflector cowl 25, 40

Florence 263, 277, 279, 282
Flotation device 119
Fluid Flywheel 210
Flushing 162
Flying Dustbin 107, 109
Formation Signs: Armoured
    Brigades and (Army) Tank
    Brigades 275; Corps 271
Fritton Decoy 142, 144

Gabes Gap 241
Gazala 249, 252, 269, 294, 297
Gearbox 210; Maybach 286;
    Merritt-Brown 22, 23, 25, 91, 104
Geilenkirchen 164
George VI, HM King 86, 237, 290
Gheel 170
Gothic Line 282
Gournay-en-Bray 249
Greece 241, 244
Grigg, Sir James 18
Groesbeck 171

Harris, Maj. K. P. 289
Hingen 161
Hobart, Maj.-Gen. Sir Percy 41,
    114, 129, 130, 131
Hobart, Lt.-Col. P. R. C. 21, 41
Hobo's Funnies 175
Hollands, Capt. E. D. 85
Home Guard 233, 234
Hong Kong 42
Hopkinson Mission 214
Horrocks, Maj.-Gen. B. G. 6
Huon Peninsula 78

Icks, Col. R. J. 50, 51
Invasion plans 147
Italy vii, 240, 253

Japan 76, 256, 272
Jeffries Plough 120
Jungle 76, 258, 268

Kippenberger, Maj.-Gen. Sir
    Howard 278
Klein, Col. Harry 280, 281
Korea 42, 288

Labuan 83, 257
Lakeman anti-aircraft mounting 12
Lakenheath 237
Landings 150
La Romola 296

LCTs 149
Le Havre 129, 156, 158, 180, 251,
  252, 253
Le Kef 292
Levant 246
Libya 16, 92, 197
Liddell-Hart, Capt. B. H. 21, 265,
  289
Light carrot device 110, 112
Linney Head 144
Littlejohn attachments 205, 215,
  299, 304
Lobster flail 122
Log carpet device 111
LST (Landing Ship, Tanks) 78, 146
Lulu, roller device 120, 121

Maastricht 170
Macarthur-Onslow, Brigadier 78
McNaughton, General A. G. L. 260
Madagascar 285
Maginot Line v
Maltot 248
Malaya 256, 269, 277
Mandalay 272
Mareth, Battle of 17
Martel, Lt.-Gen. Sir Giffard Le Q.
  viii, 237, 239, 294, 301
Martel, Maj. 132, 299
Mary of Arnhem 173
Mat laying devices 108, 110
MDI Plough 120
Mechanical charge placers 112
Merritt, H. E. 87, 91, 286
Merritt-Brown gearbox 22, 23, 25,
  91, 104
Meuse river 172
Middle East 228, 232, 256
Middleburg 162
Miller, Maj.-Gen. Charles H. 176
Mine, anti-personnel 170
Mine-clearing devices 15, 98, 120,
  121, 135, 137, 138, 249, 308
Minesweeping 135
Montgomery, Field-Marshal
  Viscount viii, 40, 41, 129, 245, 293
Motor-cycle units 259, 281
Munro, Ross 258

Nash and Thompson hydraulic
  system 3
New Guinea 256, 257
Nijmegen 166, 171, 286
Normandy v, vii, 21, 22, 26, 96, 109,
  135, 143, 145, 157, 175, 176, 177,
  215, 245, 246, 247, 248, 261, 264,
  297
Normandy cowl 25
North-West Europe campaign vii
Nuffield, Lord 2
Nuffield Mechanisations
  and Aero, Ltd 4, 6, 8

Obstacle Assault Centre 120
Odon 247, 251
Oke, Maj. J. M. 114
Onion (Jones onion) device 110,
  112
Operation "Battleaxe" 16, 286, 287
Operation "Crusader" 1, 272, 277,
  286, 291, 296
Operation "Goodwood" 248
Operation "Husky" 302
Operation "Overlord" 109, 143
Operation "Totalize" 59, 155, 262,
  264
Operation "Tractable" 155, 264,
  297
Operation "Veritable" 61, 144, 166,
  169, 171, 175, 195, 251, 252,
  264, 290
Orford 146
Orne canal 160
Ortona 261

Paget, Gen. Sir Bernard 9
Palestine 223, 244
Pennants 12, 13
Periscopes 110
Petroleum Warfare Department 113
Phillips, N. C. 279
Plough devices 120, 147
Po Valley 282
Pocock, Brig. J. G. 267, 268
Pontoon ferry 278
Poole, Maj.-Gen. 282
Postan, M. M. 285
Pram Scorpion flail 122
Puckapunyal 256

Radar station 155–56
Rees 172
Reichswald Forest 101, 166, 169
Remagen 171
Renton, Lt. J. G. 85
Rhine 164, 170, 171
Riley, Percy 236
Rimini 279
Roller fascine 123
Romagna 279
Rommel 269, 272, 277, 297
Ronson flame-throwing equipment
  114
Royal Air Force 197, 202, 228, 230,
  232, 234
Royal Air Force Regiment 236
Royal Marines 26, 30, 162
Ryder, Capt. D. R. 220, 222

Sabre fighting squadron 214
Salamander flame-thrower 118
San Casciano 277

Scheldt estuary 306
Schofield, E. J. 185
Schu mine 170
Scissors Bridge 7, 15
Scorpion mine exploding devices
  121, 135, 249
Searchlight 128, 134
Sellar, R. J. B. 42
Senio Line 279
Sheppard, Maj. E. W. 265
Sherman Badger flame-thrower 118
Shwegyin 266, 273
Sicily 244, 263, 302
Sidi Barrani 16, 289
Sidi Bou Zid 292
Sidi Rezegh viii, 1, 16, 240, 286,
  296
Siegfried Line 123, 144, 166, 169
Sifton, Sir Clifford 258
Simonds, Lt.-Gen. Guy 59
Skid Bailey 127
Sledges, armoured 128
Slim, Field-Marshal Viscount 276
"Smithforce" 253
Smoke dischargers 31
"Snake" mine exploding equipment
  98, 137, 148
Sollum 269
Solomon Islands 278
South Africa 217–27
South African Reconnaissance
  Cars see Armoured cars, Marmon-
  Herrington
Spencer, Maj. J. D. 33
Spitzbergen 263
Stacey towing attachment 304
Steam Roller Farm 85
Steering 90, 210, 286
Steering unit, Wilson epicyclic 5–6,
  12, 20
Stern, Sir Albert 86
Stokes Bay 146
Straussler, Nicholas 119, 132,
  197, 228
Suspension 20, 25, 30, 43, 44, 71,
  73, 91, 104, 210, 229, 286

Tapeworm device 111
Tarakan 83, 257
Taranto 279
Terrapin 160, 168
Thompson and Nash hydraulic
  system 3
Thoren light 134
Thorpe, Maj. D. 91
"Tiger" convoy 16
"Tiger Cubs" 16
Tobruk 1, 16, 217, 218, 239, 241,
  252, 255, 282, 289, 291, 296
Track(s): and wheel drive 188;
  Carden-Loyd 191; design and
  materials 189; replacement 189;
  wear 182, 189
Track frame 184, 188

Tractor: Diamond T M20 195, 196;
  Dragon 123, 280; Field Artillery
  229; Matador 205, 210, 211;
  Ruston-Hornsby 188;
  Straussler's "Hefty" 229
Trailer: Diamond T 194; M9 195,
  196
Transmission 20, 30, 44, 64, 73,
  104, 211, 286
Transporters: 189; A.E.C. 190;
  Antar 194; Diamond T 30-ton 194;
  federal tractor truck 191; M19 195,
  196; Mack EXBX 186, 192, 193;
  Scammell 186, 191, 192, 193, 195

Trieste 278
Trondheim operation 260
Tunis 97
Tunisia vii, 86, 92, 242, 251, 253,
  279, 291

VE-Day 254
Venice 252
Verney, Maj.-Gen. G. L. vii, 1
Villa, Leo 236
von Koch, Gen. 85
von Rundstedt 164

Walcheren 156, 162
Watkins, Brig. Bill 291
Watson, Col. W. D. 65
Wavell, Field-Marshal Earl 2, 16
Western Desert 214, 297
Wheel and track drive 188
Wilson epicyclic steering unit 5-6,
  12, 20
Wireless 9, 13, 19, 25, 30, 44, 73,
  90, 102
Worthington, Col. F. F. 45, 47, 49,
  50, 64, 258